**FROM**

**DEPARTMENT** OF **PUBLIC INSTRUCTION**
**DOVER, DELAWARE 19901**

Training Program for Acquisition
Of Skills in Curriculum Development
and Evaluation

November 1970

Property of: **LEKOPPENHAVER**

RETURN POSTAGE GUARANTEED

# SCIENCE TEACHING AND TESTING

**LEO NEDELSKY**

*The University of Chicago*

# SCIENCE TEACHING AND TESTING

Harcourt, Brace & World, Inc.

New York / Chicago / San Francisco / Atlanta

PICTURE CREDITS:
page 1, Courtesy Mott Foundation Program, Flint Community Schools
page 235, Hays from Monkmeyer

Library of Congress Catalog Card Number: 65-19846

Printed in the United States of America

# CONTENTS

# PART II
# SAMPLE EXERCISES WITH COMMENTS

# INTRODUCTION

This book is addressed to teachers and prospective teachers of science in college and high school. It deals primarily with the student's first course in a given science; most of its illustrations are from my own field, physics, but analogues of the illustrations will readily occur to teachers of other physical sciences and, with a bit of imagination, perhaps even to biologists.

Science is now taught badly. Little effort is made to give the student an understanding of what science is like or what scientists do; one result is that the student cannot rationally decide whether or not he should become a scientist. Science teaching is unimaginative, dull, and highly authoritarian: we lose some of our best prospects to other fields. Science courses stuff their students with facts instead of giving them understanding and teaching them how to learn, yet it is the last two abilities that the students would be most likely to retain and to use after their course work is completed.

The causes of this sad state of affairs are political, economic, social, and pedagogic. This book is an attempt to do something about this last cause. The job is a hard one: school teachers do not know much science, and learning science is a slow process; college teachers neither know much pedagogy nor are they willing to learn. Some progress is being made in helping teachers learn more science and in providing them with better tools—texts, apparatus, buildings—but the teacher's behavior in the classroom has remained unchanged. It seems likely that students' learning has not changed much either.

Teaching is partly a science; therefore valid generalizations can be formulated about it and applied to particular situations. But teaching is also an art and thus depends on the motives, tastes, and talents of the teacher. This book is designed, then, not so much to tell a teacher how to teach as to show him how he can learn from his own teaching. It does give advice on how to teach what is now neglected: understanding; ability to learn; and intuitive, disciplined, and imaginative thinking. But the major portion of the book is devoted to testing for these abilities—to advice on writing tests, on appraising the value of published ones, and on using tests for assigning grades, for counseling, and for experimenting with teaching methods. Once the teacher knows what his students have or have not learned he can, if he wishes, improve his teaching.

My own physics course is intended to increase the students' knowledge, understanding, and ability to learn. Of these objectives, ability to learn is the most important. It is also the most important aim of this book. Throughout the book I make, explain, and defend assertions primarily to enable the reader to use them as tools for studying his teaching and his students' learning. The reader should treat my assertions heuristically —modifying or discarding them as his learning progresses. It is not that I have not done my best to select the most respectable of educational and psychological generalizations. However, none of these is as unshakable as Boyle's law is and parity conservation used to be, and all are difficult to state briefly and understandably as well as with precision. I have tried merely to supply the teacher with methods for studying his teaching that he can easily use and that will not mislead him in the initial stages of self-study, and I refer him to more learned treatises for further progress. I should like to add that studying one's teaching is fascinating.

### Organization of the book

Chapter 1 of Part I argues that the terminology of a subject is not enough if teachers want to discuss and solve problems of teaching, and it contends that of the two usable pedagogical languages—those of learning theory and evaluation—the latter is much easier to learn. Finding out what their students learn is, for most teachers, the simplest road to course improvement. Chapter 2 gives a rather detailed list of possible objectives of an introductory science course, explains the classification scheme and the terms used, and illustrates these terms by examples from physics. The objectives are divided into three classes, knowledge, understanding, and the ability to learn, and include disciplined, imaginative, and intuitive thinking. (Additional and more specific objectives that apply primarily to laboratory work are treated separately, in Chapter 6.) Chapter 3 defends the importance of these objectives by looking at the probable academic and post-academic future of both science and non-science majors, by analyzing a particular subject, and by quoting scientists and science teachers. The chapter also explains how a teacher can prepare his own list of objectives. Chapters 4, 5, and 6 show that the objectives described in Chapter 2 are realistic, that is, that they can be attained with the present facilities (time, personnel, and equipment), and that, nonetheless, the majority of introductory science courses fail to reach some of the important objectives. The chapters go on to describe and defend changes in teaching methods that may make it possible to remedy these failures.

Chapter 7 explains the meaning of the most useful test statistics verbally, mathematically, and by illustration; for instance, it shows what happens to students' grades if the tests used are of low validity or low reliability, or if they show low intercorrelations. It discusses factors that influence the values of various statistics and methods for improving tests. Chapters 8 and 9 present the basic principles of test theory and show how science teachers can prepare valid tests for all the major objectives of their courses and judge the appropriateness of published tests. The chapters discuss special problems in writing tests on understanding, learning ability, and disciplined, intuitive, and imaginative thinking. Chapter 10 concerns oral, essay, objective, and performance tests: their general strengths and weaknesses and their appropriateness for measuring the attainment of various objectives. Chapter 11 outlines the steps for preparing and criteria for judging various forms of test questions, and it explains how these criteria can be used to evaluate the teacher's own tests and commercially available ones. Chapter 12 states and discusses the criteria a collection of test exercises must meet if it is to be used as an achievement test. The discussion is illustrated by a full description of a good achievement test in physics. The chapter also deals with weighting, scoring, and assigning grades and shows how to improve an achievement test on the basis of statistical analyses. Chapter 13 discusses the design of tests suitable for counseling and educational research. It argues that good achievement tests, both homemade and prepared by outside agencies, if specially scored, can be used for these purposes. It describes and illustrates the usefulness of properly interpreted test results in discovering the strengths and weaknesses of a student, a class, a teaching method, or materials of instruction.

Chapters 14 and 15 contain annotated bibliographies of books on science teaching and testing and of published tests. A special feature of Chapter 14 is a topic—or question—index. The index lists some fifty-nine questions that may occur to a teacher who wants to improve his teaching and testing and refers him to relevant portions of the present book and of the sources included in the bibliographies. The index is also used as a list of references. In every chapter of the book the reader will find numbers in parentheses, usually at the end of the sentence in which a new topic is introduced; these are the numbers of the questions in the index under which the relevant literature is listed. Readers familiar with pedagogical and testing theories may prefer first to review the questions in the index, choosing those that interest them, and then to read the relevant chapters. Others may want to read the chapters in order. But perhaps all readers should look briefly at the topic index—which is a good capsule summary of the content and intention of the book—before reading much further.

Part II of the book contains a large collection of test exercises, most in physics and some in chemistry, arranged according to the objectives listed in Chapter 2.

# SCIENCE TEACHING AND TESTING

# PART ONE
# THEORY AND METHOD

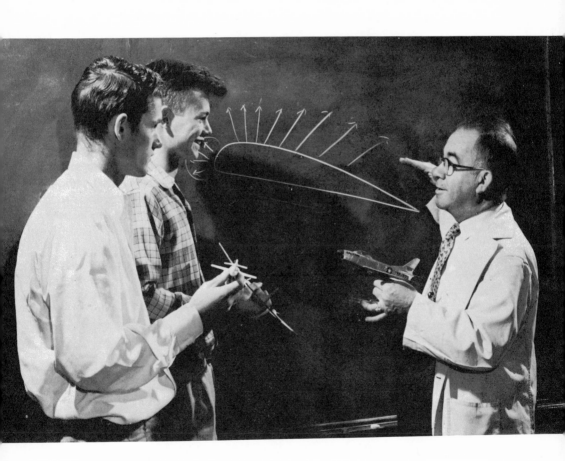

# 1

# TEACHING AND TESTING

In schools and colleges, testing is commonly used for student admission and placement and for course grades. But testing can also be used for a more important purpose: to improve teaching and to make it more exciting and satisfying to the teacher (26).* Later chapters will discuss the use of test *results* for both of these purposes. This chapter presents an analysis of teaching, using concepts and terms that have been developed primarily by test-makers, and shows how such an analysis can help to rationalize teaching.

## 1.1  TEACHERS NEED A PEDAGOGICAL VOCABULARY

To improve their teaching or just to keep it alive, teachers must learn to be analytic about it; they must be able to think and talk about it in an orderly, organized fashion. At present, most brilliant teachers can give us no more illuminating and convincing account of their success than a centenarian can of his longevity. The first requirement for any analysis is a set of appropriate concepts and terms. In turn, however, the results of an analysis are strongly and sometimes crucially influenced or predetermined by the choice of concepts. It would therefore be preferable that the terms of analysis of teaching be developed from studying teaching rather than testing. Such terms exist in theories of learning, but they are hard to learn, and besides they can be applied more easily to elementary education than to high school or college. Evaluation concepts are simpler and better suited to amateur teaching research. Section 1.4 will show that, as things stand at present, teaching research cannot all be relegated to departments of education or psychology but must be carried out by teachers themselves. Since most college professors (even those whose main interest is teaching) and many school teachers are not analytic about their teaching and do not pursue educational research, we should like to recommend

* See question (26) in Section 14.3 for references.

to them, as a provisional set of terms of analysis, those used in evaluation.

College science teachers are prone to underplay the word *teaching* in the phrase *science teaching*. The greater prestige associated with *science*, with its implications of research, is undoubtedly in part responsible, but the main reason is probably that scientists understand and love science while they can only love teaching. Their lack of clear understanding of even those aspects of teaching that can be understood results mainly from their failure properly to analyze any of the three aspects of teaching: content, method, and objectives. Only two questions are normally asked about content: Is the material an important part of a science? Is it teachable? As a result, as science grows so does course content. Thus these two criteria are clearly not enough even to keep course content within reasonable limits. The discussion of methods of teaching is limited to crude and sometimes superficial distinctions that reflect a very limited conceptual vocabulary: lecture, discussion, laboratory, types of demonstration apparatus, and sequences of topics taught. Objectives are commonly specified in terms of content only; what a student should be able to *do* with or within the content taught is seldom stated more explicitly than that the student should understand it and be able to solve problems.

Without a more explicit consideration of desired ends of instruction or of conditions conducive to learning, it seems *a priori* unlikely that science teachers could successfully and profitably think about or discuss teaching problems. Facts seem to substantiate this opinion. Methods of science teaching in the college have changed but little in the past few decades (11). Most scientists seem to have inherited their courses and their texts uncritically; others have tried earnestly to improve their teaching but in ways that are piecemeal, opportunistic, unanalytic—in short, unscientific. Physicists' committees, for instance, preoccupy themselves with the design of apparatus and buildings not because they believe that these are most in need of improvement, but because they know how to talk about them (14). Papers devoted to teaching, such as those presented at meetings or published in journals, are predominantly descriptive—of a method of presenting a topic, of a piece of demonstration apparatus, of a laboratory experiment. Presumably these innovations are intended to help the students to a better—broader, deeper, or different—understanding of physics. The authors of the papers are seldom moved, however, to state or to defend their theses. Their lack of explicitness is probably the result of their unfamiliarity with either of the two vocabularies that would lend themselves naturally to such defense—that of learning theory and that of testing. The theses that are defended are defended inadequately: the authors estimate students' interest from casual observation, judge quality of teaching entirely on the logic and clarity of presentation, and do not cite empirical evidence for students' achievement. In fact, more often than not the thesis seems to be, "This is how I do it and I like it," although the same professors would indignantly reject such a defense if it were offered in support of a scientific theory. Teaching is not all science, but it has enough science in it to make the "I like it" defense of a teaching method sound both arrogant and frivolous to the present writer.

The analysis of a course may proceed in either of two ways: by observing teaching materials and processes and gauging them against an accepted standard or by measuring the results of instruction, the students' achievement. With the observation technique, a textbook is read, apparatus is inspected, a teacher is listened to, and the students' reactions are noted. Since all these observations are to be used to decide whether or not conditions are conducive to learning, the observer should base his conclusions on a knowledge of some learning theory, with its terms of motivation, reinforcement, inhibition, attention, and so forth. However, with respect to theories of learning, most college science teachers are ignorant (10), suspicious, belligerently defensive, and, when opportune, jubilantly offensive. This attitude has a strong irrational component, for it is reassuring to think that what one does not know is not worth knowing, and it would probably be futile to suggest that professors master this theoretical language. They would find the chore arduous and the results probably meager; it may be wiser to depend on common sense than to brave the dangers of little learning. Nevertheless, without a theory of learning, a systematic, communicable criticism of teaching on the basis of observation is impossible.

We must therefore turn to the other technique of obtaining information on the quality of teaching, the measurement of how much students learn. This technique, in principle if not always in practice, is congenial to scientists, for it is largely empirical and can be readily mastered.

## 1.2  EVALUATION CONCEPTS ARE USEFUL IN TEACHING

The concepts and terms of evaluation can be used for an analysis of teaching goals, of content or subject matter, and of methods of presentation.

### Analysis of teaching goals

An essential part of measuring and judging the results of instruction is a statement of the desired results or objectives. The statement should be sufficiently detailed and explicit to guide the test-maker. To him it is immediately and painfully clear that descriptions of course content only are inadequate as objectives. He needs to know in addition what the students are expected to be able to *do* with the content; he needs to know the so-called behavioral objectives of the course. Nor can he be satisfied with the statement that the student should understand the content and be able to do problems, for there are many levels and kinds of understanding and of problems. The abilities to restate the content of a specified text or lecture and to work routine problems closely patterned after those in the text are of course quite unambiguous objectives; in our system of classification we include these under *knowledge.* Knowledge is a necessary aspect of understanding science, but to be satisfied with it seems inexcusable at the high school or college level, for by itself it is useless to the student and is therefore quickly forgotten (7).

Unlike test-makers, teachers are not forced to have a clear idea of their behavioral objectives. Some of them (but not many) nevertheless teach well through sheer genius; they do give the students a deep and lasting understanding and appreciation of the subject. Perhaps their thinking is angelic in that it dispenses with intermediate steps and arrives directly at correct conclusions and proper action. Whatever it is, it is private and rare, and it is buried with the artist. Most of us need clear and explicit reasons for choosing the right path. We need them for thinking and talking about teaching, and for learning how to teach well.

Once science teachers have acquired facility in the vocabulary of behavioral objectives, conversation about teaching becomes richer and easier. When, for instance, a physics teacher says that a student is familiar with ("understands") Newton's laws, he may imply one or more of the following behavioral objectives. The student should be able to state the laws; he should know their historical development; he should understand their relation to conservation laws and perhaps to relativity and quantum mechanics; and he should also understand their status, that is, in what sense each of the laws can be said to be true and what its general function in physics is. He should be able to use them to solve routine numerical problems and to analyze at least partially problems that are genuinely new to him or quite complex, and he should be able to read, without help, a chapter on, say, kinetic theory, in which Newton's laws are used. Some teachers may also want to use the content of Newton's laws for its *illustrative* value and will expect their students to be able to give at least partial answers to the following questions: How are definitions formulated in physics? What are the criteria of their excellence? Can a definition ever be found to be wrong? To what extent does the choice of concepts and definitions influence the progress of physics or even color our knowledge of reality?

A laboratory experiment can also be used for a variety of purposes. For instance, the classic one on measuring the heat of fusion of ice can be designed with some of the following objectives in mind: to give the student a better understanding of the concept *quantity of heat;* to teach him how to use a thermometer; to train him in the methods of tracking down error; to illustrate the proposition that in attacking an experimental problem he must make assumptions and working hypotheses, for instance, he must assume provisionally that some factors are negligible.

These examples show that the concept of behavioral objectives introduces a new dimension into the discussion of teaching a particular content. An explicit statement of the teacher's objectives will make it clearer to him, to his students, and to others just what he wants to accomplish by his course. It will make it possible to define adequate and excellent understanding of an area of science more accurately, perhaps even to define them in some absolute sense rather than as relative to the achievement of the rest of the class. The language of teaching is made both richer and more precise by adding the terminology of behavioral objectives to that of topics and areas of content.

Descriptions of behavioral objectives, such as knowledge or ability to apply principles, are much more general than descriptions of content, such as kinematics or hydrodynamics. Descriptions of behavioral objectives can be used in identical or nearly identical form for all the physical sciences and, with some modifications, for the biological sciences as well. It is important, however, that the modifications be made by biologists, because behavioral objectives can guide the teacher in his teaching and testing only if they are well articulated with the content. There have been attempts to state behavioral objectives so generally that they seem to apply not only to natural and social sciences but even to the humanities (6). Such generalization seems premature; it can be used only with great caution, lest formal similarities be taken for substantive ones. The kinship between understanding a poem and understanding how an ammeter works, though present, is really slight.

Even though the behavioral objectives of a science course may have a completely clear and usable meaning only to the teacher of that science, they can be understood fairly well by most teachers. The description of a course whose content is specified only in quite general terms, such as nuclear theory, acids, bases, and salts, evolution of stars, Shakespeare's dramas, or the federal government, can be made truly meaningful by stating its behavioral objectives. This kind of description of a course can be understood by all the teachers of a college, its students and deans, even perhaps by its president and alumni. Better communication among these people, made possible by the language of behavioral objectives, would make for a better college. Our main concern here, however, is better communication among subject-matter specialists, teachers of various courses, for without such communication a rationally designed curriculum is impossible. But, for reasons that transcend academic boundaries, we should like to see a physicist and a social scientist explain to each other just what kind of understanding they want their students to acquire.

**Analysis of content**

Behavioral objectives are also useful in choosing content (21) and, in particular, in solving the now very pressing problem of reducing content. A topic in science is commonly taught for its intrinsic value as part of a body of knowledge and also as an illustration of an aspect of the science that is relevant to other content areas. Thus the discussion of an experiment that supports a particular theory can be so conducted that the student learns some of the *general* principles and methods used to interpret data and to assay the cogency of evidence. In fact, some topics should be taught entirely for their illustrative value; the obsolete caloric theory, for instance, lends itself particularly well to bringing out criteria used to judge theories and to illustrating physics as a process of inquiry. The relative intrinsic value of topics has been admittedly an insufficient reason to include them in courses. There are now too many "basic" parts of physics and other sciences, and it is difficult, perhaps impossible, to order them in a hierarchy of intrinsic importance. To consider whether a given group of students can understand the topic is very helpful, but the question is elastic; many topics become teachable, given enough time. The illustrative value of a topic supplies a useful additional criterion for the choice of content, because topics differ widely in their aptness as illustrations of particular methods or aspects of a science. Thus, to limit ourselves to just one behavioral objective—an understanding of the relations between disciplines—kinematics is particularly useful for elucidating the relation between physics and mathematics; relativity, between philosophy and physics; and Faraday's laws, between chemistry and physics. Similarly, in the physics laboratory, the Ohm's law experiment lends itself readily to illustrating one aspect of the ever present interaction between the measuring instruments and the objects studied—meter resistance changes the resistance of the circuit. Calorimetry experiments, on the other hand, are useful for teaching some of the general principles of tracking down error. These few examples, you will note, also point up the virtual impossibility of avoiding the language of behavioral objectives in discussing the illustrative value of topics.

The preceding paragraph defends the use of the illustrative value of a topic—and consequently of the relevant language of behavioral objectives—as a way to reduce course content. But choosing subject matter without considering its illustrative value is inexcusable under any circumstances. The intrinsic importance of topics is properly the guiding principle in designing advanced specialized courses; the very short courses for nonspecialists, on the other hand, can hardly do more than exemplify various aspects of a science. But the one- or two-year introductory courses, with which this book is primarily concerned, must be strongly influenced by both criteria. If the prospective scientist does not learn in the introductory course the criteria for good definitions and for cogency of evidence or the power of operational definitions, he is not likely to hear them discussed in later courses. What is perhaps more important, if the illustrative value of topics is not emphasized, and the topics are presented as unique and autonomous elements, the student will have a fragmented and distorted picture of what a particular science is like. A consequence of college-wide importance is that he will not be able to make a rational choice of his major.

**Analysis of method**

Not only the choice of content but also the method of presenting it should be guided by the behavioral objectives that the teacher considers important. Information is most economically and most thoroughly obtained from books, though more painlessly from lectures. Lecture demonstration apparatus is almost always a good aid to memory. It must be specially designed and manipulated, however, if the objective is to convince the student of the correctness of a generalization or to give him a better understanding of it. Laboratory work is usually too expensive to be widely used to engender such convictions and understanding; it is practically irreplaceable, however, for helping the student understand the relation between theoretical "book" science and real phenomena and for helping him develop certain attitudes and habits. A discussion session is the best place to discover a student's misconceptions; to criticize and improve his reading habits, in particular, to develop his awareness of an author's implicit assumptions and his ability to evaluate the author's argument; and to give him an understanding of both the subtler and the more general aspects of a science. The discussion is more expensive and not much better than the lecture for teaching students how to solve stereotyped numerical problems—the use to which most discussion sessions or, more accurately, recitation or quiz sessions in physics are now put. Homework is the best way for the student to acquire information; it can also be used to improve reading habits, provided the material is not repeated in the lecture.

The above analysis of the relation between behavioral objectives and appropriate teaching methods is superficial: there are, of course, different ways to lecture or to conduct discussion sessions and laboratories that are best suited for attaining specific objectives. Very different treatments should be accorded to a topic depending on whether its main value is propaedeutic, intrinsic, or illustrative, and if illustrative, illustrative of what. Similarly, the main purpose of a laboratory experiment in a given area may be manipulative training or the understanding of control or of systematic error. The design of an effective experiment must suit its purpose; experiments "designed" to teach all about a topic are likely to fail to teach anything. Further, the method of attaining a particular course objective may well vary with the caliber and the major field of the students.

Not all the assertions in the preceding two paragraphs are equally well supported by empirical evidence (20). The main point, however, is merely that both a rational time allowance for lecture, laboratory, and discussion and the conduct of each must proceed from a consideration of behavioral objectives. Consideration of chosen content is, of course, also desirable; however, the choice of an appropriate teaching method should be guided primarily by behavioral objectives.

## 1.3  TEACHERS SHOULD FORMULATE THEIR OWN OBJECTIVES

Since it would be impossible to discuss the various ways to understand a science without a list of objectives, such a list appears in the next chapter. But every science teacher should prepare his own list, for each teacher has his own image of his teaching goals, even if they are not explicitly stated, that is congenial to him. He will not feel really easy with anyone else's scheme; he will find it difficult or awkward to use a borrowed plan to guide his teaching and testing. Most of the objectives in Chapter 2 are probably basically acceptable to a science teacher; nevertheless, he should reword them to fit his own habits of expression, perhaps after consulting his colleagues.

Where several instructors teach the same course they must arrive jointly at a formulation of their common objectives. The agreement cannot be perfect; each instructor will have his own objectives in addition to the common ones, and that is as it should be. Teaching is an art, and therefore, for a full utilization of the teacher's talents and knowledge, a great degree of freedom should be allowed him in the choice of content, methods of instruction, objectives, and, certainly, the *formulation* of objectives. But teaching also is, or should be, a science. Therefore a good deal of systematization and agreement on teaching goals and their description is possible. Paradoxically, such agreement will increase rather than decrease the individual teacher's freedom. To make sure that various members of a staff do indeed teach the same course, the current practice is to make them use the same laboratory experiments, the same textbooks, and even the same chapters. Such uniformity becomes much less important once the course is defined in terms of goals and not in terms of means. Naturally, most of the content must remain common to all instructors, because a knowledge of content of high intrinsic value will be one of the objectives of the course, but its treatment and the choice of illustrative content may be left to individual preference.

To reach agreement on objectives and content, members of a staff must not only reconsider all phases of their teaching but must also talk to each other about them. Both these activities are highly recommended. A long, hard discussion that suggests a *variety* of appropriate teaching methods and test exercises as well as alternative wordings of the objectives should bring out the real differences of opinion among the teaching staff and resolve disagreement that is only apparent. Objectives arrived at by this method will introduce clarity into communication among the participants and aid them in teaching and testing. A list of objectives prepared by an outsider and accepted by a teaching staff that has not gone through the process described above can only bring apparent clarity and may lead to confusion. On the other hand, once a teacher has formulated his own objectives he will find translation between them and another set, such as the one in

Chapter 2, surprisingly easy, and the agreement on the total range of objectives will almost invariably be close indeed.

Chapter 3 describes methods for formulating objectives from three different starting points: the future of the students, the nature of the discipline taught, and the kind of course already in existence.

## 1.4  TEACHERS SHOULD ENGAGE IN EDUCATIONAL RESEARCH

Section 1.1 advanced the thesis that teachers should think and talk about their teaching systematically and analytically, and that to do so most of them need a better conceptual pedagogical vocabulary. Teachers should also experiment with their teaching; such experimentation by college teachers whose interest is primarily teaching should probably be at the level of research (15). Serious analysis of teaching, and research on or even experimentation with teaching, require a great deal of time. Unfortunately, not much time is allowed for these activities by either schools or colleges. In particular, introductory college science teaching is commonly relegated in "strong" departments to people who regard it as a chore, and in "weak" departments to people whose teaching load is so great that they have no time for scholarly activity and must be content with a routine performance of teaching duties.

Yet it is generally admitted that science teaching needs improvement and that college professors must be scholars, which usually means that they must do publishable research. The necessity for improving physics teaching, for instance, is strongly suggested by the lack of change in teaching methods over the years, by the prevalent student distaste for physics courses (12), and by their consequent general dislike of physics. This dislike is unjustified, because very few introductory physics courses show or even attempt to show what physics is like; physics as a process of inquiry is barely mentioned and physics as a body of knowledge is fragmented until it is unrecognizable. The widely held opinion that we need more scientists has resulted in some efforts to make science courses richer and more interesting. The more vigorous and imaginative of these efforts, however, have been directed *by* college teachers *at* high school courses (13). It is true, of course, that schoolteachers have had better, or at least more, training in pedagogy than in science, and that an interest in science is not likely to be engendered by a teacher who doesn't know science. On the other hand, a dislike of science is even more likely to result from pedagogical mistreatment than from the teacher's lack of knowledge of his subject; in this respect, colleges are at least as blameworthy as schools. Yet various organizations that are concerned with college physics teaching, for instance, seem to tiptoe around teaching proper and to feel much happier with peripheral, though useful, activities such as designing buildings or apparatus and preparing better texts (14).

The rather gingerly approach of organizations to the real problems of teaching, the problems of pedagogy, has some justification, for fundamental progress is contingent on the individual teacher's struggle with these problems. But an organized effort should be made to mold public opinion toward a recognition that pedagogical research by practicing pedagogues is both necessary and respectable, perhaps as respectable as research in science. That the prestige of these two areas of research is now enormously different is obvious from the allocation of salaries and promotions, from opinions both implied and openly expressed, and from the available outside financial support. It is comparatively easy for a college profesosr to get a federal grant for "improving his teaching" if his method is to learn more science, and very difficult if his method is to learn pedagogy. Public approbation and support are our society's most powerful tools for making an activity flourish. There is a good deal of truth in J. R. Oppenheimer's remark that research, like marriage and poetry, should be discouraged, and that it should occur despite discouragement. But research in science teaching is now so anemic and discouragement of it so great that there is little danger in the foreseeable future of overproduction of cheap goods or of intellectual corruption of the participants by rewards of any sort. Research in physics and other sciences, on the other hand, has not been able entirely to avoid these dangers.

Offhand, it would seem that in this age of specialization educational research should be, as it usually is, left to departments of education. There are two reasons, however, for supplementing the professionals' research with local effort: one is the already discussed desirability of developing better communication among teachers; the other is the difficulty of applying to local teaching problems the information found in educational literature. Education is still a crude science, partly because its problems are exceedingly complex, so complex in fact that it is quite generally considered not one science but a mixture of several, and partly because, at least in recent years, it has not been able to attract enough talent. Professors of education are aware of this, and their professional dignity is as shaky as that of physicists who do no research in physics. Researchers in education and other social sciences look enviously at the more prestigious natural sciences and often choose problems more for their amenability to exact solution than for their importance. All these factors are responsible for the general opinion that educational literature is more voluminous than it is nutritious. To find answers to a teacher's problems in this literature is possible—and, in fact, sometimes necessary—but difficult. Moreover, the answers are likely to be rather abstract, and their application to a specific problem will usually require from the teacher additional research of his own.

A university is a community of scholars. That, and not the teaching of specialized courses, is its distinguishing characteristic, for such courses are taught in trade schools and dancing academies. Most universities sanction only one scholarly activity—research in one's own field. The "field" is also defined narrowly: physics, but not teaching, is said to be the physics professor's field. Unfortunately, his scientific research is unlikely to make the professor a better teacher at the undergraduate level, partly because such research demands a great deal of time and physical and emotional energy and partly because much of it is not scholarly. But the most important factor may be that many scientists, especially if they are young, consider teaching a separate, rather low-class activity that competes for time with research. The reason for this negative attitude of young researchers toward teaching may be that they have been mistreated pedagogically, that they lack experience and instruction in teaching, or that they are assigned to teach courses that do not readily permit them to use their newly acquired insight into science. It is therefore fortunate that there exists a scholarly activity—research in teaching—that makes the scholar a better teacher. If research is a college professor's obligation, it is the college's obligation to provide him with time and facilities for research in almost any field within his competence, certainly in a field as closely associated with his scientific activities as the teaching of his own subject matter.

At present the duties of college scientists are commonly defined as teaching and research—in science. But many scientists are not provided with the facilities necessary for modern research; some could not do scientific research even if so provided; and some would rather do research in teaching. For all these people, research in the very broad field of teaching is the only way to become or to remain scholars and, for most, the only way to maintain or regain their self-respect. The respect of their colleagues and administrative recognition will follow, though perhaps slowly. It can be speeded up, as indicated a few paragraphs back, by propaganda from various organizations, but only moderately, because beating drums for an almost nonexistent but "necessary" activity is an ambiguous gesture. A better starting point is an increase in teaching research by science teachers. They have formidable obstacles to overcome, but their rewards will be great. They will learn, if they do not know it already, that teaching associated with scholarly pursuits is an exciting and highly rewarding activity. Scholar-teachers will produce better scientists and thus contribute to the progress of science; it is they and not researchers in science who can engender a rational respect for science instead of the awe generated by sputniks and miracle drugs. They will be able to leave their knowledge of teaching to posterity: at present the death of a great teacher is like the death of a violin virtuoso before recording was invented.

# 2

## SUGGESTED OBJECTIVES FOR
## SCIENCE COURSES

Chapter 1 pointed out the value of a fairly detailed set of teaching objectives: They provide a vocabulary that facilitates communicating with colleagues, administrators, and students; carrying out educational research; and designing a course. In addition, a teacher's notes for a lecture, discussion, or laboratory are not complete unless they include behavioral objectives as well as a list of topics, for the objectives will determine the teacher's best method of presentation.

Explicitly stated objectives are thus directly useful in the teaching process. This book, however, attacks the problem of improving teaching indirectly; it uses objectives primarily to analyze problems of testing. One way to help teachers learn how to teach is to show them how to construct and recognize good tests and how to interpret their results. A good test will tell the teacher what the students learn from his course and what they do not, and this is the beginning of teaching wisdom.

The importance of explicit and fairly detailed behavioral objectives in testing becomes quite clear when one is asked to write or recommend a test for someone else's course. Teachers might also try analyzing and criticizing the accuracy of their tests as estimates of the extent to which their students are prepared to meet various future situations. They will find that deciding what the student should be able to *do* as a result of his training is a necessary step in such an analysis. They may also resolve that they will never again write a test without being guided by the explicit goals of the course.

This chapter lists the kinds of competence that may constitute the objectives of a course in one of the physical sciences in college or high school and explains the meanings of the terms and the classificatory scheme used in the list. (Modifications of the list to make it suitable for biological sciences should readily suggest themselves to teachers of those sciences.) Most of the explanations will indicate how to test for various objectives, that is, will help define the objectives operationally, since the list of objectives will be used in most of the book as a guide for test construction and criticism. To define an objective as clearly as possible, a test exercise is described that would measure essentially that objective only, even though the exercise may not in fact be practicable. The competence that a test exercise measures depends on the students' preparation; the students to whom the illustrative test exercises are directed are those taking their first college-level physics course. (An increasing number of high schools teach such courses.) Sometimes, to avoid circumlocution, the word *physics* is used in stating an objective. Although the statement might well remain valid if *chemistry* or *astronomy* or perhaps even *physiology* were used instead, such substitution will be left to teachers of those sciences.

## 2.1   A LIST OF POSSIBLE OBJECTIVES OF A COURSE IN A PHYSICAL SCIENCE

The three general types of competence, or *ability*, in the list are 1, knowledge; 2, understanding (both analytical and intuitive); and 3, the ability to learn. Each ability is further subdivided into that concerned with symbolic (verbal and mathematical) subject matter and that concerned with real phenomena. Besides the numbers 1, 2, and 3, the letter $I$ is used to denote intuitive understanding and the letter $L$ to denote laboratory competence. Altogether eight abilities are listed: 1 and L1; 2, I2, L2, and IL2; and 3 and L3. The next subclass, indicated by the first decimal, is objectives: these objectives usually show the broad realm or field (such as the nature and structure of physics) within which an ability is to be exercised. For example, listed under theoretical or book knowledge are objectives 1.1, possession of information, and 1.2, knowledge of relations. The *content* within the realm or field is indicated by the second decimal; for example, 1.22, theories and phenomena. Spelled out, 1.22 stands for verbal and mathematical knowledge of the relation between those theories and phenomena that have been taught in the course.

The list of objectives, because of all the numbers, decimals, and letters, looks more formidable than it really is. The reason for the complex scheme is that it facilitates reference to Part II of this book, in which the same numbers are used to classify a large number of test items and exercises. The reader should give the list in this chapter just a brief look at this point and then consult it only as the subsequent text refers to it.

### A list of possible objectives of a course in a physical science

(Statements in parentheses after the name of an objective refer to testing for the attainment of the objective. Most of them are examples of possible test questions.)

**Ability 1. Knowledge: verbal and mathematical**
(Tests of knowledge should be restricted to contexts very similar to those in which the subject matter has been presented in the course.)

Objective 1.1. Possession of information about
1.11. Laws and principles   (State Boyle's law.)
1.12. Theories   (State the electromagnetic theory of light.)
1.13. Facts   (What determines the period of a simple pendulum?)
1.14. Definitions of physical quantities   (Define *volt*.)
1.15. History   (When and by whom was the neutron discovered?)
Objective 1.2. Knowledge of relations (explicitly treated in the course) between:
1.21. Empirical generalizations (laws of nature) and specific phenomena   (Calculate the acceleration of a system.)
1.22. Theories and phenomena   (Give evidence for the photon theory of light.)
1.23. Instruments or experiments and conclusions   (Describe the action of a cyclotron.)
1.24. Broad concepts or classifications and specifics   (Define and give examples of a postulate of a theory, statistical evidence, experimental control.)

**Ability L1. Laboratory knowledge**
(Laboratory skills are not included under laboratory knowledge. See objective L3.2. Tests should be restricted to experiments very similar to those performed in the course; apparatus is normally required.)

Objective L1.1. Knowledge of apparatus and materials   (Read a vernier setting. Estimate the resistance of a wire.)
Objective L1.2. Knowledge of laboratory procedures   (Set up a potentiometer and measure the emf of a cell. Knowledge of procedures that require skill beyond the student's ability can be tested by asking him to direct and criticize someone else's procedure.)
Objective L1.3. Knowledge of relations between data and generalizations from the data   (Give important sources of error in the Atwood machine experiment. Atwood machine is present for the student's inspection.)

**Ability 2. Understanding: verbal and mathematical**
(Disciplined and highly imaginative thinking are not included under understanding. See objectives 3.3 and 3.4. Tests of analytical or intuitive understanding should be based on situations that have important elements new to the student.)

Objective 2.1. Understanding the individual topics and principles taught in the course

2.11. Empirical generalizations   (A brick can be pulled along a surface with a string; however, the string would break if jerked sharply. Explain.)

2.12. Theories   (Give evidence for the assertion that radioactive disintegration is *not* the result of interatomic collisions.)

2.13. Experiments that can be understood without laboratory experience   (Describe an experiment for measuring the heat conductivity of mercury.)

2.14. Concepts   (PE + KE of a freely falling body remains constant even though a force acts on the body. Explain.)

Objective 2.2. Understanding the interrelationships of physics principles and their relationships to principles of other disciplines

2.21. Situations involving more than one area of physics   (Droplets of water are suspended in oil in a rapidly rotating drum. Describe and explain the motion of water droplets.)

2.22. Situations involving more than one physical science   (What role does mathematics play in physics? A mixture of oxygen and hydrogen reacts violently when illuminated by sunlight. Explain.)

2.23. Situations involving nonphysical sciences   (What are the main complicating factors in applying Bernoulli's principle to the circulation of blood? A brief description of the relevant anatomy and physiology is available to the student.)

Objective 2.3. Understanding the nature and structure of physics

2.31. Physics as a body of knowledge: criteria for empirical generalization, theory, model, experiment, concept, and definition   (What are the advantages of assuming that the sidereal day—rather than the solar day—does not vary in length in the course of a year?)

2.32. Physics as inquiry   (Do modern physicists try to anticipate the results of a new experiment? Give an example. Why is the wave theory of light still used despite the discovery of the photoelectric effect? What is the relation between experimental data on blackbody radiation and the quantum theory of *light*?

**Ability I2. Intuitive understanding**
(The subject matter of intuitive understanding is listed under 2.1, 2.2, and 2.3. Tests must be based on situations that are novel and sufficiently complex to preclude an analytical solution. Example: The three free ends of a T-shaped wire are kept at constant temperatures. Estimate the temperature of the wire at a given point.)

**Ability L2. Laboratory understanding**
(Tests must be based on situations that have important elements new to the student. Apparatus is normally required. Laboratory understanding does not include imaginativeness or skill. [See objectives L3.2 and L3.4.]

The teacher can test a student's laboratory understanding by asking him to perform a task, to direct another student's performance, or to criticize another student's performance. The first method is best, but it can be used only if the student is *known* to be adequately imaginative and skillful. If he lacks the necessary skill he should be asked to direct a performance, and if he lacks both skill and imagination he should be asked to criticize. For brevity the examples below describe only the task to be performed.)

Objective L2.1. Understanding of processes of measurement
   L2.11. Apparatus   (Set up apparatus to verbal or symbolic specifications; describe verbally or symbolically apparatus already set up; determine, from an inspection of a mechanism, how it functions or why it misfunctions.)
   L2.12. Measurement   (Select proper apparatus, carry out specified measurements, and interpret the results. For example, measure a very high or very low resistance.)
Objective L2.2. Understanding of experiment: understanding the relation between theoretical or "book" physics and phenomena   (Find out experimentally what factors determine the electrical resistance of a salt solution.)
   L2.21. Experimental design   (Make a preliminary design of an experiment.)
   L2.22. Experimental process   (Perform an experiment.)
   L2.23. Interpretation of experimental data   (Interpret the results of an experiment.)

**Ability IL2. Intuitive understanding of phenomena**
(Tests must be based on situations that are novel and sufficiently complex to preclude an analytical solution. Example: Estimate the distance a spring gun will project a pellet. The student should be allowed to handle both the spring and the pellet.)

**Ability 3. Ability to learn**
(Tests should be based on material that is new to the student.)

Objective 3.1. Ability to understand prose
   3.11. A brief statement   (A statement of a principle new to the student is followed by a problem based on the principle.)
   3.12. A passage   (What are the author's assumptions, methods of argument, conclusions?)
   3.13. A chapter, article, or book   (Summarize the main content; state the author's thesis.)
Objective 3.2. Ability to understand nonverbal symbolism
   3.21. Symbolically indicated operations   (Given:  $F(a,b,c,d) = ac - bd$. What is $F(1,2,1,1)$ equal to?)

3.22. Graphs, drawings, photographs, tables (Given a table of properties of several materials, choose the material that is best for a specified purpose.)

3.23. Spatial relationships (Two identical cubical containers are filled with equal weights of copper spheres. What does this imply about the spheres' sizes?)

Objective 3.3. Disciplined thinking

3.31. Possession of, or at least an ability to conform to or to imitate, scientists' modes and habits of thought and action and their attitudes toward inquiry (For example, the ability to suspend subjective beliefs and likes. The student is asked to complete a syllogism some of whose premises he considers false.)

3.32. Ability to organize and formulate ideas (Compare, systematically and critically, two competing theories, such as the kinetic-molecular and caloric theories. Write a report on the Boyle's law experiment.)

Objective 3.4. Imaginative thinking; ingenuity (For example, the ability to think up questions about a phenomenon new to the student, to imagine possible answers, to formulate hypotheses, and to suggest methods of attack; the ability to orient oneself in a complex or very novel situation and to see possible connections among elements that are diverse or apparently inconsistent.)

Objective 3.5. Knowledge of sources of information (What reference would you use to learn how to prepare a small amount of hydrogen chloride?)

**Ability L3. Ability to learn from experiment or observation**

Objective L3.1. Ability to pursue experimental inquiry (Find out experimentally what factors determine the electrical resistance of a salt solution.)

Objective L3.2. Possession of laboratory skills (These skills require good muscular control, good eyesight, and so forth. Without these skills a student may be able to direct an experiment but not to perform it himself.)

Objective L3.3. Disciplined thinking (Same kind of tests as for 3.3, except that these involve real apparatus and phenomena.)

Objective L3.4. Imaginative thinking in the laboratory (Same kind of tests as for 3.4, except that these involve real apparatus and phenomena. Example: Design an experiment to measure the electrical resistivity of human skin, perform it, and interpret its results. Explain why a cloud in the sky has a particular shape.)

## 2.2   MEANING OF TERMS AND CONCEPTS IN THE LIST OF OBJECTIVES

**Explanation of the classificatory scheme**

(The numbers in parentheses on this page and the following page refer to entries in the list of objectives.)

*1. Knowledge*   A student has adequate knowledge if he can recall the content, that is, laws, theories, and other assertions, presented in the course (1.1, information). The objective 1.2, knowledge of relations, also includes the ability to reproduce derivations and other arguments and to recall and follow various "recipes," for example, quite explicit rules for solving problems closely patterned on those discussed in class or in the text. Acquaintance with materials, apparatus, and processes of the experiments performed in the course is listed under L1, laboratory knowledge. Content entries 1.21 through 1.24 correspond to 2.11 through 2.14. There are no content entries under knowledge that correspond to those under 2.2 and 2.3, because to *know* that mathematics is the language of physics or that operational definitions are desirable is essentially useless unless the student *understands* the full implications of these assertions.

*2. Understanding*   A student understands a particular portion of the subject matter if he can use his knowledge of it in a context or situation so novel that the situation cannot be analyzed simply by following explicit rules taught and practiced in the course (but not so novel as to require highly imaginative thinking). For instance, he understands a law if he can use it to solve a problem different from those he has been taught to solve in the course (2.11). He understands a theory (2.12) taught in the course if he can assess the cogency of experimental results *not* presented in the course as evidence for the theory. If the student can solve a problem that involves two or more principles taught separately in the course (2.21) or that involves principles from other sciences, such as chemistry (2.22) or biology (2.23), he shows an understanding of the interrelationship of the principles involved. The information outside physics, however, must usually be furnished. An understanding of the general criteria for theory or definition (2.31) can be tested by asking the student to criticize a theory or definition not taught in the course. His understanding of physics as inquiry (2.32) involves understanding the goals, attitudes, and methods of physicists, and the growth of physics. An understanding of the principles and processes of measurement (L2.1) can be tested by asking the student to direct or criticize a measurement new to him. (Performing the measurement may require skills in addition to understanding [L3.2].) Testing understanding of experiment (L2.2) requires a more complex laboratory problem than does L2.1; the student should decide *what* to measure as well as how.

If a student arrives at a correct or nearly correct conclusion without being able to identify the logical steps that lead to the conclusion, he has reached the conclusion through the use of intuitive understanding (I2 and IL2).

3. *Ability to learn*    A student has an ability to learn if he is able to acquire knowledge and understanding of new material on his own. Learning from any kind of situation requires that the student be able to think in a disciplined and organized fashion (3.3); for example, his conclusions must correspond to the data. It may also require imagination (3.4 and L3.4); for example, the student may have to formulate searching questions about the situation or invent ways of modifying the situation experimentally. An ability to learn from written material requires an ability to read and interpret prose (3.1) and nonverbal representations (3.2). Under 3.5 is included a knowledge of references or sources of information. An ability to learn from experiment or observation (L3) may be tested in exactly the same way as L2.2, understanding of experiment. In some cases, however, laboratory skills (L3.2), imagination (L3.4), or both may be necessary for learning from experiments.

### Explanation of concepts
*Knowledge*    Knowledge has been variously described as possession of information, grasp of the subject matter, acquaintance with the main facts, and remembering what was taught in the course. The last is nearly, but not quite, the sense in which *knowledge* is used here. A student *knows* (rather than *remembers*) how to solve stereotyped problems. The same word would describe the competence of a bricklayer, who surely does more than *remember* how to lay brick (though he may do less than *understand* the task). Success on a test designed to measure knowledge, especially knowledge of relations, will probably depend on the ability to organize and relate the materials studied as well as on memory; this ability in turn depends on the student's verbal and mathematical facility and on his intelligence. It must be emphasized, however, that in testing for knowledge the ability to organize should not be measured directly; it is to be of help to the student primarily as a mnemonic device. Some students will answer what is meant to be a knowledge question not from memory but by a process of deduction that requires understanding. Such a process usually takes more time than straight recall. Its use may be prevented, if the teacher wants to test knowledge only, by decreasing the time allowance for the test. A test for knowledge must usually be a closed-book test.

*Understanding*    Understanding has been variously described as ability to use methods of science, working knowledge of science, possession of the intellectual skills used by scientists, and critical thinking in science. The last is perhaps closest to the meaning of analytical understanding as used here, but the other descriptions are also relevant. In testing for knowledge, the student is asked essentially to reproduce or imitate what he has heard or read in the course; in testing for understanding, the student is asked to work more or less on his own, and it is therefore necessary that test exercises contain elements that are new to him. However, the situations should be of the same *kind* as those studied in the course, for otherwise more than understanding of the course materials may be required. The subject matter of understanding is essentially the same as the subject matter of knowledge: assertions, arguments, relations, and patterns studied in the course. The differences lie in the teaching and testing methods. Teaching of understanding usually requires explicit emphasis on the illustrative value of subject matter; testing for understanding requires situations that could have been, but were not, used as illustrative examples. There are rules, of course, that the student can follow in analyzing exercises requiring understanding. For instance, a rule for attacking any numerical problem may be to write down relevant laws, ignoring factors that are not likely to be important, to write down data, and so forth. But this rule is not specific enough to be called a recipe because no explicit rules exist for deciding what is relevant or what is important. In contrast, recipes do exist for solving highly idealized problems about statics, floating bodies, and so forth. Knowledge of such recipes is sufficient, though of course not necessary, to solve such problems.

The attentive reader will have noticed that *knowledge* was defined without reference to subject matter: "Remembering what was taught in a course" applies equally well to science and to poetry. Similarly, in a test for knowledge, students will understand the task to "state in your own words what was said in yesterday's lecture," and they will write fairly comparable essays. *Understanding*, on the other hand, has close ties with subject matter and is therefore hard to define in the abstract. A test exercise that asks the student to "apply the material of the lecture to a new situation" is ambiguous. There will be as many different answers as there are students. To specify the new situation it is of course necessary to refer to the relevant subject matter.

The above paragraph sketches a difference between the words *knowledge* and *understanding* that is reflected in the definitions. This difference is also important in choosing appropriate teaching methods and test exercises.

*Intuitive understanding*    We are all aware that some students and scientists can reach correct conclusions in theoretical or experimental situations without being able to tell us how they have done so. We disapprovingly call the mental process leading to such a conclusion a lucky guess if the conclusion is reached by a student, but we call it scientific intuition or a stroke of genius if reached by a scientist. Some students, however, are "consistently lucky" in their guesses. Intuitive understanding seems a good name for their enviable talent, for consistent luck is a concept foreign to science (2, especially Bruner).

Perhaps all nonsyllogistic "reasoning" or weighing of alternatives is intuitive. Many good speakers and writers form their sentences intuitively, without conscious use of grammar. Some can spell intuitively, by seeing whether the arrangement of letters seems "right," but they cannot explain what orthographic rules they have followed. Similarly, to decide that a peg will not fit a hole one does not analyze the geometry of the two objects and use axioms and theorems; rather, one automatically selects and reacts to the relevant pattern of geometric facts. Perhaps good intuitive thinking depends on choosing patterns aptly, so that their relevance to the situation at hand is immediately apparent. Intuitive understanding thus employs an analysis of the problem, but the analysis is implicit, whereas with analytical understanding it is explicit. Dissimilarities in the two kinds of understanding may also lie in the different uses they make of one's complex mental cross-reference system. Furthermore, intuitive "thinking" makes greater use of nonrational processes than analysis does; for instance, to estimate how far a compressed spring will project a pellet, a student may, without being aware of it, empathize with the spring kinesthetically by tensing his muscles.

This discussion of intuitive thinking is of course tentative and partial. It is only meant to indicate what the phrase means in this book and to point out that we all think intuitively and use both intuitive and analytical understanding in solving almost any problem.

*Laboratory understanding*  The entries under laboratory understanding refer to an understanding of science that requires, or at least is enhanced by, contact with phenomena. These entries illustrate perhaps more clearly than others that, in the ascending hierarchy of intellectual virtues—memory, critical thinking, and imaginative thinking—critical thinking is the upper limit of understanding.

Skills—mostly manual skills—are separated from understanding of measurement. Although some people may not be able to understand measurement without mastering certain skills, others can, and they can show their understanding by directing another person who does not understand measurement in performing it.

Understanding of experiment means understanding the total process by which a scientist, starting from known concepts and generalizations, adds to them, makes them more general, or otherwise modifies them through experimentation. The core of this understanding is therefore an understanding of the relation between verbal-mathematical science and phenomena. Understanding of experiment as it applies to introductory courses is discussed in Section 6.1.

*Ability to learn*   Under ability to learn are listed skills, abilities, and talents that will enable the student to add to his knowledge and understanding without a teacher's help. It may be argued that some of the objectives, such as the ability to organize one's thoughts, could also have been placed under understanding because the ability to state things clearly is a good sign of understanding. It probably is, but it is a sign or a symptom, not a part, of understanding. It is certain, however, that a student who is working independently will find the *acquisition* of understanding of any new and complex subject matter difficult, if not impossible, unless he can organize his thoughts.

The same test can be used for L3.1, an objective under the ability to learn from experiment, as for L2.2, understanding of experiment, not because the ability and the understanding are the same, but because one test can elicit symptoms of each of the two, and because a test for understanding alone would be cumbersome. The two objectives are not easily separated, for understanding how scientists learn from experiment is just what is meant by understanding of experiment. Actual learning by the student from a particular experiment, however, may require not only understanding, but also certain attitudes or beliefs, ingenuity, and skill.

*Disciplined thinking*   It is doubtful that a student's deep-seated convictions and attitudes can be changed through any kind of academically organized effort, especially through repeated assertion or argument or through grades (5). It is for this reason that disciplined thinking is limited here to the ability to conform to rules of logic and evidence. Hopefully, a student who has repeatedly imitated scientific behavior may find that it has become a habit, perhaps even an aesthetically pleasing one. For a young man of our science-permeated civilization may well find that the required scientific behavior conflicts with his own predilections in only a few isolated instances. Section 5.1, however, argues that scientific attitudes and modes of thought cannot be assumed to exist in our students, and that disciplined thinking must therefore be taught and tested. Without disciplined thinking a student may acquire knowledge but not an understanding of a science, either as a body of knowledge or as a process of inquiry. Disciplined thinking is therefore a legitimate subclass under ability to learn. This classification should also throw further light on what is meant by disciplined thinking: it is the kind of thinking that is an aid to learning.

*Imaginative thinking*   Much of what has been said about disciplined thinking applies to imaginative thinking as well. The best way to develop the student's imagination and ingenuity is to allow him to exercise it (5). An imaginative student thinks of many questions, only a few of which are relevant, and of many solutions, none of which may be possible. He plays with the topic under examination, tosses it about, turns it upside down.

In the classroom, he is a pest—to be cherished. The drive behind the student's questions and answers may be curiosity—hopefully about science, but possibly about his own mental processes or about the instructor's or students' reactions. Imaginative thinking does not include curiosity; it is limited here to the more easily teachable or at least detectable talent or competence. Whatever the drive, however, learning with understanding is impossible without formulating questions. In this kind of learning it helps the student if someone acquaints him with relevant classes of questions. For example, what assumptions has an author made and what *kind* of argument does he use? Similarly, the student can be acquainted with the types of question he should ask himself as he designs and carries out an experiment. A student who learns to ask questions may not increase his imaginativeness, but he will be able to use it more effectively.

### Relativity of competence

The type of competence required to accomplish a task depends on the student's preparation. (This point is elaborated in Sections 8.3 and 11.1.) A problem in mechanics, for instance, may demand ingenuity of a high order from a beginning student, only a good understanding of the laws of mechanics from a more advanced student, and a routine sort of knowledge from a student familiar with Lagrange's equations. Similarly, it requires a high degree of manual skill and ingenuity for a beginner to measure the diameter of a sphere with micrometer calipers, but the task can be done relatively easily by most students once the proper procedure has been demonstrated. Roughly speaking, a test exercise will measure knowledge if its ingredients and their patterns are familiar to the student, understanding if they are a mixture of the familiar and unfamiliar, and ability to learn if they are new to the student. A test exercise cannot be classified in any absolute sense; the competence it will measure depends on the degree and kind of novelty it has for the student taking the test. Illustrative test exercises in the list of objectives in Section 2.1 must be judged accordingly; usually, they will measure the competence under which they are listed when administered to the average student in his first college-level course in physics (32). Such courses are now commonly taught in the first or second year in college and with increasing frequency in senior high school. It should be noted that unlike test exercises the objectives are valid in a wide educational range, from grade school to graduate training.

### Nonoperational language of the objectives

Strictly operational language has not been used here to define the main objectives. A student possesses knowledge if he can *recall* content, understanding if he can handle a situation that is *novel to him*, and an ability to learn if he can increase his knowledge and understanding without a teacher's help, but no operational definitions of "recall" or "novel to him" are given. For, if a student can do a specified exercise, that does not necessarily prove that he has knowledge or understanding or ability to learn. A particular competence is not always necessary for solving a problem: there may be several quite distinct mental paths toward the solution (33). Therefore it is better to treat the student's ability to answer a test question not as proof but as evidence of a competence, in the sense that the accomplishment of the task can be explained by assuming that the student possesses the competence. This is the way the parenthetical suggestions for measuring a competence that appear in the list of objectives in Section 2.1 should be interpreted. However, a student's ability to accomplish a great *variety* of properly chosen tasks should be a fairly reliable index of his competence. A variety of tasks or exercises is the best safeguard and assurance of the validity of test results.

## 2.3   CLASSIFICATION OF OBJECTIVES

### Schemes of classification

Objectives must be systematized as well as stated if they are to serve effectively their triple function of improving communication, teaching, and testing. Adequate classifications of content are well known. One such classification divides the field of physics into mechanics, heat, and so forth. Schemes of classification of behavioral objectives are less well known and therefore merit discussion (6). The writer is familiar with and has himself experimented with the following primary or fundamental bases: memory *vs.* mental skills; analysis *vs.* synthesis; inductive *vs.* deductive thinking; quantitative *vs.* qualitative thinking; simple *vs.* complex mental processes; knowledge, critical ability, and creativity; and others. A choice of one of these bases as the primary one does not imply giving up distinctions inherent in other bases. Thus, in a memory *vs.* mental skills scheme, mental skills may be subdivided into those required for inductive and deductive processes of thought, and each of these may be applied to qualitatively or quantitatively described material. The classification of objectives that is used in this book will be defended later in this section.

### The overall objective of science courses

It would be convenient to find a word that encompasses all the main behavioral objectives of science teaching just as the word *physics* describes all the content of that science. The most commonly used words of this sort are knowledge, understanding, mastery, and proficiency. *Knowledge* seems too narrow, dangerously and seductively so, for it strongly suggests that knowing how to do something is the upper limit of the student's intellectual achievement. The ability to use information in novel contexts is much better described by the word *understanding* than by the word *knowledge.* The sentence "I know the law but can't apply it" makes better sense than "I understand the law but can't apply it." *Mastery* is perhaps too broad and certainly a bit immodest. Also, one speaks only hesitantly of degrees of mastery. *Proficiency* is so obviously vague that it almost forces its user—if he is a conscientious teacher—to become more specific, to break down the term into its constituents, and, hopefully, to make him consider what a student should be able to *do* with his knowledge. The coercive nature of the term has been found very useful by advocates (including this author) of more analytic thinking about teaching. This book, however, tries to avoid all—and especially semantic—coercion; its rhetoric is intended to make things clear and leave decisions to the reader.

The word *understanding* has several advantages over those discussed in the preceding paragraph. It makes sense to speak of degrees and kinds of understanding. And the word is both noble and apt because it places introductory science courses, whether for future poets or for future scientists, where, despite their differences, they all belong—among the liberal arts. In this book "understanding science" is occasionally used to describe the total goal of science teaching. This is done for the sake of brevity only, however, for the term is really not general enough. An ability to state Newton's laws of motion, for instance, is not so much an understanding of the law as an item of knowledge that is prerequisite to understanding. It is even more awkward to use *understanding* to describe the ability to interpret a passage that is unfamiliar to the student.

The use of a word whose meaning must be stretched if it is to include certain important aspects of learning will frequently lead to a neglect of those aspects. Most science courses, for example, overemphasize the acquisition of knowledge, and this overemphasis is perpetuated by the overuse of the word *knowledge*. Despite the fact that most science teachers speak highly of understanding and the ability to learn, the word that most readily occurs to them is *knowledge*. "How much physics does he know?" "Does he know enough to take the next course?" and "He knows his chemistry" are the common forms of expression.

### The basic classification

The list of objectives given at the beginning of this chapter speaks not of one general type of competence, but of three: *knowledge, understanding,* and *ability to learn*. These general objectives were chosen for empirical and pragmatic reasons. The criteria were that the terms should be readily understandable, even familiar; that the set of objectives should include most of what science teachers consider important and achievable and little else; and that the classification should make preparing good tests and criticizing prepared tests as easy as possible. Most science teachers use *knowledge, understanding,* and *ability to learn* when speaking of their teaching to mean roughly what they do here. Although few make a special attempt to teach each of the three types of competence and still fewer to test for them, all teachers consider them desirable, most consider them important, and a good number, teachable. Under usual teaching conditions, students' attainments in knowledge, understanding, and ability to learn do not correlate very highly (18). This relative independence or lack of overlapping of the main classes of objectives makes for economy in teaching and testing. This point is taken up again in Sections 7.2 and 9.2.

*Behavioral objectives and content*    Behavioral objectives rather than content are used for primary classification because they allow a more economical discussion of principles and techniques of testing. The techniques of preparing test items on knowledge in two different areas (say, light and heat) are more similar than the techniques of writing items to test knowledge and understanding in a single narrow area (such as calorimetry). In fact, in this sense, some of the behavioral objectives are nearly independent of content. Moreover, excellent courses in introductory physics and other sciences may differ greatly in content; it is much more difficult to omit even one of the main types of competence—*knowledge, understanding,* or *ability to learn*—from a good course.

### Subclassifications

The next subclassification under the three general behavioral objectives approaches the language of content. Thus, under knowledge are 1.1, information, and 1.2, knowledge of relations; these two headings suggest the type of material the student is expected to know as well as what he should be able to do with it. This subdivision by content has been chosen from several other possible subdivisions because it separates the different *kinds* of knowledge (18): different mental processes may be required for their acquisition, and somewhat different methods of teaching and testing are called for. Thus objectives 1.1 and 1.2 are different behavioral objectives, and the fairly low correlation in the attainment of the two objectives by the students in a typical introductory course makes for economy in teaching and testing, pragmatically justifying the subclassification. What has been said about subclassification under knowledge applies in varying degrees to all the first-decimal subclasses, except that 3.3 and 3.4 are openly stated in behavioral language. The second-decimal subclasses are even more closely concerned with content, as in 2.11, understanding of empirical generalizations, and 2.12, understanding of theories.

Laboratory objectives deserve a separate classification for several reasons. The methods and materials of instruction are different; testing requires laboratory equipment; and there is considerable evidence that, as seems likely a priori, different types of ability are required in dealing with laboratory apparatus from those required in dealing with words and other symbols (2).

As stated earlier in this chapter, under the potentially wide canopy of disciplined and imaginative thinking is included only the kind of thinking that is necessary to an investigator or student, to someone who is trying to learn. This limited interpretation of disciplined and imaginative thinking means that they do belong under the general category of ability to learn.

Intuitive as well as analytical understanding are classified as *understanding* because they have certain similarities and probably occur concurrently or intermittently. Negatively, intuitive understanding hardly belongs under knowledge, for it can be exhibited only during an attack on a new problem; nor is there any reason to believe that, in general, it is any more necessary for learning than is analytical understanding.

### Implicit objectives

A very important cross-classification runs through almost all the objectives: ability to deal with nonverbal symbols as opposed to verbal statements. This cross-classification is made explicit in ability to learn, where 3.2 deals with understanding of graphs, tables, and diagrams and 3.1 with understanding of prose passages. But it is merely implicit, except for parenthetical statements, in the objectives of knowledge and understanding, where the presence of the nonverbal element will be indicated only through sample test exercises in Part II of this book. Teachers of the physical sciences will agree that the mathematical description of reality is a characteristic and fundamental property of the sciences. Moreover, the ability to deal with nonverbal symbols does not correlate highly with qualitative understanding and must therefore be given special attention in teaching and testing.

The distinction between science as a body of knowledge and science as inquiry is also not explicit in the classificatory scheme, except in objective 2.3, understanding of the nature and structure of physics. The ability to judge the cogency of evidence for a theory, for instance, is a sign of understanding of both views of science. The distinction is hard to maintain because neither aspect can be really understood without the other. In any analytical scheme, however, distinctions of this sort must be made. It seemed better to differentiate between science as a body of knowledge and science as a process of inquiry on the basis of *content* than on the basis of behavioral objectives. Acquaintance with original papers, on the other hand, is treated not as a direct objective of introductory science teaching, but as a means for understanding certain aspects of science.

Perhaps the most important quality not mentioned explicitly in the classification of objectives is depth, for instance, depth of understanding. The depth of understanding expected of a student is very difficult to specify exactly. Moreover, the required degree of competence will vary from course to course. Various degrees of attainment of objectives will be illustrated in Part II. Here it is necessary only to note that one can measure the depth of a student's ability to learn by asking him to choose a topic or aspect of science that he understands best and then examining him on it at a higher level than other topics. The simplest test form for this purpose is the essay (31, Holton).

### Objectives not included in the list

There are at least two classes of desirable qualities and attitudes that cannot be found in the foregoing list of objectives, however broadly these are interpreted. First, there are objectives that are not likely to be attained through academic means, such as scientific creativity and scientific integrity (5). Second, there are objectives that, although they can be attained through teaching, are best approached indirectly, such as interest and respect for science and its methods. It is of course good pedagogy to make a science course as interesting as possible and at times to emphasize scientists' impressive achievements. But an abiding interest in science can and should be instilled only in certain students. This is probably best done by making clear to *all* students what science is like, especially as a process of inquiry (5). The same procedure can engender respect for science. Pedagogical techniques can make the study of science either satisfying or very unpleasant, and these techniques may well influence the student in the choice of his major (17). But all study should be intellectually rewarding; if it is, the student's own interest will guide him in the choice of his career.

# 3

## METHODS AND CRITERIA
## FOR CHOOSING OBJECTIVES

This chapter discusses methods for arriving at the objectives of a science course and criteria for judging a set of objectives. For illustrative purposes, these criteria will be used to criticize and defend the list of objectives in Section 2.1, which was designed for an introductory course in physics, but the methods and criteria can be applied to other natural science courses as well. The defense is based on the future usefulness of various types of competence, the nature of the relevant science, the opinions of authoritative groups, and the present status of introductory science courses.

### 3.1 SOURCES OF OBJECTIVES

Since education is a preparation for the future, a look at the future of our students is one basic source of teaching objectives. But, at best, the future will indicate only what the total contribution of the educational process should be; the particular contribution of a science course must depend on the nature of the science.

The futures of students will vary, but it is obvious that scientific training can help them understand certain situations and their causes and consequences, resolve problems the situations present, learn from the situations, or just enjoy them. Such situations may occur in the student's next course or in his life as a professional worker or citizen. Taking another science course, doing research in any field, reading a newspaper article on satellites, gazing at stars, and speculating on the origin of life are just a few examples of relevant situations. The formulation of the objectives of a science course might start with a direct attack on the real-life situations the student will eventually face. In such a procedure, the complex competence that an enlightened citizen or a creative scientist must have would be analyzed into its constituents—knowledge, abilities, skills, attitudes, habits.

The last step would be to identify those constituents that a science course would help the student acquire. These would be the proper objectives of the course. Such a deductive method of attack, however, would present rather formidable difficulties. It would be hard to identify the requisite constituents, and even if they could be identified, they would not be likely to add up to the complex whole. The logical path from creative (or even just competent) scientist or enlightened citizen to specific objectives of a course in science is not easy or unambiguous.

An easier and far more common way to formulate objectives is to start with the science itself. The first step here is to analyze the nature of the discipline, to identify its basic parts and decide what constitutes its coherence, unity, and beauty. The second step is to determine what knowledge, abilities, and attitudes a student must develop before he can be said to possess a reasonable understanding of the discipline. A description of these desirable achievements constitutes a tentative list of objectives. The first method of arriving at objectives, which deduces from samples of real-life situations the desirable characteristics of one who has to meet the situations, will show what the educational process *should* contribute to the education of a man. The discipline analysis, on the other hand, will show what a particular science *could* contribute. To make possible a rational choice among the rich offerings of a science, objectives reached by discipline analysis should be checked against representative academic and post-academic situations in which the student may later find himself. Such a check should result in modifications of the tentative list of objectives or at least in revised estimates of their relative importance. But the most salutary result will be the teacher's realization that the choice of behavioral objectives, which specify what the student is expected to be able to do with his science training, is at least as important as the choice of course content.

Although analyses of the students' future and of the science itself should determine the choice of the main objectives of a science course, other, more local considerations will influence the relative emphasis placed on various objectives: the caliber and preparation of the students, the particular competence and interests of the teacher, the nature of the curriculum of which the course is a part, and the limitations of the available methods of instruction (for example, lecture rather than discussion) and of the physical facilities and equipment.

A combined analysis of both the discipline and the students' future is highly desirable, for an over-emphasis on either type of analysis alone leaves many questions unanswered. Most physics teachers live in the ivory tower of sheer discipline analysis. To them "physics is physics." They thus avoid the all-important question of the effect of their course on the future behavior of students, and they may fail to consider such questions as: What is the proper role of straight knowledge or information, which the students lose so quickly? Because material that interests a student is retained longer, are we obliged to make our courses interesting? Should we at least try to combat what seems to be the almost universal opinion of college and high school students that physics is dull and hard or just plain dull (12)? Should we teach our students how to learn? Exclusive preoccupation with physics has meant that, as physics grows, physics texts become thicker and physics teaching correspondingly thinner. And courses for non-physics majors, since "physics is physics," are often mere diluted or "moronized" versions of courses for physics majors, or, worse, insubstantial courses *about* physics (11).

Overpreoccupation with the future of the students and a consequent disregard for the nature of the discipline involved, on the other hand, have had even worse results. The main objective of some physics courses seems to be to prepare students to be handymen—to repair doorbells, for instance. Also, preoccupation with the future can lead to a faulty analysis of the relations between the complex competence required to deal with life situations and the specific subject being taught. The argument may be as follows. Before one can decide on an action in any situation, one must examine the situation to identify its salient features; that is, one must have an ability to interpret data. It follows that a major objective of all education is to teach students how to interpret data. In a physics course, an exercise appropriate to this objective would require the student to draw conclusions from a set of measurements. But there is very little evidence that the mental activity involved in doing such an exercise is essentially similar to the one required to assess real-life situations. The formal quasi-Platonic argument that the phrase *ability to interpret data* fits both cases is suggestive, but far from conclusive. Thus it seems safer to compare life activities and academic experiences at a very general level only and to make teaching objectives more specific by means of discipline analysis.

## 3.2  THE STUDENT'S POST-ACADEMIC FUTURE AS A SOURCE OF OBJECTIVES

All citizens need science training. They should be able to understand natural phenomena and modern technological achievements, such as television, antibiotics, and the nuclear bomb. What is more important, a society should understand its pattern of culture. Otherwise its members will be unable to interpret contemporary historical changes and to take appropriate action.

Our culture is profoundly scientific. The belief in the power of empirical science to solve many of the problems facing humanity has been growing rapidly in the past few hundred years. Science has shaped our present-day thinking probably as strongly as theology shaped the thinking of the Middle Ages. Increasingly we have come to depend on empirical evidence as the best, and sometimes the only acceptable, support for almost any kind of assertion.

Although a reasoned argument that would lead from a consideration of the student's future to a design of his first science course is enormously complicated and difficult, a look at relevant future situations can suggest general classes of objectives. Science training is useful if it helps one to understand a situation or to learn from it. It seems clear that to be able to do either, one must have at one's disposal a certain fund of information or knowledge on which to draw. Further, since the situation is most unlikely to duplicate situations analyzed in a course, the student must be able to use his knowledge to analyze situations that are in some degree novel to him. The ability to transcend the immediate context of the learning situation is here called *understanding*. Finally, the student must know how to learn. Otherwise his intellectual growth will stop after he graduates: experience is a good teacher, but only to those who can learn. An analysis of the student's future has thus yielded three basic types of competence: knowledge, understanding, and ability to learn.

## 3.3   THE STUDENT'S ACADEMIC FUTURE AS A SOURCE OF OBJECTIVES

Introductory physics courses are designed to accommodate three main groups of students: future non-scientists, future biologists, and future physical scientists. All these courses should teach knowledge, understanding, and ability to learn. There is of course considerable overlap among the three types of competence. Many teachers use this overlap to argue that possession of knowledge is a sufficient index of all three abilities; others argue the sufficiency of ability to learn.

The argument for sufficiency of knowledge runs as follows. Ability to learn is a prerequisite to understanding, and understanding is necessary in choosing what information to acquire; it follows that a student who has appropriate knowledge is certain to have attained the other two objectives. The argument has two weaknesses. First, course content is chosen not by the student but by the teacher, and, second, ability to learn stands for unaided learning, not for learning under expert guidance.

A stronger argument can be made for ability to learn as the all-sufficient objective: Learning from a situation is impossible without understanding it, and understanding has no meaning without knowledge. The trouble with this argument is that a legitimate and realistic objective of, say, an introductory physics course is not to teach how to learn but only how to learn *physics*. This narrower skill is often nearly all that a student needs for his next physics course. If he does well, the introductory course has served its main purpose. But the direct contribution that an introductory physics course can make to a student of biology, for instance, is to give him an understanding of physics. The ability to learn physics is of value to such a student mostly because it has common elements with the ability to learn biology. There is no evidence that the two abilities are identical (2).

The preceding paragraphs argue that understanding is a legitimate and independent objective of a course in science. Knowledge unaccompanied by understanding is harder to defend from an analysis of the student's future because, unless the student can use knowledge, it has little value. However, a student who has acquired knowledge from an introductory course can be taught how to use it by the teacher of the next course. The teacher may not be pleased with this additional task, but he would quite properly refuse even to admit a student who did not have the prerequisite knowledge.

### Non-science majors

Humanities and social science majors will have little opportunity, as students, to use the knowledge of physics they acquire in the introductory course. Consequently it is likely to disappear almost entirely unless joined to an understanding that may be exercised in non-physics contexts (7). The main reason that the non-scientist should attain a set of objectives like the one in Section 2.1 is that science is an important component of liberal education. The characteristic goal of liberal education is to furnish the student with intellectual tools, to give him an understanding of how the human mind deals with basic problems, an understanding thorough enough to lay a firm foundation for further learning. The student must therefore understand the nature and structure of science, both as a body of knowledge and as a process of inquiry, and he must understand its relation to other disciplines. He must also be able to use that understanding in future situations. In other words, he must have understanding and ability to learn; these of course are impossible without knowledge.

The preceding section points out that understanding of science is essential for a proper understanding of modern man and his world. That humanities majors do not understand science is therefore deplorable, although no more deplorable than scientists' ignorance of the humanities. The case of social science students is graver, for many of their professors imitate the research methods of the natural sciences. Such imitation may not be desirable in any event; without understanding the nature and structure of the natural sciences, it is dangerous.

### Biological science majors

As the student of biology leaves the physics course, he leaves behind him all frictionless planes, nonviscous fluids, and thin lenses. The knowledge he has acquired about these is no longer useful to him unless he can apply it to situations greatly different from those in the physics text, unless, that is, he has an understanding of the material. Moreover, the information in his physics text is seldom thorough or detailed enough to help him study, for instance, blood flow, radiology, or microscopy. He must be able to read up on more advanced or at least more specific physics. A physics course, then, should equip a biology student with some aspects of knowledge, understanding, and ability to learn.

An understanding of experiment and disciplined thinking are especially important for biology majors. Disciplining students' thinking, though, must be done sparingly and very conservatively. Only extreme deviations from what the teacher considers the norm should be explicitly seen to. Nevertheless, the habit, say, of not making conclusions unwarranted by data, can probably be taught and then transferred from physics to biology. The relation of book physics to experimental phenomena is of course very different from that of book biology to experimental phenomena. The generalizations of physics are broader and more abstract; observations are classical, that is, nonquantum, while many theories are not. A good deal of biology, on the other hand, concerns only the visible. These differences indicate the comparatively complex relation of physics to experimental phenomena, but this very complexity gives physics a sharper epistemological focus than biology. It is easier to show through physics than through biology that science is more than just a mirror of nature. Yet many of the terms of analysis in the two fields have similar meanings: empirical generalization, evidence, proof, hypothesis. Some transfer of training should therefore be possible, especially if teaching is reinforced by explicit comparisons of the two sciences (4). More generally, since the biologist has increasingly used physics as a model and a tool, he must understand its nature and structure.

### Physical science majors

That a physical scientist should understand what physics is like as one of the liberal arts as well as from the more technical standpoint is readily apparent, especially since today's physicists are often asked to serve as advisers on important biological and social problems. What is less obvious is that the first physics course a physics major takes should shift its center of gravity toward the liberal arts and away from pre-professional education. There are two reasons for this assertion. First, the introductory course should help the student decide whether to choose physics as a career, and a rational decision must of course be based on an understanding of what physics is, especially as a process of inquiry. Second, a student who fails to get a broad understanding of the scope and nature of the discipline before he begins a detailed study of its components is not likely to get this understanding from succeeding physics courses. These courses will be preoccupied with mathematically elegant, highly refined recipes (such as Schrödinger's, Hamilton-Jacobi, and Maxwell's equations) for solving certain types of problems. Contact with raw phenomena will be slighted, especially the origin of the recipes; these recipes will be postulated, to be justified by results. However, the postulational approach is too sophisticated for many students, probably because the introductory course has not showed them how to orient themselves among the various kinds of assertions in physics or how to understand their legitimate uses and relation to one another and to phenomena. Few graduate students, even those who intend to teach introductory physics, are able to discuss adequately such questions as: How was Ohm's law discovered (without ammeters)? In what sense does the Atwood machine experiment support Newton's second law of motion? What is the basic objection to defining 50° as the geometrical halfway mark between 0°C and 100°C on a mercury-in-glass thermometer? Can Huygens' principle be used for de Broglie or Schrödinger waves?

### 3.4  NATURE OF SUBJECT MATTER AS A SOURCE OF OBJECTIVES

The section on the students' academic future shows that an analysis of physics as one of the liberal arts can yield a set of basic objectives appropriate to any introductory physics course. (Common basic objectives do not imply that the various kinds of introductory courses should be identical, that the several objectives should have the same importance, or that all subobjectives should be pursued in any one course.) But although an introductory physics course shares with liberal arts courses the objectives of understanding and ability to learn, designing a physics course to achieve these objectives naturally requires a knowledge of the important characteristics of physics. Such characteristics are outlined in the following paragraphs; the numbers in parentheses indicate what competence, from the list in Section 2.1, indicates an understanding of the characteristic.

Physics, like all natural sciences, deals with phenomena with the aid of symbols. However, the relation between reality and symbols in physics (L2) is particularly rich and subtle because physics is a highly abstract science. Physics is characterized by unity: its parts are closely and coherently articulated (2.21). Physics is basic to the other physical (2.22) and biological sciences (2.23). Generalizations, both empirical (2.11) and theoretical (2.12), of presumably universal validity; experiments of extraordinary ingenuity and precision (2.13); and highly refined abstract concepts (2.14) are characteristic of physics. It is therefore important to understand the criteria for generalization, experiment, and concept (2.31) and the attitude toward processes of inquiry (2.32) used in physics.

The above paragraph refers to all the subdivisions of analytical understanding in Section 2.1. The entries under knowledge are prerequisite to understanding. Section 2.2 argues that all entries under ability to learn are useful and some indispensable for acquiring further understanding of physics. In addition, ability to learn is justifiable as an ability to pursue inquiry, and knowledge, as an acquaintance with the results of the inquiry. Furthermore, the nature of an inquiry and its results are often so interdependent that one cannot be understood or appreciated without the other.

Clearly, the above discussion does not prove that the objectives in Chapter 2 are a logical consequence of a discipline analysis of physics; rather it shows that the objectives are consistent with such an analysis. The discussion does indicate, however, that each objective is a legitimate part of understanding physics. For example, the common assertion, "I have time for physics only, not for its history," is more accurately, "I have no time for that (historical development) aspect of understanding physics." If such a change reveals the weaknesses of the original statement, so much the better.

### 3.5    AUTHORITATIVE OPINIONS AS A SOURCE OF OBJECTIVES

The author has found, through interviews, that the nearly unanimous opinion of many professors, heads of department, deans, and college presidents is that a student should receive from his college education—in descending order of importance—an ability to learn further, an understanding of what he has studied, and a certain amount of information. This opinion is apparently shared by employers of students with a B.A. or B.S. in physics or engineering (8). The sample of employers was limited primarily to research directors in very large corporations.

An ability to learn from his course is naturally what a teacher expects of his students. Asked to define this ability, the teacher of an advanced course will usually say that he wants students to be able to do independent reading, to organize their ideas, to understand "the very few fundamental ideas" of courses that are prerequisite to his, and to have "some" information. The hierarchy of objectives is often inverted if the teacher is asked what the students should receive from *his* course; knowledge rises to the top, and the ability to learn sinks to the bottom.

Tests given to students reflect these double standards. Tests determining the student's grade in a course stress knowledge. Prognostic tests, in particular various scholarship and talent-search tests, attempt to gauge ability to learn, partly directly (in the sense of objective 3) and partly by measuring understanding.

The opinions of educators and employers thus indicate little meeting of minds or even of parts of one mind—the mind of a professor who teaches two courses, one prerequisite to the other. A discussion of this schizoid pattern of culture appears in the next chapter; the opinions are mentioned here only to show that all three main objectives have authoritative defenders.

### Carleton College conference

The recommendations on physics teaching made by a conference composed of physics teachers (the author was one of these), administrators, textbook writers, and research physicists from universities and industry, which met at Carleton College in 1956, are quoted below * for their value as a detailed argument by authorities in the field. The objectives the group developed were endorsed in 1962 by the Commission on College Physics (6, Commission). The conference accepted the important statement made by a committee of the American Institute of Physics, which emphasized that the student "should have an appreciation for the science of physics and the mode of thought which to such a large degree has been responsible for the phenomenal development of physics over the past decades [2.31, 2.32]." It was agreed that the goals quoted below are desirable in all physics courses, whether the courses are for physicists and other scientists or for non-scientists (including those taking general education science courses). The goals describe the knowledge, understanding, and beliefs that physicists should have and should help their students to attain.

(1) The physicist is, almost by definition, curious about the physical world in which he finds himself. . . .

(2) . . . the physicist . . . learns the limitations and scope of his descriptions and interpretations [L2.2, 2.31]. . . .

(3) He has learned that there are underlying, unifying principles [2.11, 2.12, 1.1, 1.2] . . . .

(4) He knows that [one] must know something of the historical development of underlying ideas [2.32, 1.5] . . . .

(5) The physicist has often pioneered in the development of precise methods of measurement [2.13, L2.1] . . . .

(6) The physicist believes that through a proper understanding of the laws of nature, people can arrive at more objective judgments [3.3] . . . .

(7) [He has gained] a precise understanding of the basic concepts of physics [2.14] . . . .†

The conference felt that the physics teacher can introduce the student to "methods of clear and concise analysis and presentation." In particular, he can help the student to develop the ability:

(1) To approach and solve new problems, using verbal formulation, mathematical analysis [abilities 2 and 3], or experimental manipulation [L2 and L3].

(2) To read and comprehend scientific writings at various levels of complexity [3.1, 3.2].

(3) To express himself in clear, succinct, and precise statements, written or oral, qualitative or quantitative [3.3].‡

---

* Insertions in brackets are the author's; numbers in brackets refer to the objectives in Section 2.1.

† "Improving the Quality and Effectiveness of Introductory Physics Courses: Report of a Conference Sponsored by the American Association of Physics Teachers," *American Journal of Physics,* XXV (1957), 419–20. Reprinted by permission of the publisher, The American Institute of Physics.

‡ *Ibid.,* p. 420.

The objectives of curiosity and enthusiasm are not on the list in Section 2.1, although they do appear in the listed objectives of the report. But, as the report says, it is only *hoped* that the student will gain curiosity and enthusiasm. These should result from understanding and, if they do not, they should not be extraneously aroused. No attempt should be made to seduce the student into a love of physics. It will be quite enough if the teacher merely clears away the dull and the mechanical so that he can make clear the true nature of the discipline. If he does this, some students will be repelled or appalled and others fascinated, which is as it should be.

The paucity of references in the report to knowledge as an objective may be misleading; the objective is strongly implied. Though the conferees agreed that the content of introductory physics courses should be drastically reduced, they considered knowledge of certain few areas indispensable. Imaginative thinking and intuitive understanding (3.4, I2) were not discussed at the conference. Discussion of laboratory objectives (L1, L2) was left to the University of Connecticut conference.

### University of Connecticut conference

The recommendations of this conference, held in 1957 (6, Connecticut), contain the following objectives.

> The laboratory should definitely provide the student with an opportunity to know physics as a process of inquiry leading to theory [L2]. . . . Knowing also includes techniques which the student acquires in the laboratory, particularly the techniques of measurement used by the physicist [L1, L2.1] . . . . laboratory work should impart the principles and techniques by which the physicist recognizes the limitations which measuring processes put upon knowledge [L2]. . . . He should encounter the joys and sorrows of experimenting, elation and despair. . . . Having had such experience, the student . . . will have an insight into the scientific enterprise [L2]. . . . good attitudes toward physics and toward science in general on the part of students . . . often stem from satisfying experiences in the physics laboratory.*

Joys and sorrows are treated in this book not as objectives but as desirable conditions of learning; good attitudes toward science are valuable, but should arise as by-products of other objectives. Neither of these opinions, however, violates the intent of the recommendations.

### AAPT questionnaire

It seems safe to conclude that when groups of physics teachers meet to discuss objectives of introductory courses in physics they arrive at formu-

---

* "Laboratory Instruction in General College Physics: Report of the Committee on Conclusions of the Conference on Laboratory Instruction in General Physics," *American Journal of Physics*, XXV (1957), 436–37. Reprinted by permission of the publisher, The American Institute of Physics.

lations similar to the one presented in Section 2.1. The agreement is of course formal only. To clarify the meaning that physics teachers attach to statements of objectives, the AAPT (American Association of Physics Teachers) Committee on Testing, in 1956, sent out an elaborate questionnaire, illustrated by test questions, to 150 teachers of introductory physics. The question asked, briefly, was this: "If you were to use in your course a test prepared by an outside agency, what would you want it to measure?" The consensus of the sixty teachers who replied was that testing for knowledge is essential, testing for understanding important, and testing for the ability to read (3.1 and 3.2) also important but less so. Objectives 1.1 and 1.2 under knowledge were given approximately equal importance, as were objectives 2.1, 2.2, and 2.3 under understanding. Laboratory objectives, disciplined and imaginative thinking, and intuitive understanding were not included in the questionnaire.

### Conclusions

To judge from the two conferences and the questionnaire, the statement of objectives in Chapter 2 is understandable to a large number of physics teachers, and most of them consider the development of the objectives proper and desirable goals of introductory physics teaching. Taking into account that replies to the questionnaire referred to tests covering not ideal courses, but existing ones that heavily emphasize knowledge, the results of the questionnaire cannot be said to contradict the recommendations of the conferences. The available evidence shows, among other things, that physics teachers value understanding of a few topics more highly than knowledge of many.

### 3.6   PRESENT-DAY INTRODUCTORY SCIENCE COURSES AND THE OBJECTIVES

Although teachers of science agree that the objectives of understanding and ability to learn are important and say so publicly, many introductory science courses still make knowledge their main and sometimes their only specific goal (11). This section is intended to show that the other two objectives are equally suitable for introductory science courses; it also describes existing science courses and criticizes some of the more common arguments for teaching knowledge only.

### The objectives fit introductory science courses

A few examples from physics will show that the objectives in Section 2.1 do not mean that introductory science courses, even if taught as a part of liberal education, should become courses in the history or philosophy of science; on the contrary, the objectives apply very well to the standard elementary content.

Introductory physics teachers want their students to learn some of what we know about nature. Thus, some years ago we "knew" and taught that under certain conditions gases obey Boyle's law; that parity *must* be conserved; that there are only three elementary particles, electrons, protons and neutrons; and that ice melts exactly at 0°C. The first of these pieces of knowledge is still with us, the second and third have been found inconsistent with experiment, and the fourth has simply been abandoned through a new agreement on fixed points. It seems clear that knowing that the four assertions above are or were true (1.1) is shallow if not erroneous. To deepen his knowledge, the student should at least be able to place the assertions into an admittedly impermanent and rough classification: fact, theory, and definition (1.24). And to judge the probable permanence of a theory, he should know the evidence for it (1.22). These three objectives are subdivisions of objective 1, knowledge. Further, it is not enough for a student to *remember* that a given fact is evidence for a given theory; he should be convinced of it. To be convinced, he has to learn to estimate cogency of evidence (2.12). The student should also understand some of the general reasons for changing fixed points (2.31). These two objectives are subdivisions of objective 2, understanding.

The preceding paragraph argues that formal distinctions should be made between classes of assertions, partly because they may differ in stability. This type of classification may not be congenial to many scientists. For example, they may ask whether the assertion, "Molecules are made of atoms," is a fact or theory. The stability of that assertion has depended somewhat on the continuing use of the words *molecule* and *atom*, in spite of changes in our conception of these particles. The conception has in fact changed so radically that to say that a molecule *consists* of atoms is to misrepresent the modern theory, for the phrase suggests a Daltonian preservation of atomic identities. "Made of atoms" is vague enough to escape this danger and it should have a stabler future. Scientists who don't like the suggested classification might instead distinguish among the ways the assertions were first introduced (2.32): Boyle's law was *discovered*, fixed points were *agreed* on, the elementary particles were *invented* to account for facts, and symmetry laws were *assumed* without question.

If understanding is important it should not be allowed to decay, but should be used to acquire greater understanding. The student most likely to use it in this way is the student who has learned how to learn. Ability to learn depends on the habit of disciplined thinking, for instance, on the abilities to use physics terms as they are defined rather than as they are used colloquially (3.31) and to organize and formulate one's ideas (3.32). Learning from books, the main source of dependable information for most students, requires the abilities to read prose (3.31) and to interpret non-verbal symbols, such as drawings and tables of numbers (3.2). Finally, learning about things that are really new requires the ability to formulate questions and tentative answers (3.4).

Teaching intuitive understanding (I2) is discussed in Section 5.3 and laboratory teaching (L1, L2, IL2, L3) is discussed in Chapter 6.

### Objectives now attained in introductory physics courses

It is not easy to form an accurate—or an optimistic—picture of what students learn from the usual physics course. The teacher's behavioral objectives other than imparting knowledge, if they exist at all, are commonly considered unfit subjects for polite conversation; they are publicly taboo. Nevertheless, they can be deduced from physics teachers' conversations, papers, conferences, and questionnaires; from their lectures; from their texts; and from the results of standardized tests. The reader can decide himself whether the description of current introductory physics courses that follows fits his own impression of such courses—other than his own course. (One's own course, like one's own face and voice, seems distorted in any representation.)

*The lecture*   The main teaching device in college physics courses is the lecture-demonstration. A lecture is usually very much like a chapter in a yet unpublished textbook. It is a point of professional honor that this textbook differ from the one read by the students. The main effort of the lecturer is to acquaint the student with a "topic," a limb detached from the body of knowledge that is physics. Little time is devoted to showing the relation of the current topic to the rest of physics or to discussing the reasons for taking the topic up at all. Arguments, derivations, and apparatus demonstrations are used mainly to convince the student that the teacher's assertions are true. The lecture is thus used essentially to purvey knowledge.

*The recitation section*   A second teaching device is the recitation or quiz section. It is usually conducted by a graduate student who has not been fortunate enough to get a research appointment. He spends most of the recitation time in solving problems that have been assigned as homework. Often he does this on explicit instructions to "drill" the students in the solution of conventional problems. The upper limit of the pedagogical effort of the recitation instructor is similar to that of the lecturer; it is to prove that certain recipes or rules are true or usable. The students learn how the particular problems can be attacked but not how they could have arrived at the method. Methods of attack on a group of similar problems are seldom explained: "If bodies are accelerated, use $F = ma$" is a recipe, not a method or an explanation. Only rarely do students hear suggested what they should do or think about when confronted with a really new problem. It would appear that the central, explicit behavioral objective of the quiz section is knowledge, especially the knowledge of relations (objective 1.2).

*Homework*    A third teaching device is the homework assignment. By common consent, "understanding" of a chapter in the text is achieved if the student can repeat the generalizations and definitions that are stated there and solve a few of the end-of-the-chapter problems. The usual text is hardly more than an annotated handbook. To save the student the task of discovering the main points of the chapter, the parts that are to be remembered are specially marked by bold print, color, indention, or inclusion in a summary. To save him the further anguish of attacking a new problem, type problems are worked out step-by-step. Since the student can be almost certain that the formulas in the chapter will solve the assigned problems, his intellectual chore is mainly to decide where to use which certified recipe. Most of his time is spent in assigning the symbols of a formula to the numerical values given in the problem. The job may be difficult and may involve understanding and imaginative thinking, but in most cases the required competence is knowledge of relations. Those students who find even such guided reading and problem-solving strenuous know that the content of the chapter will be remasticated in the lecture, and that the problems (not type problems but *the* assigned problems) will be solved in the quiz section. Homework assignments, too, appear to be designed primarily for acquisition of knowledge.

*Tests*    Tests, viewed as a teaching device, keep pace with homework and lectures. They measure predominantly knowledge and, occasionally, ingenuity (imaginative thinking?) and an acquaintance with the teacher's foibles.

To make the pedagogical picture a bit blacker, the precautions taken in introductory physics courses against forcing a student to acquire an understanding of physics or to learn how to read a text extend to disciplined and imaginative thinking. A scientific attitude of inquiry—highly critical, if not downright skeptical, inquiry—must be hard to maintain in the face of almost purely authoritarian teaching: both the lectures and the text are commonly treated by instructors as repositories of not-to-be-questioned truth. Such authoritarianism can help develop only the lowest form of disciplined thinking—ability to conform. In the quiz sections where questions by the students are permitted, the only questions respected by the instructor are those that are narrowly and rigidly relevant to the assignment. Attempts at imaginative or creative thinking, which in beginning students must often be just flights of fancy, are likely to be squelched by the instructor, with the approval of the rest of the class: "What has that to do with the problem at hand?" or, "Consult the philosophy department."

"Check your creativity at the door" seems to be the motto in most physics classrooms, even at the graduate level.

*The laboratory*  The fourth common teaching device is the laboratory. The usual introductory physics laboratory is a beehive of overorganized, overdirected activity that allows little time for any kind of thinking—analytical or intuitive, disciplined or imaginative. Such a laboratory cannot teach much beyond an acquaintance with (knowledge of) the measuring devices and processes used in the assigned experiments. The standard tests of students' laboratory learning do not indicate the attainment of any higher competence (59). Laboratory teaching will be discussed in detail in Chapter 6.

Though most physics courses overemphasize the acquisition of knowledge at the expense of understanding and ability to learn, they do teach, probably with some success, a few aspects of these objectives. The lecture and the recitation seem designed to impart knowledge, but they may also develop other types of competence. When, for instance, the lecturer explains why a given fact is evidence for a theory, some students may abstract from the lesson the general criteria used in the argument and the general *form* of argument so that they can use it for other facts and theories. In the laboratory, too, the student comes into contact with real phenomena and may be able to generalize from individual experiments. Finally, homework gives students practice in textbook reading. But how many and what kinds of students develop understanding and ability to learn, and how well, are difficult questions.

The aspects of ability to learn that are most often taught badly or not at all are disciplined and imaginative thinking. The aspects of understanding that the student is least likely to acquire concern the nature and structure of physics, especially as a process of inquiry, its relation to other disciplines, and the relation of theoretical physics to reality. In short, introductory physics is not taught now as one of the liberal arts, and physics courses fail, for the most part, to give the student a fair idea of what physics is like. There is in fact some evidence that the image of science and of scientific activity that present courses evoke has cost science some of its most promising candidates (24, Friedenberg).

### Criticism of arguments for teaching knowledge only

There are at least three types of argument in defense of teaching primarily knowledge. Some of the arguments cite practical difficulties, others plead ignorance of how to teach understanding, and still others are based on theories of pedagogy. Practical difficulties mostly stem from administrative and departmental disinterest in improving teaching. This problem was discussed in Section 1.4. The best plea of ignorance can be made by those teachers who themselves do not understand science. For them, materials are available from various organizations (13); they might also review the small and inexpensive library suggested in Section 14.8. Below are discussed some theories of pedagogy that have been used to defend the prevalent methods of teaching science.

*There is no time for frills in science courses.*   The proponents of the no-time-for-frills theory maintain, of late usually in a somewhat apologetic tone of voice, that there is so much content to be covered that neither the teacher nor the student has time for anything but knowledge. Such arguments are based on the obvious (though seldom stated) premise that knowledge is the most important objective or that knowledge of many topics is better than an understanding of fewer. (*Knowledge* and *understanding* are used as defined in Section 2.2. All teachers claim "understanding" as one of their objectives, but what they mean by the word varies.) The more common defense of the no-time-for-frills theory consists in demonstrating that each of the topics included in the course has high inherent value and therefore cannot be omitted. A cogent *ad hominem* rebuttal is that there are many topics of extremely high inherent value that are *not* in the course. Such a rebuttal, however, may encourage the true devotee of coverage to try to enrich his course by adding more topics. A better counterargument is that knowledge without understanding and ability to learn is a most perishable intellectual commodity. If, at the end of a course, students understand twenty topics, a year later they will have retained more knowledge than if they knew a hundred topics (7). And of course one may always argue that understanding and ability to learn are not frills.

*Only knowledge should be taught.*   Science teachers who maintain that the instructor's only obligation is to impart knowledge fall into two groups. One of these holds that though students can be taught understanding and ability to learn, such teaching is a waste of effort, for these two competences require no explicit attention. They will be acquired by the students more or less automatically if the lecturer tells them clearly enough what the laws and theories of the science are, what evidence they are based on, and so forth, and if he proves all his assertions by argument or demonstration. This method of teaching, if not the theory behind it, is standard in science courses. An equally standard addendum to the method is assigning homework problems (in physics, numerical problems) and discussing them in the quiz section. The addendum shows a lack of faith in the theory, for it can surely be traced to test results showing that students do not learn how to solve problems by watching the instructor do them on the blackboard. (It is a pity that in physics even the quiz-section instructor spends most of his time in this way.) Test results will also indicate what else students do not learn when the instructor exhibits truth and the student listens silently. Available empirical evidence strongly suggests that *explicit* attention to each major objective is highly desirable (18).

The other group holds that only knowledge *can* be taught. Understanding and ability to learn, the argument goes, require that the student's native intelligence act on the knowledge acquired from the course; outside help is of little avail. Since intelligence is not teachable, the only contribution a teacher can make is to increase the student's knowledge. The disciples of this school usually seem to feel that psychology and education are not worth studying because they contain so little solid knowledge. They are similarly disinclined to try educational experimentation because the results are not likely to be precise or unambiguous. Their personal position is therefore impregnable. Fortunately, such people seldom enjoy teaching and, given a chance, will leave it for other forms of endeavor.

As a matter of fact, however, there is little doubt that it is possible to help students attain every one of the three major objectives (4). A very large number of experiments have been conducted on teaching various aspects of understanding and ability to learn. As a rule, the modern experimenter no longer tries to establish the feasibility of improving a particular competence, but to find out which of two methods of teaching improves it most.

*The objective of knowledge alone makes the course difficult enough.* A common source of pride to a college science teacher, and sometimes the main prop for his self-respect, is that his course is "tough." The teacher considers that the toughness of the course testifies to its intellectual respectability and indicates it is a rewarding experience for the hardworking student. The teacher will argue that the repetition of the same material in the text, lecture, and quiz section is obviously necessary because even with such repetition some students learn little from his course. The logical form of this argument is similar to that of "It is silly to offer steak to people who find even pap hard to swallow." It is not true that the only or the best way to help the student grasp difficult material is to restate it as many times as possible; such a teaching method seems to work fairly well in memorizing nonsense syllables, but at the higher intellectual planes (say, learning spelling) excessive repetition may actually decrease learning (22).

A liberal education requires hard thinking. Thus all intellectually respectable courses are tough; but all tough courses are not necessarily intellectually respectable. A course is usually called tough if a large percentage of students gets low grades. If this percentage is large by tradition and if, as is usually the case, it does not vary with the caliber of the students or the excellence of instruction, it is a better index of the professor's irresponsibility than of the difficulty of the course; after all, one can fail half the class in an easy course. A course can be hard for students if it uses materials and methods beyond the preparation of many students admitted to the course. Such a breach of faith with the students is usually the fault of the teacher. The fault is serious if the percentage of inadequately prepared students is high, for among these there may be good scholars who rebel against such treatment and learn to disrespect and dislike science, or potential scientists who decide that they cannot understand science and switch to other fields.

These two examples of tough courses are really examples of errors in judgment, most frequent at colleges in which "the classroom is the teacher's castle." Where administration has the upper hand, errors in judgment are likely to lie at the opposite pole: most students must pass every course however little they work or learn, and true prerequisites are waived. (The author's advice was recently sought by a physics instructor who had been asked to teach analytical mechanics to students without calculus. The author's advice was, "Don't.")

Many science courses are difficult because of pedagogy that stands in the way of or does not reward real understanding. Such a situation often occurs in courses with a bad choice, or more commonly a bad hierarchy, of objectives. The most common error in the hierarchy of objectives in science courses is overemphasis on knowledge, especially on knowledge of many topics. A course that requires learning a great deal of material in a short time is hard on students who do not feel comfortable with half-understanding or even rebel against it; they are likely to get relatively low grades. Since dissatisfaction with half-understanding is essential in a scholar, such a course penalizes scholars; it rewards memory, docility, and superficiality.

Overemphases other than on coverage vary from science to science. In physics, mathematics is commonly overemphasized, with the result that the rewards of greater learning go to students with mathematical knowledge, and those students who at the moment have less mathematics are penalized. Although there is some injustice in this practice, it is hard to avoid, for without mathematics an acquisition of understanding of some aspects of physics is impossible. There are, however, exceptional students who, despite the obstacles of inadequate mathematical knowledge, acquire good understanding of most aspects of physics taught in an introductory course, only to find that the examinations, couched in mathematical language, do not permit them to show that understanding. They get lower grades than they deserve. Besides these exceptionally gifted students, there are very large numbers of students who could have some understanding of physics but do not, because the mathematics barrier is too high. Physics courses should not be taught without mathematics, of course, but some nonmathematical material should be taught and should appear in tests in all introductory courses. Also, the student's mathematical competence should be *tested* before he is admitted to a physics course.

Some courses are difficult because they demand from students talents or abilities that are not announced prerequisites, that are not developed in the course, and that are not closely associated with understanding. One such talent is imaginative thinking or ingenuity. A good number of teachers are proud of their really tough test exercises; their pride would be better justified if such questions tested for deep understanding rather than for understanding and ingenuity or knowledge and ingenuity. Another competence that may spell success or failure in a course is the ability to stay awake during the lectures and to remember their content. Still another is the ability to divine what the instructor, who keeps the objectives of his course a dark secret from his students and not infrequently from himself, will base his grades on. These rare gifts—ingenuity, learning from dull lectures, and mind-reading—have survival value, but if they are highly rewarded, students who have nothing better to offer than an understanding of science will be penalized—they will find the course tough.

## 3.7  CONCLUSION

This chapter is an attempt to show that the objectives listed in Section 2.1 are important, that the list is reasonably complete, and that although the objectives are not too fancy for even an introductory course they are not well taught in most courses. The bases for these conclusions have been the uses students are likely to make of their training; an analysis of the discipline of physics for its main characteristics; opinions, mostly of physics teachers, on what objectives are proper and important; and, finally, arguments against the explicit teaching of knowledge only. Teachers' opinions seem to favor a shift from the knowledge of many conclusions reached by scientists to a deeper understanding of fewer conclusions and to a greater emphasis on science as a process of inquiry. This shift in objectives will involve the goals of research, the kinds of problems scientists attack, their methods of attack, and the rules and standards that guide scientists in their research and in their interpretation of results. Thus many teachers in fact recommend teaching introductory science as one of the liberal arts, however little this term may appeal to some of them.

# 4

## TEACHING METHODS:
## 1. READING AND
## ANALYTICAL UNDERSTANDING

This chapter shows how some of the objectives listed in Section 2.1 (2, analytical understanding, and 3.1 and 3.2, ability to read; the other objectives are taken up in Chapters 5 and 6) can be attained through modifications of teaching methods that need not require additional personnel, time, or money. The examples are again from physics, but the ideas apply to all the physical sciences and, with some modifications, to the biological sciences.

The general criteria for a good introductory science course might be as follows. The objectives of the course, both content and behavioral, should be written down in some detail. (The two primary guides in selecting the objectives are the students' probable future and discipline analysis, which were discussed in Sections 3.1 to 3.4.) The teacher should make a conscious, planned effort to reach each of the main behavioral objectives of his course, and he should measure the degree to which the students attain them. The course should have the main features of a true liberal arts course: it should make clear the nature of the discipline and its relation to other disciplines; it should be intellectually respectable; and a thorough understanding of most of the material should be possible and rewarding if the student makes a serious effort. The student should assume greater responsibility than now for learning, he should know the goals of the course, and each step the teacher uses to arrive at the goals should make sense to him.

Compared to present introductory science courses, a course designed to meet the criteria of the preceding paragraph will have the following characteristics. It will cover less subject matter and include more integrative material, that is, material that organizes the content into coherent units and

50

these units into a coherent whole. The course will be more difficult for some students and easier for others; it will provide some students with greater motivation for further study of the science and others with less; and fewer students will think the course dull. The instructors will have fewer but harder hours of teaching; fewer of them will find teaching dull.

The following two sections discuss methods of teaching and the objectives of science understanding that are now inadequately attained. Section 4.1 deals with content; Section 4.2, with analytical understanding and ability to read.

### 4.1   INTEGRATIVE CONTENT (CONTENT IMPLIED IN OBJECTIVES 2.2 AND 2.3)

Content that should be but usually is not included in introductory science courses is the interrelationships of principles and of disciplines, and the nature and structure of the science as a body of knowledge and, especially, as a process of inquiry. Every type of content to which objectives 2.2 and 2.3 refer cannot, of course, be fully treated in one course, but at least enough can be included in a physics course, for instance, to enable the student to understand the word *physics*. He should be shown that physics is not isolated, independent, and autonomous assertions and methods; that these, on the contrary, are interrelated; and that physics has coherence, unity, and its own kind of beauty. He should also be aware of its difference from and relation to other disciplines. Without integrative content it is unlikely that a student will reach an enduring understanding even of the separate parts into which, for teaching purposes, physics must be divided (22). The integration may proceed in several ways. For instance, the teacher may emphasize historical development or the analysis of situations that involve principles of several disciplines; or he may compare and contrast the goals, methods, and basic assumptions of physicists and scholars of other disciplines. Whatever organizing principle the teacher chooses, he should make clear to the students what it is and how he proposes to use it. Explicit pedagogy may itself be considered a type of integrative content, for it may help the student form a more coherent image of the course. Below are a few examples of the integrative possibilities of the suggested content.

### Interrelationship of principles

Situations that involve several physics principles may be used to illustrate the interrelationship and merging of two areas, for instance, of mechanics and heat in the kinetic theory of matter or of light and electricity in Maxwell's theory; or to illustrate the reinterpretation of concepts, for example, the changed meaning of "contact" and "size" on the atomic scale.

The relation of physics to other physical sciences, especially in its role as the basic natural science, can also be shown easily. Kinetic theory, Faraday's laws, and the Bohr atom relate physics and chemistry; laws of gravitation and astrophysics relate physics and astronomy. The relation between physics and mathematics is very different, and pervasive; it can be made clear in many contexts (kinematics is a particularly convenient one).

The dependence of biology on physics is commonly illustrated in the discussion of the ear and eye. At a deeper level, the inevitable interaction between the observer and the observed, expressed in Heisenberg's uncertainty principle and Bohr's principle of complementarity, can be shown to have implications for understanding what biological life is and perhaps even for the social sciences (see Oppenheimer in Section 14.7). In humanistic studies, philosophy has been profoundly influenced by modern physics. The examples in this paragraph should make it clear that the interrelationships should concern the discipline of physics and not its application; the effect on our lives of the invention of the atomic bomb, for instance, can be more profitably discussed in social science courses.

### Nature and structure of physics

Physicists' criteria for experiment, choice of concepts, and generalization should be briefly reviewed with each new example because of their cohesive value. A few times in the course the criteria should be treated in detail. A comparison of the caloric and kinetic theories of heat or of the corpuscular and wave theories of light is an excellent vehicle for a full-dress treatment of criteria for theory. The complex and often equivocal nature of scientific experiment is beautifully exhibited in Galileo's discovery of the law of falling bodies. What a physicist requires of a generalization can be illustrated by the Newtonian synthesis of Kepler's and Galileo's findings. Criteria for definitions can be made clear in many contexts. The basic requirement that a definition should result in a simple form of laws of nature is well illustrated by the changing definitions of time and temperature; other criteria can be extracted from the classical definitions of force and mass.

The differences and similarities in the attitudes of various scientists toward the final and immediate goals of their inquiries into nature should be brought up whenever an opportunity occurs, because even the differences—and certainly the similarities—can be used as a binding thread between otherwise isolated topics. Einstein's attitude toward quantum mechanics makes for a fine discussion.

The chronology of experiments, concept formation, and theories is perhaps the most natural integrative theme; it is easy to learn and to use. Although many immediate causes or triggering mechanisms for the more fundamental advances in science remain obscure, it is usually obvious what use a scientist made of then existing knowledge and how his advance was later elaborated and applied (see Forbes, Section 14.7). In mechanics, the work of Ptolemy, Copernicus, Kepler and Galileo, and Newton forms a useful chronological sequence. In light, another convenient and fruitful sequence is Planck, Einstein, Rutherford, Balmer, and Bohr; and, in atomic structure, Rutherford, Bohr, de Broglie, Schrödinger, Heisenberg, and Dirac.

### Science as a process of inquiry

The distinction between understanding a science as a process of inquiry and understanding it as a body of knowledge is not explicit in the classification of objectives in Section 2.1. Although a genuine understanding of one of these aspects of a science is impossible without understanding the other, it does not follow that both kinds of understanding will be acquired by the students if only one is taught or adequately emphasized. Rather, it is much more likely that neither kind of understanding will result. Some students, exposed to nothing but original papers, can discourse fluently on the relation between the sciences of Galileo and Newton without knowing the simplest facts about projectiles or motion down inclined planes and without being able to solve elementary problems involving acceleration. This kind of knowledge has little to do with physics, however impressive it may be in parlor conversation. The "good" students of many a conventional science course, on the other hand, if caught soon enough after completing the course, may have at their fingertips an impressive number of short declarative sentences about nature, which they "know" to be true. Imparting such truths is the main goal of many science courses and is soon accepted as such by most students. The students are conditioned to become disinterested in the sources of the truths—in methods and basic premises—and they thus remain ignorant of how these truths are related to reality. These students not only have no knowledge of science as a process of inquiry but have a distorted understanding of it as a body of knowledge. In introductory courses, science as a process of inquiry should therefore receive explicit attention, perhaps as much as science as a body of knowledge. The latter without the former is like Latin—neatly arranged, dead, and, to most students, totally unexciting.

Original research papers are by far the best and perhaps the only source available now for understanding science as a process of inquiry. This is true not because the scientist's own account of his work always parallels the actual chronology of his thoughts and actions, but because such accounts often exhibit well the complexity of phenomena and their relation to theory. There are many original papers that can be read by the student in an introductory course. However, students can get a good deal more out of most original writings if they are already familiar with a textbook treatment of the relevant subject matter. It is a good idea to use, say, the last few weeks of each quarter or semester for an analysis of an original paper, perhaps edited, that deals with some of the material studied earlier.

### Pedagogical integrative content

The student should be allowed to become thoroughly familiar with the objectives, methods, and evaluative procedures of the course. If he finds them respectable, he will be better motivated. But even if he merely understands them, he will be better able to make a coherent picture of the course. As a result, he will use his time better and be more relaxed, and he can be trusted to take a greater responsibility for learning. Some of these points will be discussed further in Section 4.2.

### Sources of integrative content

Although there are now texts that make good use of integrative material (see Section 14.5), they of course reflect the author's predilections more strongly than the conventional texts do. The latter are more neutral and encyclopedic and therefore more flexible: the teacher can, if he wishes, present the content to suit *his* predilections. To do this, however, he must use other sources in addition to the conventional text. The additional knowledge can be given the students through opportune interpolations in the subject-matter lectures, through specially designed lectures, and through assigned readings. The easiest solution is to have two required texts, one conventional and one with the desired type of integrative material. A better solution is to supplement a conventional text with various sourcebooks (see Section 14.6).

### 4.2  TEACHING ANALYTICAL UNDERSTANDING AND READING (OBJECTIVES 2, 3.1, and 3.2)

This section describes modifications in introductory science courses that are necessary if the students, in addition to knowledge, are to acquire analytical understanding and to develop an ability to read with understanding and profit. First teaching methods and then the new roles of homework, lecture, and recitation are sketched out.

### Transfer of training

Both understanding and reading ability imply an ability to deal with content novel to the student, content that differs from that taught in the course; they therefore imply transfer of training. Transfer of training will usually occur only if the student understands the transfer process and the transferable characteristics of what he is trained to do (4). The course must be planned to give the student such understanding. Transfer must be explained, and understanding and reading must be taught explicitly.

To teach understanding, it is necessary first to explain to the students what understanding means: the ability to apply acquired knowledge to new problems. Students should be convinced through several examples that many steps in an analysis they and the teacher use to solve a problem will also apply to other problems. The teacher may, for instance, solve a problem on the blackboard, assign for homework a new but similar problem, and next day compare the appropriate methods of attack and point out their similarities and differences. Another way to introduce a new problem is to simplify it until the solution is clear to the students, solve the simplified problem, and then reintroduce the complications one by one. Either method harks back to the familiar—a process that is at the heart of transfer of training.

Similarly, in analyzing a written passage, one asks some questions that will be useful, perhaps in a modified or generalized form, in analyzing another passage. Again this process should be illustrated, the students given a chance to use it, and the results of their efforts criticized.

Transfer of training from one context to others implies, of course, that the original content had illustrative value. Although there are topics in science that have both high inherent and high illustrative value, this is not generally true. If the objectives of analytical understanding and reading with understanding are taken seriously, some illustrative material must displace material that is valuable mainly as knowledge. Since several content areas may be suitable for illustrating a general proposition or process, the teacher may choose illustrative content in accordance with his tastes and special competence.

## Study methods

Proper reading of the text, an article, or lecture notes trains the student in reading and also gives him an understanding of the content. Students should probably read more and listen less. Proper reading requires that the student continually ask himself questions. He will need, at least in the beginning, explicit instructions as to how, when, and what questions to ask. Some questions about an author's statement may be: What class or form of statement does it exemplify? How is it related to previously learned material? How can the statement be verified? What deductions from it are reasonable? Can it be put into mathematical language? Thus, for instance, when the student reads for the first time that "the temperature of a gas increases as its molecules gain speed," he should ask himself: How can I classify or reformulate this statement in more general language? (His answer may be: It is an example of a theoretical explanation of a phenomenon; or, It is an example of a mechanical explanation of a thermal phenomenon; or, It is a postulate of a theory.) Can this theory explain some facts I know? What experiment will provide evidence for or against this postulate? What phenomena can I predict on the basis of this theory? Is temperature proportional to speed?

When he does the reading, the student may be able to give only partial answers to some of the questions, but when he is given satisfactory answers later in the course, he will truly understand them, for they will fall on prepared ground. He will also remember the answers for a long time.

In high school and only too often in college, the words *knowledge* and *understanding* are used interchangeably. A student who can restate in his own words the content of a passage is said to have understood it. Science teachers must thus learn how to teach students to read with understanding. In the beginning, a student may be assigned a single paragraph in the text and asked to restate its content, first as fully as he wishes, next in fewer sentences, and finally in a single short sentence that does justice to the content. In this way he will learn to use more and more general language. The next step may be to let him practice generalizing from a single sentence. In working on the sentence from kinetic theory given a paragraph back, helpful hints may be to restate the sentence without using the word *molecules*, next without the word *temperature*, next without any heat terms, and so on. Analogous training should be given for formulating other questions. In studying for understanding, the student should also practice using his knowledge on progressively more novel problems.

### Responsibility for learning

Perhaps knowledge can be dictated by the teacher or a book and passively absorbed by the student. To acquire understanding, however, and especially to develop his ability to learn, the student must assume a good deal of responsibility himself. In most high school and undergraduate courses the main reason students do not learn how to learn may be that the responsibility for learning is not theirs. They are told, often day by day and step by step, what they are to do: read a chapter, work an exercise, listen to a lecture. If they go through the prescribed routine faithfully and attentively they are guaranteed "good" results. Students with both intelligence and the ability to stay with the task get good grades; those with only one of the talents, medium grades; and those with neither, bad grades. A student can seldom change his ability for sustained concentration by an effort of will. If he is not taught how to study, unless his imagination is suddenly fired or his habits improve with age, a C student is fated to remain a C student throughout his academic career (19).

To avoid a sharp break with high school practices, an introductory course should start with clearly defined activities. The student should be told which parts of the reading assignment are important, what he should memorize, and which problems he should solve. Soon, however, the student should begin receiving instructions on how to study, especially for understanding. Finally, the student should be told only the goals that he is expected to achieve—a clear, detailed statement of course objectives richly illustrated with test questions—and allowed to choose his own methods of study. Attending classes and handing in homework for the teacher's criticism should become his privilege instead of his duty. However, until the millennium when students' main motivation will be a desire to learn, and those who are not learning will voluntarily leave, teachers must remain a certifying agency. Under present conditions, freedom of choice in methods of study has to be accompanied by good tests of all the major objectives.

## Student motivation

The student will be better motivated if he understands the goals, teaching method, organization of material, and grading system of the course. He should find the goals intellectually respectable and believe that he can attain them, and he should find the method, organization, and grading in agreement with the goals.

The prevalent motivating forces for students in introductory science courses today are, sadly enough, the desire to get good grades; the opinion that the training received will later be useful or at least required; and, last and least, interest in the materials of the course. If motivation through grades or praise is to lead to greater understanding or learning skills, the attainment of these objectives must be measured and rewarded, and the students must know that this is done. Willingness to study uninteresting material for its later usefulness depends, of course, on the students' estimate of the extent of that usefulness. Students know that the ability to learn will be useful; since understanding implies ability to deal with new situations, students can easily be convinced of its usefulness. The problem then is rather to convince them that these types of competence can be acquired. Straight knowledge is better defended as the raw material for understanding than as potentially useful, for the teacher in the next course, who himself stuffs his students with information, is likely to disparage the knowledge they have brought with them; he would have preferred "a thorough understanding of a few fundamentals."

The improvement of understanding and ability to learn requires of the student a more intimate and more active involvement with the materials of the course than normally results from motivations such as grades and later usefulness. To attain these objectives, the student must be interested in the materials and become a participant in the course rather than remain a passive observer (17).

To excite students' interest, some teachers turn their lectures into spectacles by using loud, bright, or large apparatus, by gestures and jokes, or even by acrobatics. Some teachers may give the lecture a dramatic plot or dramatic touches by unexpected or paradoxical turns. Spectacular methods may help the student retain some isolated items of knowledge, but their distractions must often bar him from real understanding. The dramatic approach, on the other hand, is probably harmless and can even be of value if the drama is that of science. However, no classroom technique alone is likely to be very effective in furthering understanding of science; the material presented must form part of a pattern that has real meaning for the student at all times, to some degree even *before* the material is explored. A classroom technique can be used to engage the student's attention for a few minutes; abiding interest requires that a student have a question that he hopes will be answered. Study within the conventional subject-matter subdivisions of physics, such as statics, radioactivity, or even the nuclear pile, does not pursue questions of genuine interest to the student. Nor is it at all likely that a beginning student will be truly or deeply interested in modern science, even though he may have a vague curiosity that can be used as a start. A student can appreciate the economy and efficiency of the usual larger patterns, such as kinematics begat dynamics and dynamics begat conservation laws, in retrospect only. When he is studying dynamics he sees the use of having studied kinematics, but the study of kinematics itself must depend on the inferior motivation of future utility.

A good organization of material helps answer questions that may conceivably interest an intelligent young man who as yet has no love or understanding of science. Such questions can be raised by various types of integrative material. Kinematics, for instance, can be studied as an example of the relation of mathematics to reality—as a partial answer to the question, "Can the results of a mathematical manipulation of symbols be trusted as predictions of phenomena?" Many students have strong feelings as to the right answer. They may believe that mathematics or, for that matter, physics has little to do with reality; they may consider the correspondence between mathematics and reality a minor miracle; or they may view the correspondence as a foregone conclusion. If criteria for theory are used to integrate course content, the kinetic-molecular theory may be studied as an answer to the questions, "How much can science tell us about objects too small to be seen, and how dependable are its conclusions?" Within the framework of historical development, the theory may be presented as a triumph of Newtonian mechanics.

Merely prefacing the subject matter with questions of general interest, however, is of little value. The questions must be kept alive throughout the course, and the progress toward answers must be clear to the students at all times. Furthermore, it is not necessary or even desirable that the coherence of different parts of the course be achieved through the use of just one type of integrative material. The length of the integrated unit may also vary with the material and the students' sophistication; at the introductory level it should probably be measured in weeks rather than months.

To achieve the goal of giving the student an understanding of the nature of a science and to maintain his interest, it is probably not enough just to organize the material to be explored into meaningful units. In addition, the student should be allowed to participate in the exploration (20, Sanford). The first step in his participation is understanding the objectives, methods of teaching, and evaluative procedures (23). The meanings of knowledge, understanding, and reading with understanding must be carefully and thoroughly explained to the student and, periodically, explicitly illustrated. The roles each lecture and assignment play in the development of the unit must be made clear to him. He should be allowed to become well acquainted with course examinations before he takes them; a convenient procedure is to discuss the objectives and the form of one of last year's tests. A more active and much more important form of student participation is afforded by the discussion session. Here students must be allowed to express and defend their opinions and to criticize any aspect of the course, in particular, opinions of the instructor and of the text.

## Choice of content (21)

The amount and kind of course content should be such that almost all students admitted to the course who are willing to make a serious intellectual effort are able to understand it. There are several reasons for cutting the subject matter of introductory science courses, perhaps by half. Understanding a topic takes longer than acquiring knowledge of it; integrative content, which is necessary either for its own sake or as an aid to understanding, takes time; and the students should perhaps have some leisure during which they can play with the ideas of the course or pursue beyond the confines of the course an idea that interests them.

A simple and rational way to cut content is based on coherence and unity. The teacher omits isolated topics, topics that it is not particularly useful to know in order to understand the rest of the course. Some isolated topics in elementary physics are: statics; hydrostatics and hydrodynamics; a good deal of material on rotation; most of heat transfer and thermodynamics; electrical circuitry and alternating currents; and geometrical optics and physiological theories of color.

In physics courses one of the most common sources of difficulty is mathematics. Knowledge of mathematics is not an objective of an introductory physics course, and only as much mathematics should be used as is conducive to a better understanding of physics. The optimum amount of mathematics depends on the students' preparation, which can best be determined by a pretest. On the basis of the discouraging news that such a pretest is likely to contain, the teacher must decide what parts of physics can be taught in his course. Many students will not understand even the non-mathematical parts of a passage or lecture if these are in geographical, chronological, or logical contact with a mathematical treatment beyond their ken; their minds seem to freeze at the sight of a formula. Such students' reactions may be so deep-seated that argument is of no avail. The alternatives are to keep students who fear mathematics out of the course or to omit topics that are too mathematical. Fortunately, the acquisition of understanding and ability to learn, depending as they do on the illustrative value of topics, can be furthered in many ways. To find intellectually respectable material in physics that can be presented nonmathematically is difficult, but by no means impossible. It is better, however, to omit a topic entirely than to teach it in a way that gives a misleading image of physics. Whenever possible, teachers should also avoid telling students that a proposition that plays an important part in a presentation could be proved, but that they would not understand the proof; such interpolations poison understanding.

### Roles of homework, lecture, and discussion

*Homework*   The student's care and attention in reading text material, and therefore his ability to learn from a book, are increased if he knows that the material will not be repeated in the lecture or discussion. Except when referring to an original paper or an exceptionally good textbook, an assignment to discover the author's goal, method of attack, and conclusions may annoy and frustrate the student, for most of our textbooks are poor examples of scientific literature. As such, however, they are open to criticism on an elementary level. Examples of homework assignments that capitalize on texts' weaknesses are: criticize the author's proof of an assertion, especially its implicit assumptions; rewrite a paragraph to make its meaning clearer; list steps that would add up to a rule or recipe for solving a good number of the end-of-chapter problems; and modify one of these problems so that it would test understanding of a chapter. Many statements in the conventional text are also amenable to the type of analysis described in Section 4.2 under Study methods. Toward the end of the quarter, a few weeks can profitably be spent reading a scientific paper; no other source can show the true flavor of science as a process of inquiry. The objective of understanding can be served by assigning problems of increasing novelty and questions on integrative content. Examples of integrative content are: the interrelationship of principles, the nature and structure of the science, science as a process of inquiry, and perhaps, occasionally, even pedagogical integrative content.

*Lecture*   There are several legitimate functions of the lecture in an introductory course, but conveying information is not one of them. Information is better obtained from written materials such as texts, sourcebooks, and the teacher's own syllabi, notes, and instructions. The lecture is particularly ill suited for presenting materials that cannot be understood without fairly long periods of reflection, for these periods will not occur at the same time or be of equal duration for all students. Without understanding, the students are obliged to copy down all that is said or written on the board. Copying, however, is best done from written pages. An example of material usually copied without understanding is complex mathematical derivations.

The lecture hall is a good place for acquainting the students with the aims and design of the course; with the intended roles of the lecture, discussion, laboratory, home assignment, and test; and with the relative value of each large topic as knowledge, as illustration, and as a prerequisite to further knowledge. The lecture hall is also the natural place for demonstration with apparatus that is bulky or time-consuming to set up. Most of the lecturer's time, however, should be spent in providing the integrative materials that are not in the text. Texts are usually quite clear, for instance, on what the kinetic-molecular theory says about matter and heat and what evidence supports it. They are often not clear on the origin of the theory and the reasons for its slow acceptance, on the plausibility and value of the steel-ball or other molecular models, and on the criteria the author uses for theory and evidence. Least of all are they likely to be clear on what the study of a particular theory can contribute to an understanding of other theories and of physics as a whole.

If the content of a course is reduced and the acquisition of knowledge relegated primarily to texts, the number of lectures can be drastically reduced, perhaps from the usual three to one a week. The student will have more time to study the text, and the instructor more time to prepare his fewer but harder lectures. Perhaps the instructor may even find time to take over a discussion section to learn what goes on in the minds of the students—something that many a proud lecturer will find, to put it in the gentlest terms, enlightening.

*Discussion section* Generally, the only pedagogically valid reason for breaking a class of students into smaller groups is to give the students a chance to bring up their individual problems. Problems that are shared by most students can be more economically dealt with in the lecture hall. The usual quiz section, in which a graduate assistant talks 95 percent of the time and solves problems that have been assigned to all students, and in which "How do you work problem seventeen?" is almost the only type of question students ask, is very wasteful. The same graduate assistant could do the same job equally well in the lecture hall before a hundred or more students. The teacher should use the discussion section to become acquainted with the processes of thought, difficulties, and misconceptions of at least some of the students and to give each student the help he needs. Fortunately, no problem a student has is entirely unique; of a group of twenty-five students there may be five or six whose problems are so similar that each of them can participate with profit in the discussion of a point raised by one. It is a rare student, however, who can clearly formulate the questions that really bother him, and it takes skill to find out what his problem is. But whatever the question, whether it concerns science, methods of study, epistemology, or grading, it should be treated with respect. (It is not disrespectful, however, to postpone discussing a question till more students can profit from it or till after class.) Even though the discussion section should be used primarily for discussion, there are situations in which the best pedagogy is to deliver a short lecture; it is also useful to have simple demonstration apparatus on hand.

The discussion section is the best teaching device for helping students acquire understanding and develop their ability to read with understanding. Understanding is a very individualized process; because it differs markedly from student to student not only quantitatively but qualitatively, the teacher's guidance should also be individualized. Since everything that can be done with a large group can also be done with a small one but not *vice versa*, the only arguments against making the discussion section the main teaching device are its greater expense and the shortage of trained personnel.

# 5

# TEACHING METHODS:
## 2. DISCIPLINED AND IMAGINATIVE THINKING, AND INTUITIVE UNDERSTANDING

These objectives of teaching are given a separate chapter because, though teachers of science may consider them important, present introductory courses do little if anything for their attainment, and especially because these objectives extend into the noncognitive domain, in the sense that students' attitudes and habits will profoundly—and often obviously—influence their attainment of these objectives. It is only fair to make clear to the reader the nature of the argument in defense of these somewhat exotic objectives. In the first place, the central thesis is not that these kinds of talent or competence be taught or emphasized but merely that they be legitimized, that the students be *permitted* to exercise them. In the second place, it seemed best in the following discussion to appeal primarily to the teachers' own judgment and experience, rather than to published authorities. The purpose of the discussion is not to convince teachers that a particular point of view is valid, but to encourage them to formulate a point of view of their own. Also, psychological literature contains few generalizations that can be readily applied to the relevant teaching methods.

## 5.1  DISCIPLINED THINKING

In this book *disciplined thinking* is limited to the kind of thinking that has been proven to lead to good results. Even such thinking, however, will be influenced by students' attitudes and habits. Thus a temperamentally rash student may not always be able to abide by data, even if shown that conclusions unwarranted by the data are often wrong. Teaching disciplined thinking is therefore difficult and may be hazardous. On the one hand, it is fruitless and perhaps dangerous for a teacher to try to change his students' deep-seated personality characteristics, and, on the other, it is not easy to tell these from the superficial cultural veneer. Nevertheless, instructors who sympathize with problems of young people and habitually treat their students gently can and should try to improve their students' disciplined thinking. The reasons are that disciplined thinking is necessary for learning science and perhaps anything else (this point is discussed in Section 2.2); that the objective of thinking like scientists will appeal to students; that many students' thinking is not adequately disciplined; and that there are methods of teaching disciplined thinking that will not harm students and may do them good (the last two points are discussed in the succeeding paragraphs).

### Nondisciplined thinking in students

The thinking of beginning students would be adequately disciplined if they could follow clearly stated rules in a given assignment for a limited time. There are at least two kinds of students who find such a process difficult: those who cannot or will not follow certain rules because they object to them, and those who cannot stick to any set of rules or any topic, except for a very short time. The latter group is probably not ready for college-level science; they may get over their problem when they are older. However, there are some among the former group who can be helped to improve their disciplined thinking. It is often difficult to diagnose the nature of a student's objection (verbalized or not) to the rules by which scientists abide; it is, of course, impossible in the lecture hall. Disciplined thinking is hard for students who find science excruciatingly dull—as so many now do—or intellectually not respectable, or inimical to originality and creativity. The difficulty here, however, is not the students but their courses, which give the students a distorted picture of science (12). A remedy is for the teacher to emphasize and treat explicitly the nature and structure of science. Disciplined thinking is also hard for students who are inclined toward rash judgments or are overcautious. To the extent that such difficulties are not deep-seated, they can be alleviated by the methods sketched under Methods of teaching disciplined thinking. There are also students, perhaps more students than one might guess, for whom understanding of science—especially disciplined thinking—is difficult because they have an anti-science or a pro-science bias.

### The antiscientific attitude

Some students think science is an unimportant activity because it is not likely to be useful or helpful in their later lives or because it is not what humanity needs now. This point of view may stem from the students' fear that they cannot understand science. The belief that most students *can* understand science would probably alleviate a variety of ostensible difficulties, and such a belief can be engendered or strengthened by argument.

The argument, however, must be supported by illustration throughout the course. Teachers should not try to convince the students that science is more important than they think. Rather, students should be shown that they can understand it with an effort that is proportionate to their estimate of its importance, that they can get a modicum of understanding without love for science. It should be demonstrated that there are rules that can be learned, just as rules of chess can, to deal with the few points at which science differs from common sense and which therefore require disciplined thinking.

Another antiscientific group distrusts the ability of science to reveal what is true even about natural phenomena. Some students quote history to show that scientists' theories have invariably been found wrong by succeeding scientists. Understanding of how science grows may help here. Others believe that magic or rather that an odd collection of magic recipes—lucky streaks, fetishes, omens—can change the course of events. Pieces of information and problem-solving recipes supplied by a conventional science course may be merely added to the collection. A better course would make it clear that science is a harmonious, comprehensive, and very successful enterprise based on the denial of magic. Although students may not henceforth abandon magic, they may come to see magic and science as competitive rather than complementary. Given time, science will win out.

It is comparatively easy to deal with belief in magic in a science course because both science and magic postulate a rational and orderly universe; they are intellectual cousins. Unfortunately, some students distrust both science and magic, perhaps because they see little order in nature. A good number of students seem to consider nothing certain; they fully expect an occasional breakdown in the laboratory of the best-established laws of nature. Some of these students may change their attitude if they see that their experiments *never* contradict laws of nature. (Chapter 6 describes appropriately designed experiments.) Other students do divide predictions into certain and uncertain, but they treat the latter class as essentially homogeneous. The many differences and distinctions that preoccupy the scientist, such as those between high and low probability, between guesses and theories, and between Bode's law (as of 1950) and Hooke's law, strike them as minor or pedantic. Although it is hard to know how to help these students, some of them may profit from a good analysis of the various distinctions, especially if a scientist's own account shows how such distinctions helped him in his research.

There is another group that may appear antiscientific but is not. In our civilization, common sense, used empirically, has so much in common with scientific thinking that many scientists equate the two. There are, however, ideas and concepts in physics, for instance, that many intelligent students find it difficult to understand or even to use because the ideas seem to contradict common sense or experience. Examples are: a stationary body can have acceleration; Newton's first law; the relativity of motion; and the relativity of up and down (antipodes). In the discussion section it is easy to discover that many students cannot accept these principles. Some suggestions on teaching such topics are given in Section 5.3.

### The pro-science bias

A pro-science bias means that the student expects more from science than it can give. Common unrealistic expectations are that science can solve all problems, that science is pure logic, and that scientists are always logical and objective. People who believe that the methods of empirical science are capable of solving all human problems and answering all "sensible" questions may get into trouble, but not as students in a science course. Students that do present a problem to the teacher are those with the idea that natural science is perfect in the sense that geometry is perfect. They are annoyed by the limited precision of empirical generalizations, uncomfortable with peaceful coexistence by two rival theories, unimpressed with experiments that fall short of proof, outraged by data that conflict with accepted generalizations, and shocked by Einstein's opinion that the path to fundamental discoveries in science is through intuition and a feeling for order. In general, they cannot act or think in a disciplined way when the well-ordered theoretical science comes into contact with the apparently disordered reality. Therefore a natural science is probably not the best place for them; mathematics or philosophy may be. It might be added, though, that the conventional science course, with its collection of not-to-be challenged truths, will neither bother the students described in this paragraph nor help identify them.

Students in high schools seem to have an ambivalent attitude toward scientists, something like: scientists are fine, but I'd hate to be one or marry one (9). The image of cold, aloof, and not quite human scientists is strongly supported by their products, the textbooks. In college, especially a large one, the image can persist because many a science professor seldom talks to his students. As time goes on, the student learns from their published statements that scientists have human frailties. Outside science, they show no exceptional ability to tell fact from fancy. But he may fail to discover that a scientist can also be warm and humane, for such discovery usually requires personal contact.

### Methods of teaching disciplined thinking

Although little can be done in the classroom to change a student's deep-seated attitudes and habits, his difficulty with disciplined thinking can probably be alleviated when it is fairly superficial, especially if it stems from the student's ignorance of science or of his own method of thinking. The first step toward disciplined thinking is naturally for the student to understand what it means. The teacher may try the following methods: present the student with an example of disciplined thinking, make clear to him where his thinking is and is not disciplined, require (as in laboratory reports) formal conformity with disciplined thinking, and argue the value of disciplined thinking. How these methods can be enhanced by a system of rewards and punishments is a difficult problem in adolescent psychology; it only seems clear that the use of high and low grades for the purpose would in most cases be futile.

*Teaching by example*    Most, perhaps all, scientists believe that the method of inquiry into natural phenomena that science is following is essentially the right one, and they want their students to share in this belief. It may be sufficient if the student can be made fully conscious of the teacher's belief and happens to be at a receptive stage of his growth. The best place for the teacher to give students an example of disciplined thinking is probably the laboratory, where there is greater likelihood of physical proximity and of preoccupation with a difficulty that is the same for the teacher and the student. For instance, if the experiment is not working right and neither one knows an immediate remedy, the teacher has a chance to show the student how a scientist behaves by the way he proceeds to locate the trouble. Behind the lectern he is more an actor or preacher and in the usual discussion section, an inquisitor or encyclopedia. Even in these two teaching situations it is of course possible to exhibit one's attitude toward science. But again, this is most convincingly done when the teacher has run into honest trouble. (Youngsters may miss the simplest point in a lecture, but they will unfailingly spot sham confusion.) It is not easy for an experienced teacher to have trouble with the material taught in an elementary science course, but in preparing his lecture he may run into a problem he is not sure how to attack. This is a golden opportunity; the teacher should postpone working on the problem till he is in class.

*Teaching by an analysis of students' thinking*    Unlike the teacher, students invariably have a plentiful supply of genuine problems. How a student attacks a problem can often be easily observed and criticized during a discussion or in the laboratory. Students only too frequently, for instance, use their own notions rather than established definitions and avoid using laws such as the first law of Newton that run contrary to their "experience." A remedy is to make clear to the student just what he is doing and occasionally to allow him to reach conclusions that he himself will recognize as wrong, provided this can be done without making the student appear ridiculous to his classmates.

*Teaching by requiring to conform*    Sometimes the student's ability or lack of ability to conform can be best observed in a somewhat artificial situation.

For instance, he may be asked to use an unorthodox definition (time defined by Galileo's water clock or temperature defined by geometrically uniform divisions on a water-in-glass thermometer) in an analysis and description of a phenomenon. The *requirement* to conform to the rules of disciplined thinking, however, should be limited to specified occasions—reports and tests—lest it become intolerable. Hopefully some students will find conforming to the rules of logic and evidence aesthetically satisfactory and will acquire a habit of disciplined thinking.

*Teaching by argument*    Argument is probably a more effective method of correcting misconceptions than of correcting the attitudes and habits that underlie nondisciplined thinking. It may be possible, for instance, to classify various interpretations of data as reasonable, overcautious, and rash (without of course establishing sharp lines of demarcation) and to argue the correctness of the divisions with the student. An argument of this sort can certainly make clear to the student what kinds of interpretations are acceptable to scientists and why. It may also help him form the habit of interpreting data with discretion without making a change in his temperament or emotional make-up, which may be generally rash or timid.

Misconceptions about scientists as human beings can perhaps be corrected by reading their biographies. The ones that come to mind are those of Galileo, Rumford, Leibnitz, Mayer, Curie, and Einstein. Students might also find enlightening J. R. Oppenheimer's letter to General K. D. Nichols, first published in 1954 in *Life*.

## 5.2    IMAGINATIVE THINKING

A scholar in the laboratory or at his desk and a student taking a course in science have essentially the same goal—to learn. The more similar their activities are, the better the student's understanding of science is likely to be. Since imaginative thinking plays an important part in a scholar's work, it should be allowed and even encouraged in students. A recent study of why students leave science suggests that some of the most promising students dislike science because they feel that science courses inhibit their creative impulses (12, Friedenberg). There are two things that a teacher can do to make it possible for students to exercise their imaginations as far as their talents go. One is to modify the course content or its treatment and the other is to teach certain procedures that are formally similar, and perhaps auxiliary, to some processes of imaginative thinking.

### Modification of content or of its treatment

Many teachers are worried when a student dismisses a text chapter from his mind as soon as he has finished studying it. He does this partly because of the rhetoric of the text—the conclusion of each chapter has an aura of resolution, finality, closure. He also does it partly because of the content—it is difficult, upon exit, not to slam the door on statics or Archimedes' principle or many other topics in the standard text. Yet there are unanswered questions even within the driest and deadest of topics; at the end of the chapter on statics, for example, the student may be asked either to solve the assigned routine problems or to analyze, as well as he can, the problem of a beam supported by three wires. The same problem may be assigned again at the end of the chapter on elasticity. A lecture can similarly end on a question—rather than on the more usual answer to a question the students never asked. Some aspects of physics seem, because of their very nature, regularly to arouse questions or at least to leave students feeling that some problems remain unsolved. Some of these problems are: the validity of operational *vs.* other definitions; the experimental support for Newton's laws of motion; the conclusiveness of evidence cited in the text, for instance, for the wave theory of light; and the aptness of conservation of energy as an *explanation* of some phenomena. In the laboratory, students may be given the opportunity to perform an experiment that requires ingenuity rather than a routine experiment; they may be asked, for instance, to determine the coefficient of friction between two vertical surfaces. In this case, as well as in the case of a difficult homework assignment such as the one discussed above, students should be allowed to choose the more conventional assignment. They should be encouraged, but not forced, to think imaginatively.

### Teaching how to ask questions

Imaginative thinking in the discussion section is most likely to be shown by questions, questions that often disregard the precepts of disciplined thinking. The instructor should be permissive; even if he does not know how to teach imaginative thinking, he can at least permit students to exercise it. But he must also be able to stop time-consuming flights of fancy without rudeness or sarcasm. In addition, the instructor can demonstrate, preferably through discussion rather than by lecture, how certain fairly standardized questions simplify an attack on a new problem. For instance, most students can be trained to ask themselves what laws of physics might be involved in an analysis of a novel problem or, in judging the cogency of data as evidence for a theory, what other theories might account for the data. Such questions, once they are standardized and learned, do not require imaginative thinking, but they may set the student on the road to it. To help students formulate questions while reading a text, it is probably necessary to give them many examples of the questions that should have occurred to them as they read various chapters. After some such training, homework assignments may ask the student to formulate questions appropriate to a particular chapter or to design a test on the chapter. Imaginative thinking does not, of course, stop with formulating a question, especially since the question posed by a student will quite possibly be improperly directed or formulated. In the discussion section, the instructor can show what value can be extracted from even a fuzzy question by analyzing it imaginatively and thoroughly. Perhaps he will be more patient and sympathetic if he realizes that many of his and the text's questions and assertions appear fuzzy to the student.

## 5.3 INTUITIVE UNDERSTANDING

The advice given here on "teaching" intuitive understanding must perforce be very brief, for the process defies analysis. One has an intuitive understanding of a situation (event, system, or problem) if one can arrive at correct conclusions about the situation without being conscious of all the logical steps involved. It seems reasonable to suppose that in an intuitive attack on a problem a student analogizes from a broad spectrum of experience, and that some of that experience may have been essentially sensory. Thus he may "remember" the weight of a brick in terms of the muscular sensation he experienced in lifting it. The extent and intensity of the student's previous experience, then, will probably influence his intuitive thinking. Such thinking should therefore find a better expression in the more familiar areas of mechanics and light than in electrical and atomic phenomena, and in the laboratory rather than in theory.

Intuitive understanding or thinking should be discussed with the students of science courses, even if only in a tentative manner. Students should know that it is a talent highly esteemed by scientists. Instructors should also argue, in class, that intuition is not magical or rare; that it is a probable ingredient in all our thinking; and that, for instance, what we call searching our memory is more intuitive than analytical. Further, successful intuitive problem-solving most probably requires a richer background of experience and training than analytical problem-solving (5, Bruner), and, in the hands of the novice, it can degenerate into wasteful, and occasionally dangerous, guessing. Finally, students might be encouraged to exercise their intuitive thinking in the laboratory, when this can be done safely; but they should be told that, like scientists, they should always check their intuitive conclusions analytically or experimentally.

Included under intuitive understanding is the ability to deal directly with the physical aspects of a problem, without using verbal or mathematical symbols manipulated by the rules of logic. All physics teachers have known students who can define a physical quantity without having a "feeling" for it or, in other words, without an intuitive understanding of it. Most students have or easily acquire an intuitive understanding of velocity, weight, and force, for instance, but not of acceleration, mass, or pressure, even though they can define these. A symptom of formal knowledge without intuitive understanding is the relative ease with which a student solves a stereotyped, as opposed to a novel, problem. Many students find repugnant the statements that a stationary body may have an acceleration, that the pressure at a point in a liquid is the same in all directions, and that pressure is a scalar. Some of them think of acceleration as a kind of velocity and of pressure as a kind of force.

Helping a student acquire an intuitive understanding of a concept requires time, but the time is well spent. Solving problems that involve pressure, for example, without understanding what pressure is must remain a formal and essentially meaningless procedure. One way to teach intuitive understanding of a concept is to discuss a large number of examples or to associate it with a concept that the students do have a feeling for. Thus the meaning of acceleration can be taught by discussing its value and sign at many points in the flight of a body that is thrown upward: at the start, on the way up, at the highest point, on the way down, and as it hits the ground. This can be followed by a discussion of the motion of an elevator, a loaded spring, and a train. Conclusions should be checked at times by a numerical example. To teach the meaning of energy, the teacher can associate it with the feeling of danger: a heavy boulder high up, a fast-flying stone, a stick of dynamite, a high electric potential. To make the very difficult distinction between kinetic energy and momentum, the teacher can point out that if a moving body is going to hit someone, the danger is better estimated from its energy than from its momentum.

It is a rare textbook that does a good job of explaining the *physical* content of a concept. The best source is often an original paper by a scientist who has struggled with the concept. Examples are Galileo on acceleration; Leibnitz on kinetic energy; Pascal or Archimedes on pressure; Rumford, Lavoisier, or Black on heat; Franklin or Faraday on electricity; and Newton on color.

# 6

# TEACHING METHODS:
# 3. THE LABORATORY

The three objectives of knowledge, understanding, and ability to learn are general enough to include what a student can learn in the laboratory. It is more fruitful, however, to look afresh at the question of laboratory teaching, separately from an analytical scheme developed primarily for other purposes.

Although there is little statistical or published empirical evidence that laboratory instruction in elementary courses contributes significantly to the student's general understanding of physics (59), it seems clear a priori that contact with phenomena is a necessary constituent of adequate training in physics. The proper nature of the contact with phenomena must be determined through clearly formulated objectives of laboratory instruction. Laboratory objectives should of course be a coherent part of the general objectives of the course. They must therefore be related to understanding of physics as a body of knowledge and as a process of inquiry. To what extent can these two general objectives be realized in the usual elementary physics laboratory?

## 6.1  LABORATORY OBJECTIVES

### Objectives that can be attained in an average laboratory

The introductory laboratory is seldom used as an important source of generalizations. To arrive inductively at as simple a generalization as Hooke's law would require a great deal of the student's time. If the time were well spent, it would not be because the student learned Hooke's law, but because he became acquainted with some aspects of physics as a process of inquiry or because he obtained some understanding of the relation between a mathematical formulation and the behavior of material objects (objective L2). The laboratory is more often used for a better understanding of a theoretical concept, such as the virtual and the real

72

optical image, or of a generalization, such as conservation of heat in calorimetry. In such cases, however, the principal contribution of the laboratory should be to give the student, through contact with reality, a different and truer idea of the concept or generalization than can be obtained theoretically—rather than merely a stronger or clearer idea of it. (This point is discussed in Section 6.4.) Another very common objective is to acquaint the student with various aspects of physics research: measurement (objective L2.1); control of variables; statistical treatment of data; and, less frequently, design of experiment (objective L2.2). A third common objective of the laboratory is to teach the student how to use certain instruments (objective L1.1), such as the potentiometer or the analytical balance. Here again, it is not the added knowledge of nature but an acquaintance with tools used in inquiry into natural phenomena that is important. Finally, some instructors hope to change the student's attitudes and habits (objectives L3.3 and L3.4): to help him acquire a respect for facts, faith in science in general, or a firmer conviction of the truth of a particular generalization; to stimulate his interest in physics; to promote alertness; to encourage him to work systematically; and so forth. These objectives, too, are more closely associated with physics as a process of inquiry than as a body of knowledge.

From this quick review of some of the more common objectives it appears that the elementary laboratory is well suited for acquainting the student with some aspects of physics as a process of inquiry, and that laboratory practices are at least superficially similar to standard scientific processes of inquiry. The laboratory's best contribution to the other major objective, understanding of physics as a body of knowledge, is not to increase the student's store of empirical or theoretical knowledge but to give him insight into what is known about reality. Since our knowledge of reality is a direct consequence of and essentially inseparable from the methods of acquiring that knowledge, a study of research methods and techniques is necessary for an understanding of the nature of physical knowledge. It appears, therefore, that the central objective of introductory laboratory instruction should be to increase the student's *understanding of the relation* between science and nature, that is, between the physicist's description of nature and nature itself, between physics and reality (objective L2, particularly L2.2).

### Relation between phenomena and their descriptions

The relation between reality and the physicist's picture of it is rich, complex, subtle, and changing. Even those aspects of the relation that can be "taught" in the laboratory cannot be described completely, but they must be analyzed at least in part to make communication possible among teachers and between teachers and students. Fortunately, in the laboratory, reality will be presented incorruptibly, if not always in keeping with the latest educational theory, by nature itself. The discussion that follows will be limited to assertions formulated to suggest appropriate illustrative laboratory exercises. The set of assertions can be modified by individual teachers in accordance with their philosophies and interests. Although it is not necessary for the student to learn a series of statements like—or unlike —those below, his laboratory experience should be so guided that he is continually aware of their cogency.

*Some principles and methods illustrating the relation between theoretical science and phenomena* The nature of the scientist's knowledge of reality is determined by the methods he uses in acquiring this knowledge. The scientist studies a phenomenon not in its entirety, for this is impossible, but in certain chosen aspects. In choosing these aspects he is guided by hypotheses (L2.21). The hypotheses and the method of attack (the research design) change as observations accumulate (L2.22). His final goal is to establish a generalization that applies not only to his experiment, but universally. Mathematics is the most precise, unambiguous, concise, and flexible language in which to express and manipulate the generalizations of the exact sciences. Scientific generalizations deal with classes of objects, not with any particular object: therefore they are abstractions that are strictly true only of idealized and nonexistent objects or processes. However, scientific generalizations nevertheless enable us to understand and predict the behavior of a wide variety of real objects (L2.23). In order for theory and experiment to agree even approximately or for a generalization to be induced from observation, it is necessary to correct for some peculiarities of the object studied and of its surroundings, and to neglect others. One of the most important ways to ascertain the corrections is to repeat the experiment under varied conditions (L2.22). Repeated accurate measurements invariably give similar but never identical results. These results must be treated statistically to determine the degree of agreement between the facts and the generalization (L2.23).

The next three sections describe conditions of learning conducive to achieving the general laboratory objectives and, after a brief criticism of prevailing laboratory practices in physics, give examples of appropriate laboratory experiments.

## 6.2 CONDITIONS OF LEARNING

A necessary condition for effective learning is hard thinking, a genuine intellectual effort (4). This hard thinking must of course be focused on a relevant object. Thus, since the *raison d'être* of the laboratory is to give the student a chance to deal with material objects, most laboratory learning must be gained through thinking that involves phenomena in their real, tangible, observable aspects. In particular, this is true of the central laboratory objective—exploring the principal features of the relation of science to reality. *Hard thinking* must take place in the *laboratory* and in the presence of the relevant material objects.

A second condition of learning is that the student's laboratory experience give him an opportunity to attain each of the major laboratory objectives. Generally it is not enough merely to allow him to come into contact with phenomena. Rather, the student's experience should be planned and guided in the light of *explicit, detailed objectives*. If there is a hierarchy of objectives based on their importance or difficulty, this hierarchy should inform the planning.

The third condition of learning concerns the *student's motivation*. The outcome of each laboratory experiment should interest the student, every step in it should make sense to him, and he should be rewarded for doing well. If the main reward, intellectual satisfaction, is to be achievable and just, the principal criteria of success must be clear to all, and they must be the same for both student and teacher. Since grades are a highly prized reward, it is essential that they be assigned on the basis of achievement of the main objectives of the laboratory.

## 6.3   PREVAILING LABORATORY PRACTICES

Methods of laboratory teaching are sometimes of the cookbook recipe type, in which the student is told precisely how the apparatus is to be set up, what readings are to be taken, and even what mathematical procedures are to be applied to the data. This sterile orderliness is often preserved by the watchful instructor, who continually guards the students against "wasting their time" gathering unnecessary data. At the other extreme is the unstructured type of experiment in which the student is asked to "find out all he can" about a phenomenon, and then left largely to his own devices. The relative efficacy of different laboratory instructional methods is difficult to gauge because reports of their successes are seldom based on clearly stated objectives or supported by the results of reliable measurements of students' achievement.

The highly structured and regulated laboratory has the advantages of compactness and efficiency. Many different kinds of experiment can be performed during the year; the laboratory can keep step with the lectures; and, usually, the cost of equipment, space, and supervision is less than that of the "research-type" laboratory. Unfortunately, the conventional laboratory does not, as a rule, adequately meet any of the three conditions of learning described in Section 6.2. For example, such a laboratory fails to allow the relevant phenomenology to figure prominently in the student's thinking at all stages of laboratory work: designing the experiment, carrying it through and collecting data, and analyzing the data.

In the conventional laboratory, the student is seldom allowed to have much say about the design of an experiment. He has little time to reflect upon his observations in order to decide on the next experimental step. In fact, during the ordinary laboratory period there is almost no time for thinking and thus for learning. The student seldom has to decide what to record about the phenomenon; he has usually been told. Conclusions are usually drawn at home, away from the apparatus and phenomena. If there is any hard thinking involved at this stage of the work, it has to do with relations between data, which have been reduced to sets of numbers, and generalizations. For a trained physicist who has lived with a phenomenon for months if not years, these numbers are an excellent representation of the phenomenon itself. For a beginning student they are often skeletons without flesh, abstractions of a higher order than the generalization he is to draw from them. There is a good deal of evidence for this contention. Students "forget" to put down units, absurd answers based on arithmetic errors are submitted in reports, and so forth.

In the less structured laboratory, the student has more leisure to think; he is undoubtedly better motivated; and he has a greater opportunity to exercise his ingenuity and to come to grips with the relation of physics to reality. However, this kind of laboratory costs more, is very loosely connected with the rest of the course, and often represents only a small amount of course content and a few, haphazard behavioral objectives. Since the instructor's touch must be light in this kind of laboratory, he needs an expert hand indeed to guide the student toward each of the major objectives. Most teachers acquainted with this kind of laboratory believe that pedagogically its advantages easily outweigh its disadvantages. Its higher cost as compared with the more conventional laboratory is probably the main reason for its comparative rarity.

## 6.4   PROPOSED DESIGN OF LABORATORY EXPERIMENTS

This section describes and illustrates, as examples, elementary physics laboratory experiments that meet the specified conditions of learning and that can be readily incorporated into the framework of the typical laboratory. In these experiments the student's goal is to acquire an understanding of relevant phenomena that will enable him to predict the outcome of a test experiment. The general and some of the specific characteristics of the test experiment are known to the student. The final step is an experimental verification of the prediction. The suggested experiments are like conventional ones in that the problems are set and rather narrowly delimited by the instructor; they are like less structured experiments in that they leave the method of attack largely to the student. They are unlike either type in design and emphasis, and in their "built-in" devices for testing the student's attainment of objectives.

The first condition of laboratory learning specifies hard thinking that involves both theoretical physics (that is, book physics) and observed phenomena, thinking that should occur in the laboratory. Each of the usual steps—the preliminary design of the experiment, the actual procedures involved, the collection of data, and its analysis—should invite or even demand such thinking from the student. In discussing these four steps, it will be convenient to refer to the following sample experiment.

### Sample experiment

Directions to the student: You are given a battery, two light bulbs, and two wire resistors. At a later laboratory period you will find these circuit elements, voltmeters and ammeters, and rheostats wired together to form an electric circuit, with the switch open. See the accompanying diagram for an illustration. (The student is given a diagram of a series-parallel circuit.) At that time, your first step will be to predict the readings of some of the meters from specified values of the readings of other meters. Your second step will be to close the switch in the presence of the instructor, adjust the rheostats settings, and check the actual meter readings against your predictions.

Your predictions of the outcome of the test experiment should specify the expected accuracy of the agreement. For example, you may predict that the reading of an ammeter will be $I = 5.0 \pm 0.3$ amperes. If the actual reading is within these limits, your prediction is correct. It is, of course, desirable to be able to predict the experimental value within as narrow limits as possible.

In preparation for the test experiment, you may spend up to five hours in an experimental study of the characteristics of the circuit elements given to you. Obtain whatever additional apparatus you need by submitting a list to the instructor. If in the course of your experimentation you find that you need other apparatus, submit a second list.

Arrange and summarize your data, and write down your generalizations from the data in such form that you will be able to make the calculations for your prediction in as short a time as possible. You will probably find the mathematical form—equations and graphs—particularly convenient. Bring these materials to the next laboratory session. You may be asked to hand them in and to include calculations for your predictions and the test-experiment results.

### Tentative experimental design

The tentative experimental design should take into account, and preferably be done in the presence of, the material objects involved. Thus, in the sample experiment, the student must inspect the four resistances and the battery before deciding on the range of the meters he needs. He will have to estimate the values of the resistances, for the light bulbs from their wattage and for the wire resistors from the gauge and length of the wire and from a handbook.

### Experimental procedure

It is important that some of the experiments be such that the original plan of attack is tentative, to be modified in light of the results of initial measurements. After he makes these measurements, the student must think about them before he can profitably proceed. Making alternate measuring and thinking necessary is probably the best way to insure the exercise of an intellectual effort concerned with phenomena. Students doing nothing but thinking, with the apparatus in front of them, should become a familiar and welcome sight in the laboratory. In the sample experiment, modifications of the original design may not be necessary, although some students may discover experimentally instead of knowing beforehand that the resistance of a light bulb varies measurably with temperature; thus they will be led to acquire originally unplanned data on the resistance-current relation.

### Collecting data

A student should be aware that the data he collects must depend on the generalization he seeks, and he should know the nature of the objects under investigation. Synthesizing instruments such as watt-hour meters or ohm-meters often obscure more than they reveal, and they should be avoided in the introductory laboratory. In the sample experiment, data-gathering will be influenced by the nature of the problem—the necessity of being able to predict the behavior of a combination of various circuit elements—and the peculiarities of the apparatus. The internal resistance of the battery may be important in some circuits and not in others; the resistance of the light bulbs is a function of the current; and the available meters limit the precision of resistance measurements.

### Analysis of data

An analysis of data can lead to a generalization or reveal a need for further experimentation. Either conclusion should be based on the phenomena; the former because a generalization requires an idealization of the objects experimented with, and the latter because a further treatment of the objects is contemplated. (Since the prediction in the sample experiment is to concern the same circuit elements that the student experimented with, the generalization he can draw will be very limited, dealing only with the general arrangement of the elements.) The student's treatment of the data will be strongly influenced by his need to be able to predict the behavior of the objects studied. Many students will want to put some of the data into a graph; for instance, they may plot the resistance of light bulbs against current and perhaps against voltage. The power and convenience of mathematical formulation should become clearer to the student with each successive experiment-predict-verify exercise. In the final step of the experiment, the data and generalizations, in the form of sets of numbers, equations, graphs, and perhaps verbal statements, will be matched against phenomena. This juxtaposition should further illustrate the relation of physics to reality.

The above analysis of the usual steps in the proposed type of laboratory experiment assumes that to extract the utmost profit from the contact with phenomena that a laboratory provides, the student should be continually thinking of the phenomena in their raw state. This does not mean, however, that the study of other phases of the relation between physics and reality, such as the relation between numerical data and generalizations or between generalizations and theory, is less important, but only that such study does not as a rule require laboratory facilities.

### 6.5   EXAMPLES OF PROPOSED LABORATORY EXPERIMENTS

To indicate how the second condition of learning, the opportunity for the student to attain explicit and specific objectives, can be met, a brief description is given below of a few experiments or parts of experiments aimed at elucidating and illustrating particular aspects of the relation of physics to reality. In the examples, the student is expected to follow the pattern of the sample experiment: experiment, analyze and summarize data, predict, and verify.

The physicist, guided by a hypothesis, studies only certain aspects of a phenomenon. This statement can be illustrated by two kinds of experiments. In the first, the student is directed to take only a limited number of measurements. In the second, a wise choice of measurements is necessitated by the phenomenon itself. An example of the first type is an experiment with a physical pendulum, say, a long triangular or rectangular board provided with a large number of possible points of suspension. The student is asked to measure the periods of oscillation for a specified number of points of suspension, choosing these so as to make the most accurate possible prediction of the period for any other point of suspension. The same pendulum can be used for the second kind of experiment if the number of possible points of suspension is so large that the student has no time to try them all.

The generalizations of science are abstractions that are true only of ideal, nonexistent objects. The abstractions must, however, enable us to understand the behavior of many real objects and to predict it approximately. An appropriate experiment should involve a phenomenon whose deviations from the straightforward, "zero-order" generalization are sizable and approximately calculable. For example, the student may be asked to measure the rate of water flow through a weir in order to predict the mass of water collected in a bucket. Most calorimetric experiments can be rewritten to illustrate this facet of the physics-reality relation unambiguously and forcefully. Mere disagreement, however, between the theoretical and the experimental values of, say, the heat of fusion of ice, is not edifying; it is merely discouraging. In a properly designed calorimetric experiment, the student must take into account the major sources of error and satisfy himself that his value is *not* in disagreement with the theoretical value. He can best prove this to himself and the instructor by correctly predicting the temperature of a specified mixture of ice and water. The procedure of tracking down error is lengthy, but it embodies an important lesson and should be a part of at least one experiment.

Repeated accurate measurements invariably give similar but never identical results. A convenient experiment involves measuring a linear dimension of an object, for example, a metal cylinder, with instruments of increasing precision: a meter stick, vernier calipers, micrometer calipers, and a microscope.

### 6.6   STUDENT MOTIVATION

The experiment-predict-verify pattern of laboratory work is particularly well adapted to providing the third condition of learning, student motivation. The experiment as a whole is an explicit challenge to the student's ability. It will be performed as a genuine search for knowledge, for the student is allowed to use his ingenuity and whatever knowledge, experimental or theoretical, he possesses. The experimental steps will make sense to the student, because he has devised them for a definite end. The last step, experimental verification, will be exciting and intellectually rewarding. The measure of the student's success, the agreement between the predicted and measured values, will appear clear and just to him. And finally, since the laboratory grade will be at least partly based on a measure of success that the student respects, the motivation it supplies will be pedagogically sound.

### 6.7   CONCLUSION

The preceding examples of experiments aimed at particular objectives show that the existing facilities of most introductory physics laboratories are quite adequate for attaining the central objective of laboratory instruction, understanding of the relation between phenomena and their descriptions. They also show that this objective is not likely to be achieved automatically. Rather, partly because the relation is often a subtle one, and partly because of the limitations of the student's time, sophistication, and initial interest, his contact with phenomena has to be carefully planned and guided. As a rule, a given experiment will touch on several aspects of the central objective, but not equally. It is only necessary to make sure that the cumulative emphasis over the year on each important aspect of the objective is adequate.

# 7

# THEORY OF TESTING:
# 1. TERMINOLOGY AND STATISTICS

This chapter defines the more important terms used in describing tests, gives formulas and methods for estimating a test's validity and reliability and for calculating the correlation between two tests, and discusses the relation between a student's competence and his grade. The chapter is most useful as a reference; at this point, the reader need not master its content; he has only to learn the meanings of the terms.

Section 6.1 discussed briefly the fluid and subtle relation between physical reality and the physicist's description of it. Not real phenomena but only conceptual models can be exactly described either verbally or mathematically. The relation between theoretical pedagogy and human behavior is not just fluid, but turbulent and opaque. The formulas given in this chapter apply only to conceptual models and not to live students, and, in addition, the models tend to be extremely technical. Nevertheless, teachers must be furnished with some mathematical tools so that they can acquire a vocabulary with which to discuss teaching, become more self-conscious and analytical, and learn to study what their students learn. The teachers who find testing a congenial method for improving their teaching will soon graduate from the crude but hopefully not misleading statistics in this book to more thorough treatments of the subject.

## 7.1  TECHNICAL TERMS AND CONCEPTS

*Ability, objective, competence*  Ability is a word that may stand for any entry in the list of objectives in Section 2.1: knowledge, understanding, ability to learn, knowledge of technical terms, imaginative thinking. Or it may stand for an unlisted objective such as a particular habit. An ability can also be called an objective: another way to speak of the ability, knowledge, is to say that knowledge is the objective of training. Competence is a

**81**

more general term; it may stand for one ability or a combination of abilities. The competence measured by a test or even by a single exercise usually consists of several abilities: knowledge, understanding, ability to read, test sophistication, and so forth.

*Test, exercise, item*   A test is any process that enables us to estimate a student's competence. A test may consist of several exercises, which are tasks or problems given to the student. An exercise may consist of several items, which are questions, subtopics, or other fairly self-contained and separately scorable parts of the exercise.

*Test forms*   The form of a test exercise may be oral, performance, or written. Performance tests involve laboratory apparatus or materials. Written tests are said to be *objective* in form if the student is asked to choose from a list of prepared *responses*, which are in essence suggested answers to a question, and *essay* if the response is to be written by the student. An item of an objective test consists of a *stem*, which is the question the student is to answer, and a list of responses.

*Mean*   The mean score M on a test of a group of N students is the arithmetical average of their individual scores X, as defined by the formula

$$M = \frac{\Sigma X}{N}, \tag{7.1}$$

where $\Sigma$ stands for "the sum of": $\Sigma X = X_1 + X_2 + \cdots X_N$. Unless otherwise specified, the summation includes all students.

*Standard deviation and variance*   The standard deviation S and its square, the variance $S^2$, of a set of scores X, are defined by the formula

$$S^2 = \frac{\Sigma(X - M)^2}{N}. \tag{7.2}$$

The standard deviation measures the spread of scores. (See under Normal distribution below.)

*Standard scores*   A student's standard score z is given by

$$z = \frac{X - M}{S}, \tag{7.3}$$

where X is the student's score, called the *raw* score, on the test. Standard scores are convenient because their mean is always zero and the standard deviation is 1. This property means that equal standard scores on different tests will assign a given student similar ranks within the group. A score of $z = 1$, for instance, places the student in the eighty-fourth percentile of the group that has taken the test, if one makes the usual assumption that the scores have a normal distribution.

*Normal distribution*   Scores, or any numbers, show normal distribution with the mean $M$ and standard deviation $S$ if the frequency $f$ with which a score $X$ occurs is given by

$$f = \frac{1}{S\sqrt{2\pi}} e^{-\frac{z^2}{2}}$$

where $z = (X - M)/S$. Table 7.1 gives percentages of scores lying within certain limits. More detailed tables can be found in most books on statistics.

**Table 7.1    Distribution of scores**

Percentage of scores whose values lie within the limits indicated if the scores are distributed normally with the standard deviation $S$ about the mean $M$. The distribution is symmetrical; for instance, 19 percent of the scores have values between $M$ and $M + .5S$, and 19 percent, values between $M - .5S$ and $M$.

| Interval | $M \pm .5S$ | $M \pm S$ | $M \pm 1.5S$ | $M \pm 2S$ | $M \pm 2.5S$ | $M \pm 3S$ |
|---|---|---|---|---|---|---|
| Percentage of scores | 38% | 68% | 87% | 95% | 99% | 99.7% |

*Error*   The measurement of the student's competence, like all other measurements, involves *random* and *systematic* error. If a test correctly estimates a specified competence of every student, it is free from error. If a test overestimates the competence of some students and underestimates that of other students, but correctly estimates the *average* competence of very large groups, it has random but no systematic error. If a test underestimates or overestimates the average competence of very large groups, it has systematic error; if it also underestimates or overestimates the competence of every student to the same degree, it has no random error.

*Correlation and correction for attenuation*   If a group of $N$ students has taken test 1 and test 2, the (coefficient of) correlation $r_{12}$ between the scores that the students made on the two tests is given by

$$r_{12} = \frac{\Sigma z_1 z_2}{N} = \frac{\Sigma(X_1 X_2) - N M_1 M_2}{N S_1 S_2}, \tag{7.4}$$

where the symbols have their usual meanings. For instance, $\Sigma(X_1 X_2)$ means that the score of each student on test 1 is multiplied by his score on test 2, and the products are added. The correlation is a measure of the agreement between the two sets of scores. If each student has identical standard scores $z$ on the two tests, then $r_{12} = 1$, and the agreement is considered perfect. (The requirement of identical standard scores is stronger than the requirement of identical rank order on the two tests.) Perfect disagreement between the two sets of scores may be said to be indicated by $r_{12} = -1$; in particular, the rank order is reversed. If the two sets of scores are unrelated, that is, if the relation between the scores is random, $r = 0$.

The smaller the tests' random errors, the more similar the competences measured by the tests, and the more heterogeneous the group tested, the higher will be the correlation between tests 1 and 2. A measure of the similarity of the competences is $R_{12}$, the correlation of the two tests *corrected for attentuation,* that is, corrected for random errors.

$$R_{12} = r_{12} \text{ (corrected for attenuation)} = \frac{r_{12}}{\sqrt{r_{11}r_{22}}}, \quad (7.5)$$

where $r_{11}$ and $r_{22}$ are the reliabilities (defined in the next paragraph) of the two tests. It follows from this formula that $r_{12}$ cannot be greater than $\sqrt{r_{11}r_{22}}$, because $R_{12}$ cannot be greater than unity.

*Reliability and parallel tests* There are several operational definitions of the reliability of a test (37). (See also Section 7.3, Reliability.) In all of them, high reliability means that repeated measurements will give nearly the same results; the definitions differ in the process of repetition each uses. For educational tests, especially those used for assigning grades, a definition by *parallel tests* is probably the best. Course tests vary from year to year in sampling of content, choice of problems, wording of questions, and so forth, but the teacher tries to make them equivalent—to make them test for the same general competence. If two tests are judged equally fair samples of the competence of a given group of students and thus equally suitable for assigning grades, and if they are equally difficult (same mean) and produce the same range of scores (same standard deviation), the two tests are parallel. The reliability of either test is then defined as equal to the correlation between scores made by a representative group of students on the two tests. The reliability of a test 1 is usually denoted by $r_{11}$, to indicate that it is a correlation with another test that is very much like test 1.

The freer a test is from random error, the more reliable it is. A quite reliable test may not, however, measure the desired competence. Thus a test intended to measure understanding may instead measure memory. Such a test may be said to have a large systematic error, since it will not correctly estimate the average understanding of even a very large group. The reliability of a given test varies with the group; it is higher for more heterogeneous groups. Therefore, strictly speaking, the word *reliability* should be used to describe not a test but a set of scores.

*Error of measurement* The error of measurement $e$ of a test is given by

$$e = S\sqrt{1 - r}, \quad (7.6)$$

where S is the standard deviation and $r$, the reliability of the test. The meaning of the error of measurement in testing is the same as in physical measurements. A test with $e = 0$ assigns each student a score $X_t$ that is a true measure of his competence—only, of course, of the competence that the test does measure. On a test with an error of measurement $e$, the students whose competence is really $X_t$ get scores that are usually assumed to be normally distributed with the standard deviation $e$ and the mean $X_t$; the probability (see Table 7.1) that a score falls in the interval $X_t \pm e$ is 68 percent, in the interval $X_t \pm 2e$, 95 percent, and so on. The error of measurement is thus a measure of the *precision* of the test as a measuring instrument; it is essentially independent of the degree of heterogeneity of the group tested.

If equation 7.6 is rewritten as

$$r = 1 - \frac{e^2}{S^2} \qquad (7.6a)$$

and if it is noted that the spread of scores S increases with the group's heterogeneity, we see that the reliability is similarly affected. To calculate the reliability for one's own students of a test prepared by an outside agency, one must know not its reliability but its error of measurement. The test can then be given to the students, S for their scores determined, and $r$ calculated from equation 7.6a.

*Validity* (32, Section 14.3)   A test is valid to the degree that it measures the *desired* competence, that is, gives proportionately higher scores to students of higher competence. A perfectly valid test would be free from systematic as well as random error. The validity of a test can be estimated if a *criterion* test C, that is, a test that is known to test the desired competence, is available. The (coefficient of) validity $V_{xc}$ of the new test X is defined as equal to the correlation $r_{xc}$ between the two tests, corrected for random errors of the criterion test. The correlation will be less than 1 because of the systematic errors in test X and random errors in both X and C. If random errors had been absent from the criterion test (as they would be in an infinitely long test), the correlation would have been given by

$$V_{xc} = \frac{r_{xc}}{\sqrt{r_{cc}}}, \qquad (7.7)$$

where $r_{cc}$ is the reliability of the criterion test. $V_{xc}$ is a measure of the *accuracy* of the scores that students get on the test, that is, of the faithfulness with which the scores reflect the students' attainment of the desired objectives. Some writers define validity as equal to $r_{xc}$ and others define it as equal to $R_{xc}$, given by equation 7.5a below.

*Relevance* A test exercise is relevant to an ability if it measures that ability, that is, if it correlates positively with the criterion test of that ability. An exercise may be, and usually is, relevant to several abilities.

*Representation* A competence or ability has many aspects. Knowledge of relations, for instance, may include relations between theories and evidence and between empirical generalizations and facts; it may also refer to mechanics or heat. If a test includes exercises that are relevant to all the important aspects of an ability, the ability is said to be represented in the test. A measure of both relevance and representation of an ability in a test $X$ is given by

$$R_{xc} = \frac{V_{xc}}{\sqrt{r_{xx}}}, \tag{7.5a}$$

where $V_{xc}$ is the validity of the test with respect to the ability and $r_{xx}$ is its reliability. $R_{xc}$ expresses the similarity of the abilities or competences measured by test $X$ and the criterion test.

*Validity as a function of representation and reliability* The test's reliability $r_{xx}$, which depends in part on the random error, puts an upper limit to its validity; as is seen from equation 7.5a, $V_{xc}$ cannot be greater than $\sqrt{r_{xx}}$. On the other hand, of course, a very reliable test may measure quite precisely a competence that is very different from the desired competence. Such a test will have low validity. The validity of a test $V_{xc}$ depends on the group tested; it is therefore more accurate to speak of the validity of a set of scores than of the test. If a test represents the desired competence perfectly, that is, if it measures all the major objectives of a course, and if the objectives are properly emphasized or weighted, the test may be used as a criterion, and $r_{xx} = r_{cc}$. The validity of such a test is, from equation 7.7, $V_{xc} = \sqrt{r_{xx}}$. Perfect validity requires perfect relevance and representation ($R_{xc} = 1$), and perfect reliability ($r_{xx} = 1$).

*Comparison of reliability, error of measurement, and validity* Reliability and error of measurement are essentially measures of repeatability or consistency. If a highly reliable test (or tests that are parallel to it) is used year after year on groups of about the same caliber and training, nearly the same standards are used for all groups, and grading is consistent from year to year. A highly reliable test also insures that, on the average, A students have come closer to the standard of achievement than B students (grading is fair or consistent within the group). If the test has a small error of measurement, consistency of grading standards is maintained even among groups that differ in caliber and training. The validity of a test is a measure both of the consistency of grading standards and of their correctness. To put the comparison in other words, small error of measurement means that the test is technically good; high reliability for a given group means that the test is technically good enough for that group; and high validity for a given group means that the test is in all important respects a good test for that group.

*Significance of a difference and level of significance*   When two measurements yield different results, say, $X_1$ and $X_2$, it is often important to know whether the difference, $d = X_1 - X_2$, is real (statistically significant) or the result of factors the experiment left to chance. To answer that question, one finds the standard error $S_d$ (of the difference) that the specified chance factors are likely to produce, calculates $y = d/S_d$, and looks up in tables suitable for the type of distribution governing $y$ the probability that this value of $y$ will occur by chance.

Suppose, for instance, that a class is divided into two groups in some random fashion. Different methods of teaching are used on the two groups, and the same test is used to measure the results of instruction. If the means, standard deviations, and number of students in the two groups are $M_1$, $S_1$, $N_1$ and $M_2$, $S_2$, $N_2$, respectively, the standard error (of the difference of means) $S_d$ and $y$ are given by

$$S_d{}^2 = \left(\frac{S_1{}^2}{N_2} + \frac{S_2{}^2}{N_1}\right)\left(\frac{N_1 + N_2}{N_1 + N_2 - 2}\right) \tag{7.8}$$

and

$$y = \frac{M_1 - M_2}{S_d}. \tag{7.9}$$

If $N_1 + N_2 - 2$ is greater than 30, $y$ is distributed nearly normally with the standard deviation of unity and mean zero. From Table 7.1 we see, for instance, that by chance (here, because of an accidental difference in the caliber of randomly chosen students) $y$ would have a value between $-2$ and $+2$ about 95 percent of the time. If the value of $y$ is 2 or $-2$, the difference $M_1 - M_2$ is statistically significant at the 5 percent *level*. For $y = 2.5$ or $-2.5$, the difference is statistically significant at the 1 percent level, and so forth.

At the 5 percent level of significance, and with much greater assurance at the 1 percent level, we may reasonably suppose that the group with the larger $M$ learned more than the other, not because it consisted of better students, but because of factors such as a better teacher, better method, or better equipment. To isolate just one of these factors as the decisive one, all other factors should be randomized just as student caliber was. Examples of the use of equations 7.8 and 7.9 are given in Section 13.2.*

---

* *Item analysis, discrimination index,* and *difficulty* are discussed and illustrated in Section 7.4, at the end of this chapter.

### 7.2   CORRELATION

*Factors determining correlation*   The correlation between a test measuring competence 1 and a test measuring competence 2 depends on the abilities making up the competences, the method of instruction, the caliber of the students, and the difficulties and reliabilities of the tests (35). The agreement between students' scores on the two tests is diminished if the scores are improperly assigned because of the tests' imperfections: $r_{12}$ cannot be higher than $\sqrt{r_{11}r_{22}}$, where $r_{11}$ and $r_{22}$ are the reliabilities of the two tests. The correlation is increased if the two competences that are tested overlap, that is, include some of the same abilities. All paper-and-pencil tests, for instance, measure intelligence, reading ability, and test sophistication. For this reason, correlation among college course tests are usually above .30. Similarity in subject matter raises correlation still higher. Science tests given at the end of a course, for example, usually have a correlation of at least .40, even if care is taken to test for "pure" abilities by measuring, for instance, knowledge in test 1 and understanding in test 2 (35). Positive correlation among tests of knowledge, understanding, and ability to learn is partly the result of intrinsic common factors—understanding and learning ability require some knowledge—and partly the result of less direct association that depends on the method of instruction. In a course in which these three objectives are emphasized in teaching and testing, their attainment is likely to correlate better than in a course in which only one objective is stressed, because each student will probably try, according to his ability, to advance in all three (18).

Finally, the correlation between two tests depends on the composition of the student body and the difficulty of the tests. The correlation rises with the heterogeneity of the group members' competence. If some students have studied very little or are not very bright, they will get low scores on *both* tests. Similarly, exceptionally bright and industrious students will get high scores on both tests. The presence of either kind of student results in a better average agreement between the scores on the two tests, that is, in a higher correlation. Two very difficult or two very easy tests will show low correlation because either pair of tests makes the group effectively more homogeneous. Thus, for instance, if all the students have the requisite competence for both tests, their scores will fall below 100 percent only because of test imperfections, including chance factors, and the correlation will be near zero. A very easy and a very hard test are also likely to show a low intercorrelation, partly because neither test discriminates well and partly because they probably do not test for the same competence.

#### Correlation and grades

Table 7.2 illustrates the meaning of correlation between two tests in terms of the letter grades the students are most likely to get on the tests.

**Table 7.2  Agreement between the grades received on two tests by a group of students, as a function of the correlation $r_{12}$ between the tests.**

On each test, the top 10 percent of students get A's; other percentages are B, 20 percent; C, 40 percent; D, 20 percent; F, the lowest 10 percent. Example: if $r_{12} = .65$, 18 percent of the students who get B's on test 1 will get A's on test 2, 34 percent will get B's, and so forth.

Grade on test 1 / Grade on test 2

|     | A | B | C | D | F |
|-----|-----|-----|-----|-----|-----|
| A | 100 |  |  |  |  |
| B |  | 100 |  |  |  |
| C |  |  | 100 |  |  |
| D |  |  |  | 100 |  |
| F |  |  |  |  | 100 |

$r_{12} = 1$

Grade on test 1 / Grade on test 2

|     | A | B | C | D | F |
|-----|-----|-----|-----|-----|-----|
| A | 78 | 22 | .2 |  |  |
| B | 11 | 67 | 22 |  |  |
| C | .1 | 11 | 77 | 11 | .1 |
| D |  |  | 22 | 67 | 11 |
| F |  |  |  | .2 | 22 | 78 |

$r_{12} = .95$

Grade on test 1 / Grade on test 2

|     | A | B | C | D | F |
|-----|-----|-----|-----|-----|-----|
| A | 69 | 29 | 2 |  |  |
| B | 15 | 55 | 30 | .2 |  |
| C | .6 | 15 | 69 | 15 | .6 |
| D |  | .2 | 30 | 55 | 15 |
| F |  |  | 2 | 29 | 69 |

$r_{12} = .90$

Grade on test 1 / Grade on test 2

|     | A | B | C | D | F |
|-----|-----|-----|-----|-----|-----|
| A | 56 | 34 | 10 | .2 |  |
| B | 17 | 43 | 37 | 3 | .2 |
| C | 2 | 19 | 58 | 19 | 2 |
| D | .2 | 3 | 37 | 43 | 17 |
| F |  | .2 | 10 | 34 | 56 |

$r_{12} = .80$

Grade on test 1 / Grade on test 2

|     | A | B | C | D | F |
|-----|-----|-----|-----|-----|-----|
| A | 43 | 35 | 21 | 2 | .1 |
| B | 18 | 34 | 40 | 7 | .9 |
| C | 5 | 21 | 50 | 21 | 5 |
| D | .9 | 7 | 40 | 34 | 18 |
| F | .1 | 2 | 21 | 35 | 43 |

$r_{12} = .65$

Grade on test 1 / Grade on test 2

|     | A | B | C | D | F |
|-----|-----|-----|-----|-----|-----|
| A | 29 | 32 | 31 | 6 | 1 |
| B | 16 | 28 | 40 | 12 | 3 |
| C | 8 | 20 | 44 | 20 | 8 |
| D | 3 | 12 | 40 | 28 | 16 |
| F | 1 | 6 | 31 | 32 | 29 |

$r_{12} = .45$

Grade on test 1 / Grade on test 2

|     | A | B | C | D | F |
|-----|-----|-----|-----|-----|-----|
| A | 10 | 20 | 40 | 20 | 10 |
| B | 10 | 20 | 40 | 20 | 10 |
| C | 10 | 20 | 40 | 20 | 10 |
| D | 10 | 20 | 40 | 20 | 10 |
| F | 10 | 20 | 40 | 20 | 10 |

$r_{12} = 0$

## 7.3    RELIABILITY AND VALIDITY

### Students' grades as a function of reliability and validity

The reliability of a test is defined as equal to its correlation with a parallel test. We can therefore use Table 7.2 for studying the dependence of students' grades on the reliability of the test. If a test is perfectly reliable, $r = 1$, the same grades will be assigned by any parallel test. But if the reliability is less than 1, what grade a student gets depends on which test the teacher *happens* to have chosen from his collection of parallel tests. (It does not matter, of course, whether the "collection" is in the filing cabinet or in the mind of the teacher.) Thus, for instance, if the reliability of the test is .65, Table 7.2 shows that about 2 percent of the students who have received A's on the basis of the test would have received D's if another presumably equivalent test had been given.

Clearly a test of reliability .65 is unsatisfactory as a basis for making any important decision about a student because it introduces serious inconsistencies. The absolute injustice done to a student may be more or less serious than the relative injustice indicated by the inconsistencies, depending on the validity of the test. Table 7.3 gives the percentage of cor-

**Table 7.3    Correct grades and validity**

(Summary of Table 7.2, with one of the tests taken as criterion.) Percentages of students whose grades differ by a given number of points from the grades they deserve as a function of the validity of the test. The difference between adjacent letter grades such as A and B, or C and D, is one point. The percentages in parentheses are calculated on the basis of a three-point scale: upper 20 percent of students get H (for honors), lowest 10 percent get F, and the rest, S (for satisfactory). The difference between H and S, or S and F, is one point.

|  | $V_{xc} =$ | | | | | | |
|---|---|---|---|---|---|---|---|
|  | 1.00 | .95 | .90 | .80 | .65 | .45 | 0 |
| Correct grades | 100(100) | 73(88) | 67(84) | 52(76) | 42(70) | 35(63) | 26(54) |
| Grades off by 1 point |  | 27(12) | 32(16) | 43(24) | 46(30) | 45(36) | 40(42) |
| Grades off by 2 points |  | .1 | 1 | 5 | 11(.1) | 17(.7) | 24(4) |
| Grades off by more than 2 points |  |  |  | .1 | .7 | 3 | 10 |

rect and wrong grades as a function of the test's validity. For instance, if the validity of a test is .90, 67 percent of the students who have taken the test will get the grades they deserve; the grades of 32 percent will be off by one point; 1 percent will get grades that are off by two points; and less than .1 percent will get grades that are off by more than two points.

If a test $X$ measures all the major objectives of the course weighted according to their importance, it can be taken as a criterion test, and its validity, according to equation 7.7, is given by $V_{xc} = V_{cc} = \sqrt{r_{cc}} = \sqrt{r_{xx}}$. The test's reliability $r_{cc}$ is of course always smaller than $\sqrt{r_{cc}}$. If $r_{cc} = .65$, $\sqrt{r_{cc}} = .81$, and the percentage of students who *deserve* A's but who are given D's is only about .2 percent. One can understand why Table 7.2 may exaggerate the real or absolute injustice done to the students by a test that measures the *desired* competence when one remembers that it does not measure the competence completely accurately. Thus, for instance, if a student gets an A on one test and a C on a parallel test, both of reliability .65, he very likely deserves neither A nor C, but B. Therefore each of the two tests is probably only one letter grade off and not two, as Table 7.2 may have led us to believe. If a test $X$ can be taken as the criterion, $V_{xc} = \sqrt{r_{xx}}$; if it cannot, $V_{xc}$ is less than $\sqrt{r_{xx}}$, and one can only say that the accuracy of the grades assigned on the basis of a test of reliability $r_{xx}$ is less than that given by Table 7.3 for $V_{xc} = \sqrt{r_{xx}}$.

## Improving letter-grade validity

The accuracy of assigned letter grades depends on the validity of the test and on the number of different grades we want to give the students. Suppose it has been decided that no more than 25 percent of the students should get wrong grades. These standards do not seem unduly rigorous, yet they require a validity of better than .95 for the test or the battery of tests used in assigning grades if we want to separate our students into five groups (A, B, C, D, and F). If, however, we are satisfied with giving H to the top 20 percent, F to the lowest 10 percent and S to the remaining 70 percent, a test of validity .80 will meet these standards, as the figures in parentheses in Table 7.3 show. If the validity of the battery is less than .95, and if the teacher accepts the standard of assigning correct grades to at least 75 percent of his students, he can maintain the standard only by reducing his scale of grading from five points to four, three, or even two. Otherwise he in effect writes his results to more significant figures than his measurements warrant. Simplified grading has much to recommend it besides honesty in reporting. In fact the argument for honesty, though valid, is less strong than it may appear. The number of incorrect grades can be reduced only by assigning the same grade to students of widely varying achievement. Better arguments for simplified grading are that there will be a relaxation of tension and fewer cases of bitterness over unjust grades; that it is much easier to write a test that will accurately place students into fewer groups (this statement does not concern the test's reliability— see Section 8.5); that most teachers have learned to spot outstanding and failing students but cannot tell a B from a C student, or a C from a D student; and that absolute standards (see Section 12.6) for grading become possible.

**Measures of reliability** (37)

The best way, and the only dependable way to estimate the reliability of a test if not all students have time to finish it is to give the same group of students two parallel tests a few days apart. If this is impractical, reliability can be estimated by the split-half method. In this method, the test is divided into halves that best satisfy the requirements for parallel tests, the test is administered as a whole, and the correlation of the students' scores on the two halves is calculated. This correlation, $r_{\frac{1}{2}}$, gives the reliability of either half of the test. The reliability of the whole test is given by

$$r = \frac{2r_{\frac{1}{2}}}{1 + r_{\frac{1}{2}}}, \tag{7.13a}$$

which is equation 7.13, given later in this section, with $n = 2$. A more usual practice, however, is to split the test in half by dividing it into odd and even items and exercises. Since adjacent items are usually interrelated by similarity in subject matter and objectives, equation 7.13a almost invariably overestimates the test's reliability. If the odd-even split is used, perhaps the best and certainly the easiest formula to use is

$$r = 2\left(1 - \frac{S_o^2 + S_e^2}{S^2}\right),$$

where $S_o$, $S_e$, and $S$ are the standard deviations, respectively, of the scores on odd items, even items, and the whole test. If the test is an objective test and the student's score is just the *number of items answered correctly*, the reliability can be estimated by using the Kuder-Richardson formula

$$r = \frac{K}{K - 1}\left(1 - \frac{M - M^2/K}{S^2}\right), \tag{7.10}$$

where $K$ is the number of items in the test, $M$ the mean, and $S$ the standard deviation. This formula gives a good estimate of $r$ if the items are homogeneous, that is, if they are all of about the same difficulty and if all measure the same ability (such as knowledge); otherwise the formula is likely to underestimate the test's reliability. If the items satisfy the conditions for homogeneity, matching of split halves is not necessary, and a *random* split may be used for calculating the reliability. Although the Kuder-Richardson formula can be derived on assumptions that are less rigorous than a perfect homogeneity of all items, the possibility of using a random split (really the average of all possible splits) enables one to understand how the reliability can be estimated from such "superficial" or gross variables as $K$, $M$, and $S$. For the same values of $K$ and $M$, reliability increases with $S$. This is reasonable because a larger $S$ means a more heterogeneous group, and heterogeneity contributes to reliability.

If a test measures several different abilities it should be divided into subtests, and the reliability of each subtest, $r_{11}$, $r_{22}$, and so forth, calculated from formula 7.10. The reliability $R$ of the whole test can then be calculated from the following equation

$$S^2(1 - R) = S_1^2(1 - r_{11}) + S_2^2(1 - r_{22}) + \cdots, \tag{7.11}$$

where $S$, $S_1$, $S_2$, and so on are the standard deviations of the whole test, of subtest 1, subtest 2, and so forth. The same procedure should be followed if test items differ greatly in difficulty; the more difficult items may be considered to form subtest 1 and the less difficult ones, subtest 2. Equation 7.11 merely states that the squares of random errors, as defined by equation 7.6, are additive, and the equation is thus quite general. Another very general equation relates $S$, $S_1$, $S_2$, and so forth, and $r_{12}$, $r_{13}$, and so forth.

$$S^2 = S_1^2 + S_2^2 + S_3^2 + 2(S_1S_2r_{12} + S_1S_3r_{13} + S_2S_3r_{23}). \tag{7.12}$$

This equation, which can be generalized in a fairly obvious manner to cover any number of tests, shows that standard deviations add vectorially if we interpret $r_{12}$ as the cosine of the angle $\theta_{12}$ between "vectors" $S_1$ and $S_2$, and so on. With this interpretation it follows, for instance, that if $r_{12} = .87$ and $r_{13} = .77$, $\theta_{12} = 30°$, $\theta_{13} = 40°$, and $10° > \theta_{23} > 70°$, because the angle between vectors $S_2$ and $S_3$ cannot be smaller than $40° - 30°$ or larger than than $40° + 30°$. Therefore we get as the limits of $r_{23}$, $.34 > r_{23} > .98$. It should be noted that the number of dimensions of the vectorial space is, in general, equal to the number of vectors.

### Effect of test length on reliability and validity

Consider test 1 of standard deviation $S_1$, reliability $r_{11}$, validity $V_{1c}$, and correlation $r_{1x}$ with an arbitrary test $X$. If we increase its length by a factor of $n$, without changing the character of the exercises, by adding $n - 1$ parallel tests to the test, the augmented test $n$ will have standard deviation $S_n$, reliability $r_{nn}$, validity $V_{nc}$, and correlation $r_{nx}$ with test $X$. These quantities can be shown to be given by equations 7.13.

$$\frac{S_n^2}{n^2S_1^2} = \frac{r_{11}}{r_{nn}} = \frac{V_{1c}^2}{V_{nc}^2} = \frac{r_{1x}^2}{r_{nx}^2} = \frac{1 - r_{11}}{n} + r_{11} \tag{7.13}$$

Thus, increasing a test's length increases all four quantities (32). In fact, it seems reasonable to suppose that any change that does not affect the *nature* of the competence measured by a test will affect the first four ratios in 7.13 in the same way.

The reliability of a test may also be increased by adding exercises that measure a competence different from that measured by the rest of the test, under the following conditions. Consider two tests, 1 and 2, of standard deviations $S_1$ and $S_2$, reliabilities $r_{11}$ and $r_{22}$, and intercorrelation $r_{12}$. Augment test 2 by adding to it $1/M$ of test 1. If we assume that the fraction

$1/M$ represents a fair sample of the exercises of test 1, the reliability of the augmented test will be greater than $r_{22}$ provided that

$$\frac{r_{12}}{r_{11}} > \frac{1}{2} \frac{S_1}{S_2} \left( n - \frac{1}{M} \right), \qquad (7.14)$$

where

$$n = \frac{r_{22}(1 - r_{11})}{r_{11}(1 - r_{22})}.$$

Here $n$ is equal to the factor by which test 1 would have to be lengthened to make its reliability equal to $r_{22}$. Inequality 7.14 can be derived from equations 7.11, 7.12, and 7.13.

In science, the three main abilities, knowledge, understanding, and ability to learn, will ordinarily have intercorrelation coefficients of not less than .45, and the reliability of a test for any one of them is not likely to be above .90. Thus $r_{12}/r_{11} > \frac{1}{2}$, and the condition becomes $S_1/S_2(n - 1/M) \leq 1$. If $S_1 = S_2$ and $r_{11} = r_{22}$, this condition is satisfied however small the fraction $1/M$ may be. In practice, condition 7.14 is usually satisfied for fairly large values of $M$, even if the reliabilities and standard deviations are not equal, provided, of course, that the added items are generally appropriate in subject matter and difficulty for the group tested. Therefore the reliability of a test on, for example, knowledge is likely to be increased by the addition of even a few items on understanding or learning ability. When all three abilities are considered important, the validity of a composite test will be higher, regardless of the degree of their intercorrelation, if augmenting the test improves the balance of the objectives.

**Validity vs. reliability**

Validity requires that the major objectives be represented in the test in accordance with their importance: it thus requires a certain variety. Reliability, on the other hand, thrives on homogeneity. (Representation and homogeneity are discussed in Section 8.4.) It has already been shown that adding an exercise is very likely to improve the test's reliability. A *substitution* of one exercise for another, however, will increase reliability only if the new exercise correlates better with the rest of the test than does the old one. In either case the validity is increased if the change introduces a better balance among the objectives. The following few paragraphs show what happens to the validity and reliability of a test if a substantial proportion of exercises is substituted.

*Reliability and validity of a combination of tests*    If two tests $X$ and $Y$ have equal reliabilities, $r_{xx} = r_{yy}$, and equal standard deviations, but measure different competences, and if the correlation between the tests is $r_{xy}$, it follows from equations 7.11 and 7.12 that

$$r_{x+y} = \frac{r_{xx} + r_{xy}}{1 + r_{xy}}, \qquad (7.15)$$

where $r_{x+y}$ is the reliability of a test consisting of all the items of tests $X$ and $Y$. If we now split the combination test into parallel halves and call each half-test $Z$, test $Z$ will be of the same length as either of the original tests (if these are of equal lengths) and will have a reliability $r_{zz}$ calculable from equation 7.13.

$$r_{zz} = \frac{r_{xx} + r_{xy}}{2 + r_{xy} - r_{xx}}. \qquad (7.16)$$

The correlation $r_{xz}$ between test $X$ or $Y$ and test $\dfrac{X + Y}{2}$ (that is, test $Z$) is calculable from equations 7.12 and 7.13.

$$r_{xz} = \frac{r_{xx} + r_{xy}}{\sqrt{2}\,\sqrt{2 + r_{xy} - r_{xx}}} \qquad (7.17)$$

The question is: In what respects is the combination test $Z$ better or worse than either of the original tests $X$ or $Y$? Let us assume, for example, that knowledge and understanding are considered equally important objectives of a course and that testing time is limited to two hours. Is it better to have a two-hour test on knowledge ($X$) or understanding ($Y$), or two one-hour tests, one on knowledge and the other on understanding, that is, test $Z$? This question is answered by the data of Table 7.4.

**Table 7.4   Reliability and validity of a test measuring one competence, X or Y, and of a test Z of the same length testing equally for both**

$$\left( \frac{X + Y}{2} = Z \right)$$

Very wrong grades are those differing by at least two letter grades, as when A is assigned instead of C, D, or F. A perfectly reliable test $X + Y$ is taken as criterion.

|  | I | II | III | IV |
|---|---|---|---|---|
| Correlation between tests $X$ and $Y$, $r_{xy}$ | .45 | .45 | .60 | .60 |
| Reliability of test $X$ or $Y$, $r_{xx} = r_{yy}$ | .80 | .90 | .80 | .90 |
| Reliability of test $\dfrac{X + Y}{2}$, $r_{zz}$ | .76 | .82 | .78 | .88 |
| Correlation between $X$ and $\dfrac{X + Y}{2}$, $r_{xz}$ | .69 | .76 | .74 | .81 |
| Validity of test $X$ or $Y$, $\dfrac{r_{xz}}{\sqrt{r_{zz}}}$ | .79 | .84 | .84 | .86 |
| Validity of test $\dfrac{X + Y}{2}$, $\sqrt{r_{zz}}$ | .87 | .91 | .88 | .94 |
| Percentage of very wrong grades assigned by $X$ or $Y$ | 5.5 | 3 | 3 | 2.5 |
| Percentage of very wrong grades assigned by $\dfrac{X + Y}{2}$ | 2 | .7 | 1.5 | .2 |

Table 7.4 is constructed on the assumption that correct grades would be assigned to students on the basis of a test of perfect reliability (infinite length) in which knowledge and understanding are equally weighted. As can be seen from the table, a combination test is less reliable but more valid than either of the original tests. Column I gives the results for $r_{xy} = .45$ and $r_{xx} = r_{yy} = .80$. These values are probably realistic for the majority of introductory science courses and good two-hour tests. The last two numbers in the column show that the percentage of very wrong grades assigned on the basis of test $X$ (or $Y$) is 5.5 percent but, on the basis of test $(X + Y)/2$, only 2 percent. Even if test $X$ is increased to four-and-a-half hours, giving it a reliability of .9, the percentage of very wrong grades is still 3 percent. The same effort put into writing items on understanding ($Y$) will result in much fairer grading.

In conclusion it should be pointed out that the teacher's goal is tests of higher validity; higher reliability is of little importance to him unless it increases validity.

## 7.4   ITEM ANALYSIS

Perhaps the most common statistical analysis used in improving a test's reliability—and if the major objectives are properly represented in the test, also its validity—is item analysis (54), in which the correlation between the test as a whole and an individual item (or exercise) is calculated. The coefficient of correlation, known as the index of reliability of the item, can be calculated in the usual way from the scores made by students on the test and on the item. The procedure is obviously lengthy, and short cuts are usually employed. The most common short cut that yields very good results is as follows.

The total score on the test is used to separate the students into "good" and "bad" or high and low groups. If the high group does much better on an item than the low group, the item is said to show good discrimination; it measures an aspect of that competence which the test as a whole is designed to measure and is, therefore, a properly designed item. (We are assuming here that the test is adequately valid or at least more valid than any one item.) If the high and low groups do equally well on an item, it has no discrimination, and if the low group does better than the high one, the item has negative discrimination. These last two types of item in a science test usually do not measure anything important, and they should be repaired or dropped, provided of course that enough students—fifty or more—were involved to make the analysis reliable.

An item may have low though positive discriminating power for a variety of reasons. It may be too easy, too difficult, or ambiguous. Such an item should either be improved or, if the teacher does not think it measures anything of great importance, be dropped. But sometimes an item does not discriminate well because the ability it measures does not play an important enough part in the test as a whole. This is likely to happen if the test measures several abilities that do not intercorrelate highly. To judge properly an item of such a test, the students should be divided into high and low groups on the basis not of their total scores but of their scores on that part of the test—the subtest—intended to measure the relevant ability. Thus, to estimate the relevance of an item testing understanding, the high and low groups are those with high and low scores on the subtest on understanding. The common practice of analyzing items on the basis of the total test and of "improving" the test by eliminating items of low discrimination must lead, if pursued systematically and long enough, to a test that measures a single ability, the predominant ability in the original test—usually knowledge.

Besides its reliability index, there are several possible numerical measures of the discriminating power of an exercise. The following formula for the *index of discrimination, D,* is simple, and usually an adequate measure of the reliability index.

$$D = \frac{H - L}{N},$$ (7.18)

where $H$ and $L$ are the average scores made on the exercise by the members of the high and the low groups respectively, and $N$ is the maximum possible score. The contribution of an item to the test's reliability is considered low if $D$ is less than .2 and high if $D$ is greater than .4. An estimate of the *difficulty* of an exercise is given by equation 7.19. Note that a difficulty equal to 1 means a very easy test.

$$\text{Difficulty} = \frac{H + L}{2N}.$$ (7.19)

The best way to divide the students into high and low groups depends on the size of the class. For larger classes, high and low groups of fifty students each, randomly chosen respectively from the highest 27 percent and the lowest 27 percent of the class, make an effective division. For classes of fifty to ninety students, the top twenty-five and bottom twenty-five students might be used, and for smaller classes, the upper and lower halves.

Table 7.5 on page 98 gives an item analysis of twelve items assumed to be five-response, multiple-choice items, with one right response $(N = 1)$.

*Remedies* *   In improving an item, the first and the most important judgment to be made is nearly independent of statistics. If, in the opinion of the teacher, an item of low discrimination, say $D = .1$, tests for something that is important, and the response marked right is the best one by an adequate margin, the item should be kept. The fault may lie not in the item

---

* See also Section 8.5 under Difficulty.

but in inadequate teaching or bad students, in mistaking the ability the item measures, in inadequate representation in the test of the ability measured by the item, or in a statistical quirk. With this caution in mind, the statistical results of Table 7.5 indicate the following. Items 3 and 11 are probably of no value in assigning students' grades and should not be used in their present form. The rest of the items probably contribute to the reliability of the test and therefore to more accurate grades. They should be dropped only if shortening the test is important. Otherwise they should be replaced by other items, repaired, or left as they are. The following comments suggest general rules for item repair. Items 2, 5, 6, 7, 9, and 10 are all right. Item 1 should be made harder. This is done by making the right response *relatively* less attractive. The present right response may be too attractive because of the wording of the stem; because the response is very long, studded with qualification, or too much like a statement in the book; or because the wrong responses are too obviously wrong. Usually the safest process is to make the wrong responses more nearly right. Items 8 and 12 should be inspected for ambiguities and, if they are not apparent, made easier by making the right response relatively more attractive. This can be done by making it more obviously correct or by mak-

**Table 7.5  Numbers of students who have answered a particular item correctly**

The high and the low groups consist of fifty students each from the highest 27 percent and the lowest 27 percent of the class. (For item 1, $H = 50/50 = 1$; $L = 45/50 = .9$; $D = (1 - .9)/1 = .1$; and Difficulty $= (1 + .9)/2 = .95$.)

| Item no. | 1 | 2 | 3 | 4 | 5 | 6 | 7 | 8 | 9 | 10 | 11 | 12 |
|---|---|---|---|---|---|---|---|---|---|---|---|---|
| High group | 50 | 50 | 40 | 40 | 40 | 40 | 30 | 20 | 20 | 20 | 8 | 10 |
| Low group | 45 | 25 | 38 | 35 | 20 | 10 | 15 | 15 | 10 | 5 | 10 | 5 |
| Index of discrimination | .1 | .5 | .04 | .1 | .4 | .6 | .3 | .1 | .2 | .3 | −.04 | .1 |
| Difficulty | .95 | .75 | .78 | .75 | .60 | .50 | .45 | .35 | .30 | .25 | .18 | .15 |

COMMENTS

ITEM 1.  Low discrimination because too easy.

ITEM 2.  Good item but very low discrimination at the A-B line, that is, between A and B students.

ITEM 3.  No discrimination; reason not clear without inspecting the item.

ITEM 4.  Low discrimination; probably no discrimination at the B-C and C-D lines.

ITEMS 5, 6, 7, 9.  Good items.

ITEM 8.  Low discrimination and hard; possibly ambiguous.

ITEM 10.  Good item but only 10 percent of the low group got it right; may have no discrimination at the D-F line.

ITEMS 11, 12.  Scores too near guess level; too hard, wrongly keyed, or very ambiguous.

ing the wrong responses less correct. Item 11 may perhaps be repaired in the same way.

If no serious ambiguities can be easily discovered in items 3 or 4, their repair requires further statistical data. Such data are obtained by counting the numbers of "high" and "low" students choosing each *response*. Table 7.6 gives item-response analysis for items 4, 11, and 12. In item 4, the right

**Table 7.6  Numbers of students who have chosen a particular response to each item**

The high and the low groups consist respectively of fifty students from the highest 27 percent and the lowest 27 percent of the class. The right response is A for each item.

| RESPONSE | ITEM 4 | | ITEM 11 | | ITEM 12 | |
|---|---|---|---|---|---|---|
| | *High* | *Low* | *High* | *Low* | *High* | *Low* |
| A | 40 | 35 | 8 | 10 | 10 | 5 |
| B | 8 | 8 | 12 | 5 | 30 | 15 |
| C | 2 | 4 | 10 | 10 | 5 | 10 |
| D | 0 | 3 | 5 | 15 | 5 | 15 |
| E | 0 | 0 | 15 | 10 | 0 | 5 |

response A can be changed in a formal (rather than substantive) way, by making it shorter or less technical sounding, in the hope that the poorer students will then find it less attractive. Response E should be made more attractive. In item 11, the right response A should be made more nearly correct and responses B and E, less correct or less attractive; at present only response D functions properly. In item 12, the difficulty is caused by response B. The easiest way to improve the item is to throw out response B. Another possibility is to change response B so that it, instead of A, is the right response.

*What to do with improved items*  Local conditions determine diffusion of information about a test among students and thus determine the safety of reusing test items. If test booklets are not retained by students after the examination, it is usually quite safe to use about 25 percent of the items the next year. Passage of time and changes in items, however slight, make reuse much safer. A reservoir of five different quarterly examinations should allow a teacher to do a good job of testing even though no more than 25 percent of his test items are new each year.

# 8

# THEORY OF TESTING:
# 2. GENERAL AND QUALITATIVE

## 8.1 NATURE AND FUNCTION OF EDUCATIONAL TESTS

### Educational tests are basically similar

In education, tests can be used in many ways: as teaching devices; for certification, prognosis, and counseling; and for analysis and improvement of a course or a curriculum. All educational tests, however, have a great deal in common. Whatever its intended function, each test is fundamentally diagnostic, for it tells only what the student is like at the time of testing, what kinds of competence he possesses, and what he has achieved up to that time. In this sense all educational tests are also achievement tests. Aptitude and intelligence tests are achievement tests in that aptitude and intelligence are inferred from the relation between the student's achievement on the test and his age and background. College entrance tests, though designed for prognosis, measure achievement through high school. Conversely, as is shown in the next section, the main function of a certification test (a test used for assigning grades and thus a typical achievement test) is prognosis. The usual educational test is thus an achievement test in its structure and content and prognostic in its function.

This chapter develops a theory of testing with particular reference to achievement tests that measure what a student has learned from a course. The theory will be general enough, however, to apply to all educational tests that a teacher is likely to use. In other words, achievement tests that satisfy the criteria of the theory can be used, with only minor modifications (see Chapters 12 and 13), for the purposes listed in the first sentence of the chapter.

### The main function of a certification test: prognosis

Tests in courses are most commonly used to assign grades. Grades in turn are sometimes used by the teacher to encourage or warn the student, as rewards for effort, and as measures of progress. Fortunately, the therapeutic use of grades in college is not very common, for it is a potent weapon and should be entrusted to experts on adolescent psychology or at least to those who are well acquainted with their students' interests, attitudes, and emotional needs. The use of grades as rewards for effort and as measures of progress will be discussed in Chapter 12.

But the most frequent use of grades is as indexes of future achievement, as estimates of students' ability to think and act effectively in various situations that they will face later on. This use is apt, for most of us teach science because we hope that its study will influence the student's future behavior. Certainly, the prognostic use of grades is the only use meaningful to teachers of succeeding courses, advisers, and employers. Also, since grades in science may determine whether the student will choose to make science his career, they must be based on a standard relevant to that choice.

There are many qualities or characteristics of a student that can be measured and have a good prognostic value for almost any career. Among these are native intelligence, curiosity, good memory, good health, industry, and keen eyesight, as well as the components of general and liberal education acquired in non-science courses, such as the ability to read and write, that have presumably been described or recorded in various course grades. The natural or more stable endowments are usually noted as IQ scores and in other ways. The total picture of the student is therefore clarified if these natural endowments are not directly incorporated into grades for science courses. Furthermore, it is pedagogically sounder to include in tests measuring results of training only that competence which is improved by the training. Good memory, intelligence, and other gifts and competences acquired in previous courses will then be rewarded indirectly, to the extent that the student uses them to achieve the objectives of the course.

Generally, then, tests used for assigning course grades should cover course objectives with high prognostic value. Chapter 3 pointed out that teachers' experience, theories of learning, and prevailing practices in college and industry all argue for the high prognostic value of understanding and ability to learn (8). Knowledge has a low prognostic value because tests of knowledge probably invite cramming, which makes for unreliable results; because memorized knowledge is quickly lost by the student; and perhaps also because accumulating such knowledge appeals to the less promising students and disseminating it, to the less thoughtful teachers. It would seem, therefore, that though knowledge is considered important in itself, and though without it understanding and ability to learn are impossible, testing for knowledge is not important. This conclusion, however, would be incorrect for several reasons. Understanding cannot be tested without testing for knowledge, and an absence of test questions on knowledge may misguide the students in their study habits and make counseling difficult. There are also other, more technical reasons that will be taken up in Section 9.2.

Prognosis in absolute terms, that is, predicting how well a given student will do in the future, is very difficult unless the student is exceptionally good or bad. Usually one must be satisfied with a prognosis of relative future success. The achievement test for a course should therefore separate the class into groups according to how well they have attained those abilities taught in the course that have the highest prognostic value. Some tests are good enough to separate students into two groups, others into five groups, but no test—written, oral, or any other kind—is good enough to separate one hundred students into one hundred groups. This is fortunate, because although it may make sense to say that *on the average* students in one large group know more physics or are brighter than students in another large group, no usable meaning attaches to the statement that the students in a class are ranked in order of their brightness or their knowledge of physics. Intelligence and knowledge are not one-dimensional quantities—they have many components. Large differences in these abilities may make educational sense, but small differences do not.

Of a single exercise, one can demand only that it make *some* contribution to separating students into groups. An objective item, for instance, can be valuable even if some A students choose a wrong response and some F students recognize the right response, provided the item discriminates properly and well on the average. Before an exercise is included in a test, the test-maker must ask himself what it will predict (on the average) about students who give or do not give the right response. An honest treatment of this question, which implies that a test is essentially useful only for dividing students into a small number of groups, is likely to obviate a lot of silly arguments about whether it is "fair to the students" to include a particular question in the test; whether the right response in an objective item is strictly correct or even the "best" response (because it agrees better with the latest research findings than the other responses); and whether an individual item is likely to penalize an exceptionally good student. An item that penalizes no exceptionally bright students, no exceptionally imaginative students, and no students with an exceptionally good sense of what is worth studying probably does not exist. If it did it would very likely penalize a large number of more ordinary students (58).

### Importance of variety in test exercises

The arguments of the preceding paragraphs seem to indicate that exercises that test for knowledge, understanding, and ability to learn will add up to a good achievement test in science. We should remember, however, that these three abilities are not final, but only proximate, objectives of science training. The final objective is to prepare the student to deal with situations in which scientific competence is useful. Such situations, here called criterion situations, may occur in the student's academic career, his life as a citizen, or his work as a scientist. The direct way to test the student's competence to deal with criterion situations is to present him with realistic problems, with situations that closely resemble those he is likely to face in the future. A "synthetic" test of this kind is quite valid, but it is almost prohibitively cumbersome and expensive, for genuine problems facing a scientist or a citizen are usually very complex and only seldom entirely of the paper-and-pencil type. Further disadvantages of such a test are that it is difficult to assemble an adequate sample of problems and to communicate about the precise nature of the test and of students' "scores." A less direct but more practical way to test is first to analyze the complex competence required to solve genuine problems into its constituents and then to test for the more important but still tractable of these. Such an "analytic" test has all the usual shortcomings of an analytic representation of complex and incompletely understood phenomena. All the constituents are not known, nor, if known, would they add up to the whole. In addition, some of the more important constituents, such as habits and attitudes, cannot be conveniently or accurately measured. Finally, the beginning student is not taught a true and direct part of the eventually desired competence, but either a modified version of it or a competence that is merely prerequisite to acquiring it.

The discrepancy between testing for the criterion competence and testing for its presumed constituents—knowledge, understanding, and learning ability as these are exhibited in the context of a course in science—is of unknown magnitude and kind; quite probably it is large and various. We cannot eliminate it, but we can at least alleviate it by including exercises in the test that evoke in the student a great variety of mental processes in varied patterns. The test-writer can in some respects transcend statements of objectives and come closer to the criterion competence by varying test exercises as widely as the broadest interpretation of the formally stated objectives permits. Thus, for instance, in testing for the ability to interpret scientific data the following variations are possible. The question may deal with general principles of data interpretation or it may refer to specific data; the data may be graphical, numerical, or verbal in form, simple or complex, self-consistent or not; and the data may refer to different areas of subject matter. The student may be asked to collect the data in the laboratory and to draw possible conclusions, to assess the consistency of the data within themselves or with other data, or to estimate the cogency of the data as evidence for a generalization. The form of the test may also vary: oral, essay, objective, or performance.

Variety in test exercises is important not only because most educational tests are indirect and therefore likely to be inadequately comprehensive or inclusive, but also because every test exercise measures many abilities besides the desired one. Some of these auxiliary abilities are educationally unimportant; for instance, knowing the teacher's foibles and possessing test sophistication (some students write their essays just ambiguously enough not to be counted as wrong, and others can spot clues in objective items). A test that is completely essay or completely objective in form will reward one of these "talents" more than the other. Variety in test exercises thus both increases the chance that the test will cover desirable aspects or patterns of abilities and evens out the chances of students with various irrelevant skills.

## 8.2    VALIDITY

A test designed to measure a competence should be valid; it should make it possible to assign grades that accurately reflect the degree to which students possess that particular competence. Whether a test measures the desired competence must in the final analysis depend on someone's judgment. A reliable judgment will be objective, which means that most properly trained persons can be convinced of its correctness. A test is said to be a *direct* test if its validity is clear on inspection. (It is easy, for instance, to prepare a direct test of the ability to carry out long division.) The inspector must of course know how the test will be scored and graded. The validity of essay tests, for instance, cannot be estimated by inspection unless the inspector can see the directions that the grader will get and knows the grader's competence. (The high reputation of essay tests as measuring instruments probably thrives on their obscure validities; the absence of required directions and specifications invites one to assume that readers possess wisdom, sensitivity, and erudition.)

Most educational tests, however, are indirect; they usually become more indirect as the competence to be measured becomes more complex. The validity of an indirect test can be estimated by inspection or, empirically, by finding its correlation with a test of known high validity. The validity of the latter (criterion) test must be determined by inspection. Moreover, empirical validation can be obtained only after the test is taken by a group of students. In practice, therefore, the initial validation of any test must be done by inspection.

A test usually consists of several parts or exercises. An exercise may be objective, essay, oral, or performance. The exercises in a valid test must be relevant or appropriate; they should measure some aspects or components of the desired competence. Further, the essential constituents of the competence must be properly represented in the test as a whole. The word *essential*, as used here, implies that the constituents are important (that is, that they play a major role in the competence) and that they are independent (that is, that their intercorrelation is so low that a student's competence in one such constituent does not insure his competence in another). Finally, the test must be reliable; the achievement of those constituents of competence that *are* represented in the test must be dependably reflected in the grades assigned on the basis of the test. Exercise relevance and proper representation of constituents assures that the test measures the desired type of competence; the reliability indicates the precision of the measurement.

## 8.3   RELEVANCE

An exercise is relevant to an ability if the possession of the ability increases the student's chances of doing the exercise satisfactorily; conversely, such an ability may be said to be relevant to the exercise. In the most economical and useful exercise, one ability, the *principal ability*, is much more relevant than any other. The principal ability or the ability the exercise measures can best be defined as follows. If the exercise is performed successfully by one group of students and unsuccessfully by another group, the principal ability of the exercise is the ability in which the two groups differ most. The other abilities relevant to the exercise are auxiliary abilities (and the two groups are likely to differ to some extent in *each* of the auxiliary abilities).

Although it seems clear at the outset that the principal ability of an exercise depends on the abilities of the whole group as well as on the nature of the exercise, there is a prevalent misconception that the ability measured by a test is a function of the test alone. Some test-makers seem to think, for example, that a test designed to pick out students that are promising college material in an eastern preparatory school can do the same job effectively when given to the students of a rural school in the South (32). This is far from certain, as the following example shows.

### Relevance depends on the group tested

A group of students is presented with the following exercise: It is possible to hear the sound of a fountain behind a brick garden wall although the fountain cannot be seen. This phenomenon (a) can, (b) cannot be explained by the fact that long waves are diffracted more than short waves.

The group will be divided into two subgroups: those who pass (by choosing the right response [a]) and those who fail. How do these subgroups differ? That is, what *relative* ability or knowledge does the exercise test for? If the group consists of graduate students of physics at a Spanish university, it seems probable that the two subgroups will differ most in their ability to read English, for it may be safely assumed that all members of this group possess the requisite mastery of physics but that only some know English. The next group consists of students who have had a year of physics that included a good discussion of diffraction of both light and sound but no treatment of the relevant similarities between them. Let us assume that most of these students know that sound waves are longer than light waves. In this case, the two subgroups are most likely to differ in their ability to surmise that the principles of diffraction apply to the situation described in the exercise, an ability that may be considered part of the more general ability to relate generalizations to specific situations. The last group consists of students to whom the particular test situation—the sound of a fountain behind a wall—was explained in a class or textbook. Their ability to recall the situation may be influenced by a variety of factors, especially if the explanation of the phenomenon was not emphasized. The main difference between the two subgroups is hard to determine and may not depend on anything educationally significant. An exercise-writer who uses situations very similar to those in the textbook, even in a test of pure information, is on slippery ground.

It is sometimes argued that either pair of English-speaking subgroups discussed in the preceding paragraph exhibits the same important difference—the passing group knows the answer to the question while the failing group does not—and that, in measuring the general mastery of physics, it is of secondary importance how the various students arrive at the correct answer. This argument is based on at least two questionable assumptions. One is that it is important to know the answer to the exercise question. Surely, unless the student is going to be a landscape-gardener or fountain-builder, we are interested in his ability to answer not this particular question but this kind or class of question; that is, we are interested in his attainment of the objective being measured. Let us assume, however, that it is important for the student to know the answer to some particular question, for, of course, there are such questions in science. Granting this, a second false assumption is that it is sufficient for the student to know the answer on the date of the examination. For the student's ability to answer the question some months after the examination date will depend crucially on how the student arrived at the correct answer in the first place; if he merely memorized the answer, for instance, the retention time will be short (7).

Although the sample groups are extreme in their differences, it is nevertheless quite generally true that a given exercise will measure different abilities if used with different groups. And although the illustration is an objective exercise, the argument and the conclusion are valid for any kind of test.

### Necessary and sufficient abilities

In general, the relative test scores of the members of a group will depend only on the factors in which the group is heterogeneous. For example, the Spanish group was homogeneous at the requisite level of mastery of physics but heterogeneous in its ability to read English. To know the relative standing of the members of a group on the principal ability of the exercise, this ability should clearly be necessary for doing the exercise, and the group should be fairly homogeneous in all other (auxiliary) necessary abilities. Necessity is adequately served if only the exceptional students can successfully deal with the exercise without possessing the desired competence. The homogeneity of the group in the auxiliary abilities that an exercise requires is best attained, especially in a diagnostic test, by writing the exercise so that the level of auxiliary abilities required is quite low, below that of most of the group. If a single grade is to be assigned on an achievement test, it is sufficient to keep the required auxiliary abilities below the passing level. In no case, however, is it enough to assert that the students *ought to* possess the auxiliary abilities; it is necessary to ascertain that the majority of them in fact do.

The principal ability of the exercise ought to be not only necessary, but *sufficient* for dealing with the exercise. The following example will clarify the meanings of necessary and sufficient. The student is asked, "What is the product of 3 and 7?" The ability to multiply is not necessary here because the problem can be solved by addition. Nor is it sufficient, for the word *product* must be understood. It should be clear that to make the principal ability effectively sufficient, the auxiliary abilities must be kept at a low level. If the principal ability is necessary but not sufficient, those who can do the exercise have the ability and those who cannot may or may not have it. If the ability is sufficient but not necessary, those who cannot do the exercise do not possess the ability and those who can may or may not have it. An exercise that meets the necessity and sufficiency conditions is said to be *perfectly* relevant to the competence being measured. Such an exercise must measure the relevant aspect of the competence directly; it must be based on a situation that defines the competence. A long-division exercise can easily be made perfectly relevant to the ability to perform long division. In achievement-testing, both the necessity and sufficiency conditions should be approached as closely as possible, although one often has to be satisfied with only relative success, as when, for a given test group, the measured ability is the one most likely to spell success or failure in dealing with the exercise.

*"Pure" ability exercises*    The more nearly an item satisfies the necessity and sufficiency conditions, the more "purely" it measures the principal ability. Although an occasional item in a test may well measure several abilities, for variety and for a better approximation of criterion situations, most of the items should be fairly pure. Pure items can be grouped according to principal abilities. This grouping has several advantages: accurate weights can be assigned to various objectives; students' weaknesses and strengths can be diagnosed in detail and used in counseling and to assess the strengths and weaknesses of the course; the total test score can more readily be

made reliable than the score on a test in which each item measures a mixture of abilities (41); and, finally, both validation and improvement of the test through item analysis is easier and more meaningful.

### Students' mental processes and relevance

There are statistical methods helpful in finding out just what ability an exercise measures. They all involve an analysis of results after the test has been given. One such method, item analysis, was discussed in Section 7.4, and the point will be taken up again under Measurement of relevance in Section 8.6. The exercise-writer must still depend mainly on his opinion of the students' mental activities as they are working the exercise. One of the guides in identifying the measured ability is a formal analysis of the test exercise. If, for example, in an objective item, the word *data* seems to apply to the information given the student, and if the responses among which he is to choose can be legitimately characterized as *interpretations* of the data, it is usually assumed that the exercise measures the ability to interpret data. Studies indicate, however, that students vary a great deal in their methods of arriving at correct responses (33). Some of them read the stem (in this case, the data and the question), arrive at some interpretation, and look among the prepared responses for a similar one. Others test each response in turn against the data and reject the inconsistent ones. If the inconsistencies can be established by inspecting parts of the data only, the right response can be chosen without understanding even the general trend of the data. Not only in this example but generally, the abilities required in going from the question to the responses and vice versa may be quite different. It is difficult, for example, to use objective exercises for a reliable and consistent differentiation between the "ability to interpret data" and the "ability to apply principles," especially in physics and chemistry—sciences that are based on well-articulated and very widely applicable principles. The classification of objectives in Section 2.1 has therefore been so chosen as to depend on the nature of the situation as defined by both the question and the responses; the distinction between exercises in interpretation of data and exercises in application of principles is useful primarily to insure variety.

### Relevance and the objectives in Section 2.1

The writing and detailed analysis of an exercise, and the criticism of its relevance, are discussed in Chapter 11. Here, though, are some fairly dependable rules for judging the relevance of an exercise to an ability. If the answer to an exercise can be found in a paragraph of the course text or if the exercise is very much like a homework assignment, the most relevant ability is probably knowledge. If the exercise is suitable for illustrating a generalization taught in the course but has not been so used, the most relevant ability is probably understanding. If the material of the exercise is as new to the student as a new text chapter would be (say, a chapter on the kinetic-molecular theory after previous study of mechanics and heat), the most relevant ability is probably the ability to learn. Disciplined thinking is probably best measured by an exercise that is too complex for an analytical attack, and imaginative thinking by an exercise amenable to a variety of attacks, only a few of which occur readily to the test-writer.

## 8.4    REPRESENTATION AND SAMPLING

The first requirement of a valid test of a competence, the relevance of the exercises, has been discussed in Section 8.3. The second requirement is that the test contain exercises severally relevant to every one of the major constituents of the competence that is not highly intercorrelated, and that the emphasis or weight given to each essential constituent should correspond to its relative importance. An analogue of this requirement in public opinion polls of voting preference is the requirement that the major, relatively independent populations, such as rural and urban, Republican and Democrat, be sampled. The populations are major if each of them has a large number of voters. They are relatively independent if the likelihood of difference of preference exists or, more strictly, if similarity of preference has not been established. The results of a poll are more reliable and more economical if representation, or systematic and directed sampling, is carried further: the rural group may be subdivided by age, sex, or income, or all of these. In every poll, however, a point is reached at which one resorts to random sampling. Table 7.4 contains conclusive evidence for the importance of testing for all important abilities that have low intercorrelations.

### Identification of essential constituents

A systematic way to identify the essential constituents of a competence is to analyze it in terms of behavior-content objectives and the patterns in which these occur. Such identification, which is probably as useful in teaching as in testing, is easier if the classification of objectives for a course is based on both the importance and the low intercorrelation of the objectives. In such a classification the intercorrelation of the major classes of objectives should be so low that they may be considered essential constituents of the broad competence for which tests are to be designed. Each of the essential constituents of a competence must be represented in a test for that competence. The subclasses of a major objective should have higher intercorrelations than the major objectives. A comprehensive *sample* of the subclasses may therefore be sufficient. In the classification given in Section 2.1, knowledge, understanding, and ability to learn are viewed as essential constituents of understanding a science; each of them should therefore be tested. Other constituents that are essential but not explicit in the main classification are the abilities to deal with qualitative, quantitative, and laboratory exercises. Similarly, the student's grasp of very different areas of or approaches to the subject matter, such as heat and mechanics or the body-of-knowledge and process-of-inquiry points of view, must be tested.

The most economical, convenient, and dependable representation of a competence is achieved by having a separate part of a test devoted to each essential constituent: knowledge, understanding, and ability to learn. Further, representation, or directed and systematic sampling, should probably be extended to the next step (the first decimal) in the classification. For instance, the knowledge part of the test should have exercises on 1.1, information, and on 1.2, knowledge of relations. It is also important to include, in the totality of tests used for assigning grades, subclasses 2.1, 2.2, 2.3, and 3.1 and 3.2. (Since these subclasses refer to very different kinds of content rather than to very different abilities, not all of them may be relevant to a given area of subject matter.) The objective of understanding, for instance, is not likely to be adequately represented by a more or less random sample of "thought" questions and intricate problems. Such exercises, though they are usually relevant, may touch on only a few isolated aspects of understanding and may measure imaginativeness or general intelligence to an undesirably high degree.

Ideally, systematic sampling of content and objectives should guide the choice of every exercise in a test. When the requirements of importance and of low intercorrelation cease to offer clear guidance, the test-maker should turn to the requirement of variety. Variety, the value of which has been defended at several points in this discussion, serves representation better than it serves relevance. It may work against reliability, but it almost certainly increases validity, and validity is the test-maker's goal. Some arbitrary or random sampling is unavoidable in any test of finite length. If a test has room for only one problem on, say, Archimedes' principle, the choice of the problem may well be nearly random. It is at the random level of sampling that parallel tests (defined in Section 7.1) should differ; they should have very similar representations of the desired competence.

The requirements of good representation, including variety, often lead to a test that is too long to be given all at one time. Fortunately, it is only necessary for the desired competence to be well represented by the combination or battery of all the tests that determine the students' grades. Most of these tests will usually be written; but some may be oral, as in discussion sections, or performance, as in the laboratory. Some may be given under examination conditions, others as assigned homework. In fact, the requirement of variety makes it undesirable to assign grades on the basis of a single form of test.

**Weighting the parts of a test** (40)

Good representation requires not only that all the essential constituents of a competence be measured but also that appropriate weights be assigned to these constituents. If a valid test is available, there are statistical procedures for assigning weights to parts of another test to make it as valid as possible. In the absence of empirical validation, the weight assigned to the set of exercises measuring a given constituent should depend on the importance of that constituent, on the relevance of the exercises, and to a smaller degree on the set's reliability. It has been found empirically and can be shown theoretically that the effective weight of a test part rises with its standard deviation and its correlation with other parts of the test, especially with the parts that have large standard deviations. By far the best method of raising the effective weight of a given ability, therefore, is to increase the number of items (or recordable student decisions) measuring that ability. As equations 7.13 show, all three relevant quantities—standard deviation, correlation, and reliability—increase with an increase in the number of items.

Increasing the weight of a part by multiplying the scores made on it by a numerical factor is much less satisfactory than increasing the number of items, for the multiplication does not increase the reliability of the part and may decrease the reliability of the total test. If multiplication must be used to correct a bad unbalance among various objectives, the scores of a part measuring a particular ability $X$ should be multiplied by a factor $F_x$ given by formula 8.1,

$$F_x = \frac{W_x}{e_x}, \tag{.81}$$

where $W_x$ is chosen to correspond to the importance of the ability, and $e_x = S_x\sqrt{1 - r_{xx}}$, where $S_x$ and $r_{xx}$ are the standard deviation and the reliability of the part-scores. Dividing scores by the error of measurement $e$ corrects to some degree for differences in $S$, $r$, and the intercorrelations of various parts of the test; in particular, it corrects for accidental differences in part-scores due to different systems of scoring the parts (40, Gulliksen). Differential weighting is the more important, the fewer part-scores there are to be weighted and the lower their intercorrelations. A convenient rule of thumb is that when there are only three or four part-scores of moderately high intercorrelation, such as scores on knowledge, understanding, ability to learn, and laboratory abilities, arbitrary changes of about 25 percent in weighting factors are entirely permissible. Thus, if the calculated factors are $F_k = 1$, $F_u = 1.3$, $F_a = 1.8$, and $F_l = 2.2$, we can, to simplify calculations, set $F_k = F_u = 1$ and $F_a = F_l = 2$ without introducing any great error. It is not often that nonintegral values of weighting factors have to be used. Within this accuracy, it is often possible to estimate the values of $e$ from previous experience rather than to calculate them afresh. Similar considerations apply to weighting sets of exercises dealing with various areas of subject matter.

## 8.5  RELIABILITY

### Representation vs. reliability

A valid test must consist of exercises that are relevant to the desired competence; the totality of the exercises must represent the competence; and, finally, the test must be reliable, for the validity of a test cannot be greater than the square root of its reliability. What measures can and should be taken to insure adequate reliability? The question is not a simple one because, although increasing relevance will increase reliability, the requirements of representation and reliability are in some respects contradictory. Representation thrives on heterogeneity as measured by low intercorrelation: the greater the differences among the constituents of the competence, among various contents, and among the forms of exercises, the more important it is that each heterogeneous element be included in the test. Reliability, on the other hand, increases with the homogeneity of the exercises, which is measured by high intercorrelation. If for simplicity it is assumed that all the exercises among which we are to choose have equal degrees of relevance, then representation (and thus variety), not reliability and homogeneity, deserve first consideration (38). Evidence that representation is more important than reliability is contained in the data of Table 7.4, and the teacher who is writing a test should therefore be guided by the requirements of good representation: importance, low intercorrelation, and variety. If representation were easily measurable, the teacher could well forget about reliability. However, since reliability is easier to measure than representation, the following ways to improve both reliability and validity are offered so that the test-writer can check, by measuring reliability, the effectiveness of his efforts to improve validity. Some such methods are maintaining certain kinds of homogeneity, using proper sampling techniques, lengthening the test, eliminating extraneous factors, and ensuring a proper degree of difficulty of the exercises.

### Homogeneity and sampling

To be valid, a test must measure all the main abilities. If each ability is measured by a subtest, the subtest should be homogeneous in that each exercise should test for that ability. If it is to correlate highly with a parallel subtest—which is best viewed as prepared independently by another writer—the sampling of the different aspects of the ability should be wide and characterized by variety. Thus a test that consists of subtests, each measuring essentially one ability, can meet the requirements of validity and reliability.

Complete homogeneity of exercises, which testing for a pure ability implies, is impossible. It is possible, however, to devise exercises that require auxiliary abilities of such a low level that most students may be expected to have reached it. For example, in testing for an ability whose definition does not include a knowledge of technical terms, these nevertheless may have to be used. In such a case it is advisable to explain the terms, unless it seems likely that, say, 90 percent of the students understand them. An objective paper-and-pencil test can also be made more homogeneous with respect to an ability if the right response is attractive to students with high ability and, in addition, the wrong responses are made attractive to students with a low degree of the *same* ability. On such a test, high and low scores are likely to be obtained by students who are respectively high and low in the particular ability the test is designed to measure. Finally, homogeneity relative to an ability is aided if the student tries to exhibit that ability. Test directions should therefore be clear and quite explicit as to the most effective method of attack: whether the student should try all the exercises, whether he should make considered guesses, and how he should budget his time. The scoring system must also be explained.

## Lengthening the test

The effective "length" of a test—as a determinant of its reliability—is best estimated from the number of decisions a student has to make, especially if each decision is recorded and scored. An essay test is more reliable if each important part and aspect of it is scored separately. In an objective test each item requires at least one decision; thus, increasing the number of items lengthens the test. If a student is allowed not only to choose the best response but also to indicate how certain he is of his choice, he makes two recordable decisions (44). On a five-response objective item, the student has to weigh his choice against four other responses and thus in effect makes four decisions. Such an item is likely to contribute about as much to the reliability of a test as four true-or-false items, each of which requires only one decision. If every item is scored for the right response only, however, the student's decisions are not separately recorded. Perhaps for this reason, increasing the number of responses beyond four or five does not appreciably change the item's reliability (37).

## Elimination of extraneous factors

Any factor that helps a less competent student get a higher score on a test as much as or more than it helps a more competent one will decrease the test's reliability. Perhaps the most important factor is sampling various aspects of the relevant ability. If the sampling is too small or narrow or in any way accidentally biased, chance factors become more prominent, and reliability goes down. To consider all wrong responses in a multiple-choice item equally wrong is to lump together students of unequally low abilities and thus to militate against reliability. There is evidence that scoring an item on a three-point scale by dividing the responses into right, wrong, and very wrong will increase the reliability of the test (45, Nedelsky). Such grading is discussed in Section 12.6. We assume, of course, that the scaling itself is reliable, that the very wrong responses are indeed less correct than the wrong ones. If the scale of grading is so fine that it is not highly reliable in this sense, the reliability of the test so scored is not likely to increase. Attempts to give a different weight to *each* wrong response have had little success (45, Furst).

There are factors, other than chance, whose correlation with the relevant ability is so low that they decrease the test's validity and reliability. For instance, if the test emphasizes lecture material more than text material, not because of its greater importance but as a disciplinary measure or for any other reason, the reliability of the test is likely to be decreased. The success of the test becomes dependent on regular attendance and on ability to listen and take notes—factors that may not correlate very highly with the main competence measured by the test. Other factors of this sort are the students' knowledge of the instructor's preferences, ability to decipher a badly worded question, acquaintance with the type of test used, and sensitivity to various kinds of accidental clues to the right answer.

### Difficulty (52)

A test's reliability also depends on its difficulty. A very difficult test will clearly do a bad job of separating failing from barely passing students, and a very easy test will not separate the good from the very good. Either test will have lower reliability than a test of a more moderate degree of difficulty. The best degree of difficulty depends on the level at which discrimination is considered most important. For the students near that level, the difficulty of the test should be 50 percent. Thus, if a test is designed to identify the upper 10 percent (A students), its difficulty should be such that the borderline students, the lowest A and the highest B students, get on the average 50 percent of the maximum possible score. If all levels of discrimination (A-B, B-C, C-D, and D-F) are considered equally important, the highest overall reliability, which is usually the only reliability that is calculated, is obtained with test exercises that range in difficulty, say, from 15 percent to 85 percent, with a concentration near the 50 percent mark and with the mean score of the whole class 50 percent of the maximum. If the D-F demarcation line is more important than the A-B line, the test should be made easier, with the mean at about 60 percent.

If only three grades are to be assigned, H, S, and F, the test may well consist only of difficult exercises appropriate to the H-S demarcation line and easy ones appropriate to the S-F line. If the class can be previously separated into those that have no chance of getting an H and those who are in no danger of getting an F, the latter group should be given only the difficult exercises and the former, only the easy ones. This procedure will save testing time and contribute to greater precision in assigning grades. Other advantages of simplified grading are discussed in Sections 7.3 and 12.6.

## 8.6  MEASUREMENT OF VALIDITY, RELEVANCE, REPRESENTATION, AND RELIABILITY

### Measurement of validity

The degree of validity of a test, as defined by equation 7.7, can be estimated empirically. A test is valid for a competence to the degree that it correlates with another test, the criterion test, that is known to be valid for that competence. (The test or a battery of tests that is known to be valid is often too long and its administration too expensive to be practical, except for the purposes of estimating or improving the validity of other, more efficient tests.) The correlation can be determined empirically using a sample of students. It must be noted, however, that the sample should be representative of the group one is interested in, because the correlation estimate will be dependable only for groups whose training is similar to that of the sample both in method and content, and who are not widely dissimilar in level of achievement (35). Thus, for example, a criterion test containing written and performance exercises may correlate moderately well with a written test given to students appropriately trained in both theory and laboratory, and it may fail to correlate for students trained in only one of these or for students who have had bad or exceptionally good training in both. It is therefore highly desirable that an instructor validate his tests periodically, perhaps once every five years, by giving his class a valid test and one of his regular tests and correlating the two. The first step in such validation is the preparation of a valid battery of tests.

*Test battery*  It is possible to prepare a highly valid battery of tests from tests of not very high validity. The requirements are as follows. The component tests must contain exercises that are severally relevant to the more important aspects of each of the essential constituents of the desired competence. A test-maker can be surer that the important aspects are well represented if he resorts to the device of variety by using performance, essay, objective, and perhaps even oral tests and by including many kinds of exercise in any given form. The next step is to have the number of items relevant to an aspect of an ability roughly proportional to the importance of that aspect, and the number of items relevant to an essential constituent— knowledge, understanding, or ability to learn—fairly accurately proportional to the importance of the constituent. (In counting, an item of very low relevance may be considered only half an item.) An assembly of exercises meeting the above conditions will be a highly valid test battery provided the total number of items is large and no serious errors in representation have been made; low relevance is compensated for by large numbers and variety. One can understand the possibility of such compensation by remembering that low relevance means that auxiliary abilities play an important role. These auxiliary abilities, if there is variety, will be different from exercise to exercise and not very highly intercorrelated; their cumulative effect will therefore be small, in comparison to the effect of the principal ability that is common to all items, if the number of items is large.

A valid battery of tests is usually long and takes a long time to prepare, but it does seem worthwhile once in five years to give up a few lectures and a little recitation and laboratory time to find out whether proper grades are assigned to the students. A practical solution to the time problem is to prepare the battery cooperatively with other schools or colleges and to utilize as much as possible commercial tests. It is not at all necessary to give the whole battery at the same time; it may be given in parts over a period of two or three weeks near the end of the course. The regular end-of-year or end-of-quarter tests can conveniently be a part of the battery. The total battery is then taken as the criterion test, and the validity of any part of it calculated from equation 7.7. The results of validation will indicate how fairly grades have been assigned. Also, the prognostic values of tests on various abilities can be estimated from their correlations with the battery. The validity of the battery itself can be checked by correlating the scores students make on the battery with their later academic and post-academic success.

## Measurement of relevance, representation, and reliability

Let us assume that a test consists of a subtest on knowledge and a subtest on understanding. The first step in an empirical estimate of the relevance of an exercise is to find out whether the two subtests do measure different abilities. If the reliabilities of the two subtests are $r_{11}$ and $r_{22}$ and their correlation is $r_{12}$, and the value of correlation corrected for attenuation $r_{12}/\sqrt{r_{11}r_{22}}$ is less than one, it may be assumed that the subtests measure different abilities. What these two abilities are can be decided by inspection or by correlating the tests with known measures of knowledge and understanding. Once it is known that a given subtest measures a particular ability, it is possible to estimate the relevance of any of its exercises from the exercise's correlation with the subtest. The simplest way to estimate the correlation is to calculate the index of discrimination $D$ of the exercise by using equation 7.17, $D = (H - L)/N$. In the case under discussion two values of $D$ can be calculated for each item, say $D_k$ and $D_u$, depending on whether the high and low groups are chosen on the basis of their scores on the knowledge or the understanding subtest. An exercise designed to measure understanding should have $D_u$ greater than $D_k$. Item analysis of this sort affords good training in recognizing the principal ability of an exercise.

It is well to repeat here that, however strongly statistical measures speak against an exercise, it should not be dropped if the teacher is convinced that what the exercise is intended to measure is important. Rather, since the fault may be a technical one (such as ambiguity), the exercise should be improved. And it is of course always possible that the low value of $D$, provided the value is positive, is due to an inadequate representation in the test of the aspect of an ability that the exercise measures.

There are no numerical measures of representation as such; it has to be checked by inspection. A large value of $R_{xc}$ in equation 7.5a, however, is an assurance that both the relevance and representation are good. Numerical measures of reliability have been discussed in Section 7.3.

# 9

# MEASURING UNDERSTANDING
# OF SCIENCE

Chapters 3 to 6 showed that the major objectives of science courses, knowledge, understanding, and ability to learn, can and should be taught. This chapter ("understanding of science" in its title stands for all three objectives) is an attempt to show the science teacher that the attainment of these objectives by students can and should be tested and that he can prepare appropriate and valid tests. The argument will be divided into three parts: first, that testing for these objectives is important, and they should be included in a valid test; second, that these objectives can be and have been measured; and third, that a good teacher is competent to write good tests. The discussion will be limited to course, or certification, tests.

## 9.1  CRITERIA FOR TEST CONTENT

Generally speaking, the criteria for what should be taught and what should be tested are the same. We must teach and evaluate what is important for prognosis and what can be developed in the course. Thus general intelligence, other gifts, and many types of competence (for an obvious example, ability to spell) should not be directly measured in science tests used for assigning grades. These criteria must be modified, however, because for many practical reasons tests have to be short. Testing must therefore depend on sampling much more than does teaching. In sampling abilities, those that do not intercorrelate highly must be included, while if two abilities correlate adequately only one need be tested. The same is true for subject matter. The phrase *essential constituents of a competence* has been used to denote both importance and low intercorrelation. Therefore a certification test must measure each essential constituent of the general competence, science understanding, provided of course that adequate testing techniques are in existence and are at the teacher's disposal.

118

**Choice of behavioral objectives**

Chapter 1 argues that, in teaching a course, it is highly desirable in addition to specifying the course content also to specify what the student is expected to be able to do with that content, to specify the behavioral objectives or abilities. Such specifications are clearly necessary in preparing a test, for without them sampling of behavioral objectives is likely to be haphazard. Just as there are parts or aspects of mechanics, such as kinematics and dynamics, that are included in a good test on mechanics, there are parts and aspects of understanding science that must be included in a science test. For example, the ability to state empirical generalizations and the ability to use these to solve problems must be included, for these two abilities have quite different prognostic values. It is essential for the progress of science teaching that teachers get habituated to posing the question, "What have I taught my students to *do?*" instead of the vaguer, "What have I taught them?" They will get answers to the first question if their tests measure various behavioral objectives.

The classification of objectives in Section 2.1 has been guided by their intercorrelation. Knowledge, understanding, and ability to learn ordinarily have low intercorrelations, as do qualitative and quantitative thinking. Since all these objectives are also important, they belong among the essential constituents of a general competence in science and must be included in tests of certification. In subclasses and their subdivisions, intercorrelations seem likely to increase—provided that all the relevant content is taught—and the omission of certain subobjectives from a test becomes justifiable. The list of objectives should therefore offer a satisfactory guide for a test of limited length.

There are objectives in the list—imaginative thinking, intuitive thinking, manual skills, and spatial visualization—that are not often emphasized in science courses. In addition, they are rather difficult to test. These objectives therefore have less claim than others to inclusion in a certification test. They are included in Section 2.1 partly to encourage a more permissive attitude toward less orthodox thinking and some experimentation in teaching and testing for them, and partly to point up the pedagogical importance of preventing tests for knowledge, understanding, and ability to learn from requiring the student to possess talents to which the course contributes little. It would be a pity, for instance, to fail a student who has an excellent understanding of experiment because he lacks ingenuity, or because God gave him ten thumbs.

**Choice of subject matter**

The principles underlying the choice of subject matter for a test are the same as for the choice of abilities: importance and low intercorrelation. If mechanics and heat are taught in a physics course, both should be included in the course test. On the other hand, if time is limited, some topics in mechanics and in heat may be omitted. Note that intercorrelations depend not only on the method of teaching but also on testing, because tests influence learning. To proceed with the example above, if heat is not included in course tests, next year some students may pay less attention to heat than to mechanics, and the intercorrelation, already low, between the two contents will go down still further. This omission, if it occurs just once, however, is usually somewhat safer than the omission of the objective of understanding or of ability to learn because it is less likely to decrease the validity of the test.

## 9.2  ARGUMENTS FOR AND AGAINST TESTING KNOWLEDGE, UNDERSTANDING, AND ABILITY TO LEARN

Most science tests now in use measure primarily knowledge. They have been defended by four fairly distinct arguments: (1) only knowledge can be developed in a science course; (2) only knowledge *is* taught in a particular course; (3) a test of knowledge is a good test of the other two abilities; and (4) only knowledge can be accurately measured.

### Understanding and learning ability can be developed in science courses

Can understanding and ability to learn be taught? The usual negative argument runs as follows. Abilities included in these two objectives represent a mixture of knowledge and cleverness. Since cleverness is not teachable, the only duty of the instructor is to supply the student with necessary knowledge and to test for that only. Some students are indeed much brighter than others, and, if other variables are controlled, they will do better on most tests than less bright students. There are two kinds of evidence, however, against the correctness or prudence of classifying all abilities under just two headings, knowledge and cleverness (3). In the first place, test results show that students with apparently equal stores of information vary considerably in the pattern or profile that their various abilities present. Thus a student may be considerably above average in ability 2.1 and below average in ability 2.2. Furthermore, various pairs of abilities as measured by paper-and-pencil tests show a fairly low intercorrelation (18). (To account for this variation in the *kind* rather than the degree of "cleverness," a psychological theory must postulate an inconveniently large number of unchangeable talents or abilities, all of which are to be called "intelligences.") Direct evidence that understanding and learning ability can be improved by teaching, that the improvement cannot be explained merely by the student's increased knowledge or maturation, and that improvement is best achieved through conscious and specific attention to the desired objectives has been obtained by test and pretest methods and has been published in numerous reports (4).

Most science teachers believe that some aspects of the laboratory objectives in Section 2.1 are teachable, such as the ability to set up and use measuring apparatus (11). The author has been experimenting with laboratory teaching that enables the student to explore various specific aspects of the relation between phenomena and the physicists' description of them, and the results are encouraging. Certainly they have revealed no *a priori* difficulties in using the laboratory to make the relation clearer to students. Moreover, the usual introductory physics laboratory is so devoid of empirically demonstrable value that any experimentation should be welcome —especially experimentation with teaching the aspect of physics that makes it a natural science.

There is little published evidence on the teachability of intuitive understanding or imaginative or disciplined thinking at the college level (5). The author's own fragmentary experimentation points toward the possibility of teaching students to avoid the cruder errors of undisciplined thinking, but how permanent the results of such teaching may be is uncertain. Whether or not these talents or abilities can be fostered by any teaching method, they are valuable, and the least we can do is let students exercise them. It may help students do this successfully if we make them aware of their biases or intellectual predilections and indicate whether their attack on a problem is intuitive or analytic.

### Understanding and ability to learn are improved
### by almost all introductory science courses

Some science teachers, though they admit that understanding and ability to learn are important and can be developed, nevertheless feel that they make too little effort to teach these objectives to justify testing for them. These teachers might try to use the teaching methods outlined in Chapters 4 and 6 and thus bring their teaching into line with their convictions. If circumstances make it difficult for a teacher to introduce important changes into his teaching, he should consider it probable that he promotes these objectives better than he thinks although not as well as he could. Any program of testing and pretesting will show measurable progress in these objectives by some students in most science courses, although the progress is considerably greater if consciously sought by the teacher (18). Anyone who listens to a good lecture on, say, kinetic theory will be convinced quite aside from these empirical findings that some students can learn from the lecture how to evaluate evidence, for instance. Though there are science courses that have been so "perfected" over the years that a student can get a passing grade without cracking a book, such courses are fortunately rare. In most, students must learn to read at least the textbook. Similarly, although the student's time and efforts are badly used in many introductory physics laboratories, he is after all exposed to real phenomena and is likely to acquire at least some understanding of them and of their relation to book knowledge.

*Testing for what has not been taught*   A grade of A given to a student may mean that the student was in the upper 10 percent of the class of '37 at the College of Mugwump County; if so, it has mainly historical and parochial interest. (The iniquity of the percentage method of assigning grades is argued in Section 12.6.) Or it may mean that the student had an excellent understanding of science; in this case, the grade conveys a more useful picture of the student. If grades are to have an absolute rather than a relative meaning, certification tests must measure all the important objectives, whether or not they are taught. It may thus happen that a student who has acquired less than an excellent understanding of science through the teacher's or college's fault, not his own, is given a grade lower than A. (A more elaborate system of grading might serve both justice and mercy; the student could be given A for knowledge, B for understanding, C for the ability to learn, and A as his total or summary grade.)

### Course tests should measure all major objectives

Although teachers may underestimate their contribution to understanding and learning ability almost as often as they overestimate it, most of them are quite right when they say that they do not test for these objectives directly. This is unfortunate because the grades will not then reflect the students' ability to use their knowledge of science, and because students are likely to improve primarily in objectives that are observably measured by achievement tests (27). Some students read beyond the class text or make a real effort to understand course materials; such efforts should be encouraged at least as much as acquisition of knowledge.

Some teachers pay explicit attention to the three main objectives of science teaching but maintain that not all the objectives need be tested specifically. Their argument is commonly that the degree of attainment of all three main objectives can be reliably measured by testing for knowledge alone or by supplementary testing for some particular ability, such as the ability to solve difficult numerical problems or to write clear and precise definitions. These claims are seldom supported theoretically; they are usually given as empirical generalizations from many years of experience. As such, they are amenable to empirical verification, for they merely assert that the correlation between the abilities tested and all other important abilities in science is very high. Since the relevant correlation coefficients can be readily obtained and since their meaning and dependability can be made clear by referring to the tests used, perhaps science teachers who have been able to design a short test for an all-around understanding of science could be persuaded to determine its validity and to publish their results. Tests that are short and valid are badly needed.

All presently available data indicate that good prognosis requires measuring many abilities (2). The correlations among the three main objectives range from .3 to .6, with the larger values appearing when the three objectives are consciously taught (18). These numbers are too low to justify basing grades on knowledge alone, as is shown in Table 7.4. The correlations between manipulatory laboratory abilities and other science objectives are very low indeed (2). The correlations between understanding experiment and other objectives are probably low, for an ability that requires handling apparatus is not likely to correlate highly with book learning. Similarly, the correlation between verbal and quantitative or mathematical understanding of science is low (18).

In achievement-testing, the time for guessing and hunches not supported by empirical data is long past. After a teacher has selected his basic objectives, he must test for each objective unless he has empirically established, for *his* method of teaching, sufficiently high intercorrelations among them.

*Knowledge should be measured.*  Since tests for straight knowledge have low predictive power (8), if only two of the objectives, knowledge, understanding, and ability to learn, can be explicitly tested, it is safest to omit knowledge. This is because knowledge is required to perform all exercises in a good science test. Nevertheless, a subtest on knowledge should be included even at the expense of the higher objectives, for these reasons: exercise variety is increased by including knowledge items; wider sampling of content is possible because knowledge items can be short; and the reliability of a knowledge test is likely to be high because clear-cut, unambiguous knowledge items are easy to write and many can be included in an hour's test. Reliability is not the principal goal of a test, but since knowledge does correlate with all other abilities, a reliable subtest on knowledge, if not overweighted, will increase the validity of the test. There are also arguments for a knowledge subtest that are not directly connected with the main function of a certification test: such a subtest is valuable in counseling, and it may improve students' learning.

### What abilities *can* be measured? (31)

This section discusses the feasibility of measuring, especially by pencil-and-paper tests, various aspects of the general competence of understanding science. This general competence will be discussed first; second, the relatively standard book-learning objectives of knowledge, understanding, and ability to read; third, the subtler aspects of book learning (disciplined, intuitive, and imaginative thinking); and last, laboratory learning.

*General competence of science understanding*  Some people may think that choosing the ability to use science in real-life situations as a criterion competence is wrong because it means we must aim at a target that cannot be hit. Their main argument is that the situations a student faces in a paper-and-pencil test of manageable size are too abstract, too contrived, and in general too unlike real-life situations to be suitable for testing the very complex and not-too-well-understood ability to use science. The argument that short written tests are *in principle* unsuitable for measuring the ability to use science has a good deal of weight, because some aspects of the ability cannot be measured by a written test of any length, and a direct, convincing test of those that can must somehow present real situations that are exceedingly complex. For practical reasons, the teacher must resort to *indirect* tests. Such tests, however, can be justified or at least defended theoretically, if the mental processes employed in resolving a real-life problem and the problems in the test are in some respects similar.

They can also be justified empirically, as useful for prognosis. Previous chapters have offered both kinds of justification and recommended variety of test exercises as the main safety device. The tests that have been described may not, however, come very close to measuring the criterion competence, because prognostic validation has been limited largely to later academic rather than post-academic success (8). Nevertheless, these tests are certainly more valid than the usual tests of knowledge, and their target, the ability to use science, is the right one, even if they sometimes miss it.

A more frequent and more specific argument denies the validity of tests of understanding. It states that, among all the aspects of the general understanding of science, only knowledge and to a lesser extent reading ability can be measured with any accuracy by written tests. The argument says that tests of understanding, even those written by presumed experts, are almost always ambiguous because essay questions allow the student to play the field, and the "right" response in objective items is neither strictly correct nor even clearly better than some of the "wrong" responses. The objections of abstractness, indirectness, and ambiguity will be taken up when testing for various objectives is discussed below.

*Tests of knowledge, understanding, and ability to learn*   It is generally agreed that pencil-and-paper tests are adequate for measuring knowledge and reading ability. A look at the universally accepted written tests on information and numerical problems demonstrates, however, that they are open to some of the same objections as tests of understanding and must be justified on the same grounds. They are indirect, for really the student's ability, for instance, to calculate the time of descent of a body on an inclined plane, is of no intrinsic importance. Such exercises are included in tests in the *hope* that they are indexes of a real understanding of physics. An attempt to do what is so seldom done, to justify this hope on theoretical or empirical prognostic grounds, reveals that justification is hardest for tests of knowledge and easiest—almost by definition—for tests of the ability to learn.

In avoiding ambiguity, on the other hand, tests of knowledge win easily over all other tests. The best response to a knowledge item can be strictly and uniquely correct. Commonly the answer is either vouched for by a handbook or dictionary, or obtained by manipulating numbers or words according to definite rules. The path from an unambiguous question to an unambiguous answer must always, of course, be controlled by iron-clad rules, by algorithms. But when we try to simulate real-life situations, we must resort to equivocal questions and answers. If, for instance, we want to measure by a paper-and-pencil test the student's understanding of the motion of a *real* block of wood down a plane, a sharp division of data into relevant and irrelevant becomes impossible, and there are no unique, perfectly correct conclusions, for, of course, no real objects or processes can be fully described. Thus the problem is not completely defined by the standard qualifications of no air resistance and a given value of the coefficient of friction. The student is still faced with such questions as the following: Is the gravitational field uniform? Are all the bodies perfectly rigid? Is there any rotation or turning? Is the coefficient of friction the same for all points of the plane and for all speeds, or is the value given an average value, and if so what sort of average? What are the effects of air buoyancy and turbulence? There are two ways in which the student can proceed. He can weigh these factors and use his judgment—and one might call that *understanding* of physics. If he does, both the question and the answer have elements of ambiguity. This ambiguity is particularly great in an essay test. The teacher can, of course, give the student extra credit for discussing various factors, but if the student does this, he may have no time to finish the test. The student is usually expected to proceed knowing that when he is given an inclined-plane problem, the local tribal customs sanction the use of formula X. Here the ambiguity disappears; so does most of physics.

We can put some of the physics back into the problem by listing the allowable assumptions—not all of them of course but, say, those that are likely to occur to the average student. The average student can then operate completely syllogistically. A test of this sort may measure knowledge, intelligence, ingenuity, and disciplined thinking. It may also test an aspect of the general competence of science understanding, but a very narrow aspect indeed. Bohr's principle of complementarity appears to operate between the test question's clarity and univocality on the one hand, and its contact with reality on the other. We can have precision if we shut ourselves into the beautiful theoretical structure of physics and deal only with its unambiguous and impregnable assertions about man-invented models.

But if we wish to treat physics as a natural science, we must teach our students something about the uncouth reality and its fluid and equivocal relation to theory—and we must test what they have learned. An understanding of this relation must accompany the student when he looks up a coefficient of friction in a handbook if he is not to misread science as a body of knowledge. When science is viewed as a process of inquiry, ambiguity is present not only in tests but in the inquiry itself. The truly important questions of science, those whose resolution has brought about revolutionary advances, are necessarily ambiguous, for their full meaning can never be clear until after they have been resolved.

Let us remember, finally, that the main function of an achievement test is to separate students into groups according to their understanding of science. If the teaching staff agrees on theoretical, empirical, or authoritarian grounds that a given response is more likely from good students than from poor ones, then for testing purposes it may be considered the right response. If no such agreement can be reached, the exercise is probably fuzzy and should not be used. It is assumed of course that the staff consists of competent *teachers,* who not only know their science but also know their students, which is possible only by reading students' papers or hearing them talk. To avoid measuring the attainment of an important objective because the measurement is imprecise is hardly logical; omitting the objective from a test will effectively prevent the accurate measurement of students' achievement, as was shown in Section 7.3. An analogy from determining the volume of a solid would be to omit the measurement of one of the orthogonal dimensions (lack of correlation among objectives is analogous to orthogonality) because it can be measured only very roughly.

*Tests of disciplined, intuitive, and imaginative thinking*    The ability to view a problem as it would be viewed by a modern scientist is tested indirectly in almost all tests of understanding. To test for disciplined thinking directly is not very difficult; it is only necessary to offer the student a chance to go astray by following his misconceptions, prejudices, or intellectual predilections. (The skeptical reader might look at the relevant exercises in Part II of this book.) Nor is it difficult to test for intuitive thinking; it is only necessary to present the student with a problem he cannot solve by analytical, step-by-step reasoning, because he lacks the analytical tools or the time. What *is* difficult, and requires experimentation, is pitching the problem at a low enough level of difficulty. Part II offers a few sample problems that some students have solved nonanalytically, but, clearly, testing for intuitive thinking in science is in its infancy. Imaginative thinking in science, too, involves nonanalytical jumps and presents testing difficulties primarily because it is hard to devise simple enough problems. Again, a few workable test exercises are offered as samples in Part II.

*Laboratory testing* Laboratory testing for knowledge and the lower levels of understanding is quite simple and probably valid. Judging from the paucity of empirical studies, testing for understanding of the relation between book, or theoretical, science and real phenomena is not yet well known. The technique of testing is, however, not difficult. If it is possible to design a laboratory experiment that requires of the student the understanding in question, then a successful performance of the experiment is evidence of the understanding. Chapter 6 described a few such experiments and a way of testing the student's understanding by asking him to predict from one set of measurements the outcome of another set. Section 10.3 will describe in greater detail how to evaluate the student's laboratory performance. As more science teachers learn to test for laboratory objectives, laboratory teaching is sure to improve.

## 9.3   SCIENCE TEACHERS SHOULD PREPARE THEIR OWN TESTS (48)

There are at least three reasons that science teachers should write their own tests. First, since the ability measured by a test depends not only on the nature of the test but on the students' preparation, no one else is in a position to write an entirely apt test. Second, the process of preparing a test for specific objectives is a fruitful source of ideas for improving teaching as well as testing. Third, any experienced teacher of science, armed with a list of objectives, can write a valid and adequately reliable test covering all the major objectives. The first point is discussed in Section 8.3; the second and third, below.

### Preparation of a test as a fruitful source of ideas for teaching

A good test represents a tentative operational definition of course objectives and thus forces the teacher to make them explicit. Further, it requires a salutary review of objectives from the fresh standpoint of what in fact has been taught and what the student can be realistically expected to have learned. Preparing an objective test is particularly valuable here, for it involves deciding not only what questions to ask but what answers, both right and wrong, to expect. The following two remarks, typical of teachers who prepare their own tests, illustrate discoveries that are direct products of test-writing. "This would be an important question to ask, but I failed to prepare my students for it;" and "I spent two weeks of class time on topic X, but I can't think of any good questions on it." The remedy for the first difficulty is clear. As to the second, the usefulness of topic X should be reexamined. More generally, in preparing a test the teacher must ask himself what *effect* his teaching of a topic was intended to have on the students—not merely *what* he has taught but rather what he has taught the students to *do*. This question, too often glossed over, is at least as important as the relation of a topic to the science of which it is a part.

### A teacher can write his own tests

Constructing a good test on important behavioral objectives requires time and energy, but it is not difficult, for it involves no special knowledge or analysis of subtle points. Neither is it hazardous, for there is little danger that the students' grades will be adversely affected. Indeed, this danger is much greater if no real effort is made to evaluate the students' attainment of each important objective. A valid test, as was pointed out in Section 8.4, must contain exercises relevant to all the essential constituents of the desired competence, and the exercises should comprise a reliable sample. A good teacher can assess the relevance of an exercise by inspection. Deciding what ability a given exercise measures is the most difficult problem a test-constructor faces, but teaching experience should help here, for it involves constant probing of the student's mind and thus acquaints the teacher with the mental processes of the student faced with a problem. The closer an exercise comes to perfect relevance, that is, the more necessary and sufficient the principal ability is for working the exercise, the fewer exercises are necessary for a valid test. (Expertness in determining necessity and sufficiency is probably best acquired by performing item analyses.) Similarly, *economical* representation of the various aspects of the principal ability requires good classification of subobjectives, but wide sampling is adequate. For, if a subobjective is accidentally omitted from a test, other subobjectives that correlate with it will compensate for its absence. (Incidentally, professional test-writers depend on teachers for checking representation.) Finally, adequate reliability is obtained by wide and generous sampling, and reliability can almost always be increased by increasing the number of items.

The importance of high reliability in tests has been overemphasized by many professional test-makers (38). The error of measurement, which expresses the test's precision, is related to the standard deviation, $S$, of students' scores and the test's reliability, $r$, by the equation, $e = S\sqrt{1 - r}$. To reduce the error of measurement by a factor of 2, then, the reliability of a test must be increased, for example, from .50 to .88, and to reduce it by another factor of 2, the reliability has to become .97. In a two-hour quarterly, to make its reliability less than .50 would require not mere ignorance but actual malice; reliability of .88 would show considerable expertise; and reliability of .97, compulsiveness or unlimited spare time.

An experienced science teacher can therefore make a valid test provided he is guided by an explicit statement of his objectives and is willing to use a test that is longer than one prepared by an expert. His main concern should be relevance; the list of objectives will guide him in representation; and he should not be overly concerned with reliability. Section 7.4 shows how a test can be improved by repairing items, or shortened by discarding ineffective items on the basis of item analysis of students' scores. Chapter

10 discusses appropriate forms of tests and Chapter 11, the writing of relevant exercises.

*Ambiguity of tests of higher intellectual processes*    The most searching questions in a science test are likely to have elements of equivocality; for instance, a response marked wrong may be defensible on some grounds. Many teachers find it embarrassing and tedious to argue with their students about the relative correctness of various responses, and makers of published tests are sensitive about criticism of their objective items. These facts are probably responsible for the prevalence of objective tests whose items are as clean as a whistle and just about as valuable. We must, however, test for what is important and not for what is easy to test accurately. To discuss frankly with students what we are trying to measure and the shortcomings of our measuring instruments is desirable and profitable, first because it makes the student a more active participant in the course, and second because his lively interest in the discussion helps him learn more science. The teacher should be ready to admit that a test suitable for most of the class will almost certainly penalize some of the best and the weakest students. A strong argument for a challenged best response is that the majority of high scorers on the total test have chosen it. If a student wants to defend another response he should do it in class. If the teacher becomes convinced that the item has been wrongly keyed, the scores of all or no students should be changed. The reason for this advice is that understanding of science and willingness to argue with the teacher do not always correlate highly.

## Tests not prepared by the teacher (48)

Although a teacher can and should write test exercises, it is a good idea to let some control over the more important tests rest with someone else (see Section 10.2). The degree of control permitted an outsider may well vary, as it does in college with examiners, from allowing him to choose which teacher-written exercises should go into the test all the way to having him write the whole test. In all cases, however, the objectives and their relative weights are determined by the teacher; in most cases the teacher also inspects and criticizes the whole test.

In a different category belong tests that are prepared and published by some central agency and used without modification by several institutions. The proper use of these tests is discussed in Section 10.2, and an annotated list of published tests appears in Chapter 15. Here it is necessary to note only that most of them have small errors of measurement and are therefore reliable unless the group tested is much more homogeneous than the average. Using published tests allows a comparison of scores among institutions, although since what a test measures depends on the method of teaching and the caliber of students, an interpretation of differences in scores is difficult unless the differences are large or the objective is knowledge. In measuring understanding and ability to learn, the degree of novelty of the exercise is crucial; yet it varies from class to class. Measures of these higher intellectual processes are also hard to compare because both essay and objective tests of these processes are ambiguous, as was discussed in Section 9.2 and will be further discussed in Chapter 10.

Published tests, then, are likely to be precise measures of very limited educational objectives. This was especially true in the past, when tests of straight knowledge, almost the only kind available, were bestowing a national sanction on rote learning. Students, teachers, departments, and whole colleges were judged on the basis of such tests. How far science teaching was set back as a result is not easy to estimate, but many teachers must have been delighted at an official sanction to impart only information. Recently testing agencies have been more inclined to measure understanding, because they recognize the very limited prognostic power of tests of knowledge. Progress has been slow because it is hard to make such tests short and reliable, because science teachers suffer from inertia, and because respected scientists have leveled the expected unsophisticated criticism at the tests for their ambiguity. The pressure of empirical data is hard to resist, and the progress will continue, but at present good science tests must, by and large, be written by teachers themselves.

Before a published test is used, it is necessary to find out what it tests and how well. Unfortunately, validity data are seldom furnished, and the teacher must judge exercise relevance, representation, and reliability separately. The relevance of each exercise to knowledge, understanding, or ability to learn can be determined by inspection, following the rule of thumb given in the last paragraph of Section 8.3. How well various objectives and content are represented and sampled is always best judged by inspection; representation is discussed in Section 8.4. Finally, the reliability of the test for a given group of students can be calculated from equation 7.6a.

Teachers who use published tests should press the publishers for estimates of the tests' validities. These can be in the form of correlations with students' success in later courses or, better, with tests of known high validity for each major objective. It is not difficult to construct a highly valid test of a single objective in a narrow area, for instance, understanding in electricity, as was shown in Sections 8.6 and 9.3. This is true provided that the test is very long, say three hours, and has a great variety of exercises, including objective items and essays. A collection of highly valid tests for the main objectives and content would be much too long for use in assigning grades, but such tests can be used by the publishers to validate shorter tests.

Once the teacher knows the objectives measured by particular published tests when they are given to his class and can therefore assign proper weights to them, he is almost certain to gain by supplementing his own tests with published ones. This is primarily because such supplementing will increase that most important characteristic of a test measuring a complex competence—variety. There is another reason for using published tests that most teachers recognize and most administrators do not. Published tests are like ready-made clothes: they are designed only for average fit and therefore are not so good but cheaper than the custom-made variety. The analogy assumes that the teachers' time is valuable and that it can be evaluated in terms of money. Because teachers are not paid by the hour, such evaluation is unfortunately considered too abstract or simply unnecessary by most institutions' financial officers.

# 10

## FORMS OF TESTS

Understanding of science has been measured by written, oral, and performance tests. There are two distinct kinds of written test: objective, in which the student chooses among prepared responses, and essay, in which he writes his ideas in paragraph form. In a performance test the student handles or at least observes real materials and apparatus. Each of these four forms has its strengths and weaknesses and each can, if certain conditions are fulfilled, be the most valid form for measuring a particular objective. To pick an obvious example, the choice among the oral, essay, performance, and objective forms might depend on whether one wanted to determine, respectively, a student's ability to speak, write, act, or make a choice among given alternatives. These four forms of tests are discussed below, especially their appropriateness for measuring various kinds of competence.

### 10.1 ORAL TESTS (56)

The main advantage of an oral test, beyond the obvious one that it tests directly whether the student can speak and otherwise behave well under special and trying circumstances, is that as the test progresses the examiner knows more and more about the student and can therefore ask more and more probing questions. After a few years of experience, the examiner learns to anticipate probable answers to his first question and formulates ahead of time his second, follow-up question. Beyond that, the number of possibilities becomes too large, and the examiner must react to the student's answers more or less spontaneously. Once oral testing has arrived at the unrehearsed stage, the interaction of idiosyncrasies of the examiner and the student can play an important, almost uncontrollable, often unnoticed, and certainly unrecorded role in the test. Under these circumstances, the reliability of the test can be scandalously low even for tests conducted by a panel of subject-matter specialists with years of examining experience behind them. The oral test is the most expensive form, and a better job can often be done with other forms of tests, even though the advantage of follow-up questioning is lost.

In introductory science courses, formal oral examinations are very seldom used. When, however, a teacher says that, despite a student's fairly low laboratory and written test scores, he knows that the student deserves a high grade, he is almost certainly relying on oral tests. These "tests" take place in discussions, in class or outside. The knowledge of the quality of students' understanding of science, both as a class and individually, that can be obtained from their answers and questions in oral discussion is extremely important and can legitimately influence students' grades, especially if such information is gathered *and recorded* about all students and not only about those who volunteer to speak. All the pitfalls of formal oral tests, however, are present in testing by discussion. In college, the use of discussions for evaluating students runs into a special difficulty: students may ask some questions just to impress the teacher and suppress others for fear of showing their ignorance. In schools, on the other hand, the image of the teacher as a judge seems ever present anyhow; students' recitations can therefore properly be used for evaluation. Other difficulties of oral tests remain, of course, so it may be advisable for the teacher to check and reinforce his impression of the student by asking him, immediately following the recitation, to write down very briefly his replies to the teacher's questions.

The oral test is the most flexible and potentially most searching form of evaluation of science understanding, but to be at all reliable it requires not only expertise but talent, and such talent is rare. Even though the reliability of oral tests is therefore likely to be low, their *relevance* to disciplined, imaginative, and especially intuitive thinking is likely to be higher than in the usual written test. If a problem is to be solved intuitively, there are no hard-and-fast rules on what information is relevant and what is not. The test-maker must either be very generous in supplying even remotely relevant data or must supply them on request. The latter process is practicable only in an oral test. Moreover, oral tests contribute to variety; they may bring out aspects of a competence that are almost entirely absent from other forms of tests, or even aspects of a competence that have not been explicitly included in the teacher's list of objectives. For these reasons it would be a pity to disregard the evidence that can be obtained from students' spoken questions and arguments, provided of course that evidence only of the desired competence and not of manners is gathered.

The college teacher might try in his class to engage most of the students in discussion but, not to interfere with his role as teacher, should make no conscious effort to evaluate their competence at the time. At the end of the class he should nevertheless be able to remember those few who have shown high competence and assign to them the grades of "good" or "very good." These grades, provided they are recorded, can be given some weight in assigning final grades for the course or can be used only to raise the grades of borderline students. Lowering course grades of bad discussants is unwise, for the poorer student may decide that it is best to keep his mouth shut. The students should, of course, be informed of the grading practice.

## 10.2   WRITTEN TESTS

This section discusses the advantages of the essay and objective forms, and of forms that combine the two. A more detailed discussion of objective test forms, such as multiple choice and master list, appears in Chapter 11. The abilities or aspects of the general competence of understanding science for which the objective or essay test seems particularly suitable will be indicated. The two forms differ most in the degree of spontaneity and freedom permitted in students' responses and in the clarity with which the students' task can be defined. These two elements in turn bear on the feasibility of an unambiguous interpretation of students' responses and on the validity of the test.

### Spontaneity of response

The source of the essay test's strength is, of course, the spontaneity of the student's response. He is free to say what he wants; he must organize and formulate his ideas; and he is not prompted, handicapped, or annoyed by someone else's phraseology and organization of the task set before him. The essay form is therefore clearly the preferred form for testing imaginative thinking. It is also best for measuring the student's ability to deal with a complex task. The individual questions on an objective test are necessarily directed at certain subproblems or aspects of any complex task and thus effectively lay down a rigid analytical and organizational framework. If this particular breakdown or organization of the task is uncongenial to the student, he is handicapped in solving the problem. What is more important, the student has no opportunity to show whether he is capable of devising an appropriate framework of his own. If the student's opinions are very different from the more commonly accepted ones, the self-consistency of his set of opinions can be measured by an essay test much more easily and directly than by an objective test. (In introductory science, however, an interest in a student's unorthodoxies is likely to be primarily diagnostic.) Finally, clear analytical (as distinguished from intuitive) thinking and clear speaking or writing are highly—some people think, perfectly—correlated. Consequently an essay test can be a valid, ideally even a direct, measure of the student's analytical thinking.

Objective exercises can measure the student's ability to organize and formulate his ideas and to think imaginatively, and the self-consistency of his concepts and ideas, only indirectly and rather awkwardly. The more usual objection that, on an objective test, the student needs less knowledge or understanding because he is prompted rather than allowed to decide on his own answer is only formally true. Students exhibit a tremendous variety of attacks on the problem of "choosing" the right response to an objective item. Moreover, as is shown in Section 11.5 under Spontaneity, it is often possible to be virtually certain that the student arrives at his own formulation of a response before selecting his preference among the given ones.

### Definition of task

The task that the student is expected to perform in an essay exercise becomes easier to specify, the simpler and the more routine or traditional it is. Thus, in solving a routine numerical problem, perhaps most, though usually not all, students may be expected to know from their previous experience with a particular teacher what formulas must be derived; what simplifying assumptions will be allowed and which must be explicit; whether significant figures and units must be used; and, if so, which symbols, if any, must be defined at every step and in the answer, and how much algebraic and arithmetical detail must be shown. Even in the simplest of all essays, it seems, the student's task is imperfectly defined, for many teachers enjoin their students in irritable and desperate capitals to show ALL work, even though they may not want to see some arithmetic, such as long division. In fact they would rather not see it because it is likely to be written diagonally across the more interesting parts. And almost certainly they do not welcome the usually undecipherable record of the most difficult part of the task, the path the student has pursued in *deciding* what formulas to use. In self-defense the teachers add, "Be brief and be neat," and ensure the briefness, at the expense of neatness and comprehensiveness, by limiting the allowed space. The student who can briefly and neatly show all work is an exceptional student. He is a highly cherished student though not necessarily a promising scholar. The rest of the students must weigh for themselves the relative values of comprehensiveness, brevity, and neatness and hope that their estimates coincide with the teacher's.

The difficulties of making clear to the student what is expected of him in a routine exercise like solving a numerical problem patterned on those discussed in class or writing a definition of a frequently used term are perhaps more annoying than serious. But when the test exercise has important elements of novelty to the student, as it must to measure objectives other than knowledge, the difficulties of communication are great indeed and can be adequately handled only by an expert; they cannot be entirely obviated (57). There is no way of telling the student exactly how deep, broad, or circumstantial his treatment of the subject and how nice his distinctions should be; whether he should be critical and conservative or original and imaginative; and what assumptions he must state and what assertions defend. Some students, and not necessarily the poorest, may even fail to understand what the intended main task is. It is true, of course, that the ability to understand the implications of a well-stated question and the ability to decide on the necessary and sufficient ingredients of the proper answer are important abilities. But if the whole test is in the essay form, these abilities are weighted much too heavily, especially for an introductory course. In fact, if the class is more heterogeneous in these abilities than in others, they may easily become the principal abilities measured by the test.

In an objective item, the formal task is defined precisely: choose the best response. A more substantive definition can also be made with greater accuracy than in an essay test because the student is presented with a sample of expected responses. These responses, as well as the question, can be used to direct the student to the desired task so that he will exhibit the degree of his attainment of a specific objective. If the problem can be attacked in several ways, the student may be asked to choose the best method, or the method may be specified for him in the responses. In either case, the differences between the correct and incorrect responses can vary in kind and in degree. They may be based, for example, simply on the correctness or the reasonableness of the assumptions involved. They may also be made gross or subtle. Even objective exercises (except those testing for knowledge) are, of course, ambiguous, as was pointed out in Section 9.3. This ambiguity, however, is inherent in all searching questions and is different from ambiguity in the definition of the task (for methods of defining the problem in objective exercises, see Homogeneity of responses in Section 11.5). Essay questions have both kinds of ambiguity.

### Interpretation of test results

Comparatively few teachers realize that the essay tasks they give their students are sometimes deeply ambiguous. A much more familiar problem is how to evaluate accurately and objectively the competence of the student who has written the essay. It is frequently difficult to know just what question the student is trying to answer or, if he omits a point, whether he did it out of ignorance or because he thought the question did not ask for it. Without such knowledge, it is difficult to appreciate even a clearly stated answer. But, as we all know, the ability to express oneself clearly is rare among beginning students and even among people in general. Equivocal questions and ambiguous responses make it difficult to evaluate the student's competence, except when the essay is excellent or very bad. Some teachers, fully aware of the near-impossibility of accurately defining the essay problem and interpreting the student's response, nevertheless maintain that an attentive analysis of the student's statements, even though they may have only a tenuous connection with the problem at hand, will show whether he "knows his physics" or not. The poorer students are more than willing to cooperate in this sort of catch-all evaluation and will often deliberately incorporate into their essays correct but irrelevant assertions. Irrelevancies, either deliberate or not, increase fortuitous differences among students' essays, make the essays less comparable in general quality, and reduce the accuracy of the grades assigned. They also make essay-reading more of a chore and, what is more important, they often make measurement of specific objectives or specific content nearly impossible.

*Guessing*    A very common objection to the objective test form is that the teacher cannot be sure whether the student knows the answer or merely makes a lucky guess. This objection is in most cases trivial, for one is seldom interested, except perhaps diagnostically, in whether a particular student knows the answer to a particular question. Insofar as the total score is concerned, guessing lowers its reliability; if the test is reliable, guessing has vitiated neither the total scores of individual students nor the score of the whole class on any particular item. Moreover, blind guessing is quite rare in course tests (58) and can be further reduced by penalties for wrong answers. It is nevertheless true that the essay form gives us information on the student's method of attack and thus furnishes otherwise unobtainable and valuable clues to his strengths and weaknesses. A related objection is that the student acquires "test sophistication," a special skill unrelated to understanding of subject matter, which helps him pick out the right response. This objection is valid, and every student should be habituated to objective tests so that he has a chance to become adequately sophisticated before given the tests on which his grade will be based. In essay tests, guessing and test sophistication come into play as the student tries to surmise what the particular teacher who has written the essay question will consider a fully relevant answer. They therefore play a more insidious and parochial role than in objective tests. Still another objection to objective tests is that one cannot be sure whether the student worked from the question to the answer or from the answer to the question in solving the problem; the abilities involved in the two mental processes may be quite different. A direct test of the ability to interpret data, for instance, requires that the student proceed from the data to the conclusions; an objective test cannot assure us that that is what the student has done. Section 11.5, under Spontaneity, discusses ways of making the desired method of attack profitable, in the sense that the students who work from questions to answers get higher scores. This, of course, is all that is necessary, except for diagnosis. If no such precautions are taken, the ability the test is designed to measure should not be overspecified; it should not depend on how the student attacks the problem. The sample questions in the classification of objectives in Section 2.1 were devised with this independence in mind.

*The exceptionally gifted students*    Section 7.3 showed that letter-grade validity or, more generally, the validity or accuracy with which a test sep arates students into groups according to their competence depends not only on the test but also on the number of groups desired. The accuracy of ranking also depends on the size of the groups. If we want most of the exceptionally competent students, say, the upper 1 percent of the class, to get higher scores than the rest, the test must be specially designed. It must have a large number of exercises on which the average score of the upper 2 percent of the class is about 50 percent. Tests not so designed will therefore penalize the exceptionally competent students. The objective form will penalize them because such students will see weaknesses in the "right" response and strengths in the "wrong" responses that other students do not. The essay form is free from this defect because the subtlety of analysis and the formulation of the response is left to the student. On the other hand, the imaginative students will apply a disconcerting variety of interpretations to the essay question, while the highly disciplined students may read the assignment so literally as to exclude the treatment of some of the main points. The difficulty of interpreting and grading those two extreme types of essays is particularly great because the beginning student assumes that the essay question has been carefully and imaginatively formulated and consequently considers it unnecessary to state *his* understanding of the question.

The difficulties described in the preceding paragraph are hard to avoid entirely. A test given to a heterogeneous group is usually designed to give good average discrimination and cannot be expected to discriminate accurately for every caliber of student. The best practice is to give as many and as various exercises as time permits. On some exercises, the student's imagination or precision of thought may lead him astray, but on others it will help. Given enough varied exercises, the best students seldom get less than an A −.

*The reader and the key*   Up to now it has been tacitly assumed that the student's essays are read by experts—readers who are highly skilled in inferring the student's thinking from his writing. This skill can probably be acquired only by reading a large number of essays and discussing them with the students; the prerequisites are expert knowledge of subject matter, patience, empathy, and lots of time. Rare as expert science teachers are (and they also must meet these prerequisites), expert readers of science essays are even rarer, for their job is less rewarding. In college, reading essays is often relegated to a paper-grader, the lowest man on the totem pole of teaching assistants, a student who does it for money and little money at that.

If an essay-reader has had little teaching experience, he is likely to commit systematic errors because he will not recognize the student's insight unless it is expressed in officially approved terms or terms the reader himself would use. Such errors can be reduced by training and guidance. The most practical method is to train the reader in the use of a very explicit key. Essay keys are discussed under Reliability later in this section. The main purposes of reader-training are to clarify the meaning of the major objectives by example, to acquaint the reader with the great variety of equally good responses, and, above all, to make it clear to him that his job is not only to note what the student says but also to *infer* his intentions and, from his statements and his intentions, to arrive at an estimate of his competence. The estimated competence must of course be the one defined by the essay question and the key.

Most teachers seem to agree that even a trained reader can do a good job only if he is considerably more competent than the best students whose essays he reads. It is therefore perhaps best not to ask the paper-grader to estimate the student's imaginative or disciplined thinking or his ability to organize, unless the grader is known to excel in these abilities. With these limitations, the reader can be trained to avoid systematic errors, but he will make sizable random errors in inferring the students' meaning. Random errors can be corrected by lengthening the test and by having more than one grader read each essay.

A fairly detailed key is useful even if the reader is an experienced teacher. In the first place, it will make it easier for him to keep grading uniform. In the second place, it is a good idea to give the key to the students, both to show respect toward junior members of a community of scholars and to enable them to profit from reading their corrected essays—students will go over their essays and compare them with the key faithfully and eagerly. It is true, of course, that this course will open the door to a criticism from which essay tests are exempted at present. A good key will weight projected student responses in accordance with the most probable degree of the students' competence and not necessarily or even usually in accordance with the responses' approximation to the findings of the latest research. Such weighting must of course occur in all tests; at present it is made openly in objective tests and privately in essay tests. Reducing this privacy should lead to a rapid improvement in essay tests; the essay form is much too valuable to be allowed to moulder as it has in the past.

### Tests combining the essay and objective forms

*Structured essays*    There are forms of tests that are compromises between the objective test and the open-ended essay. Compromise tests define the problem and the competence required of the student better than essay tests, but lose spontaneity of response. The essay task can be made more definite by specifying the subtopics to be treated. For example, if the main topic of the essay is a comparison of the wave and the photon theories of light, specified subtopics may be ether theory, electromagnetic theory, and black-body radiation, or the student may be asked to explain a list of experimental results by using the theories. The *structured* essay question will evoke from the student a response that is less spontaneous but easier to evaluate than his answer to an unstructured question. An essay can be even more rigorously structured, of course, by specifying the order in which the subtopics are to be treated or the extent of the treatment—the number of words or paragraphs or inches of space. An essay can also be structured if the teacher writes part of it; the student's task is to complete the essay. An open-ended essay, "Prove that heat is energy," for instance, can be structured as follows: "Starting with the premise that a hot body, for example, steam, can be made to do work if it is allowed to cool, one may reach the conclusion that heat is energy. What additional premises are necessary to *prove* the conclusion? Defend your statements." Still another way to define a problem is to give the student an essay containing errors of fact, of logic, or of organization and ask him to rewrite it. A highly structured essay may be based on an objective multiple-choice item: the student is allowed to write his own response if he finds the prepared responses unsatisfactory, or to criticize the prepared response he considers most nearly correct, or to defend his choice of response.

Structured essays are a very effective compromise form for testing in science. Even essays so highly structured that the student's response to each subtopic will be only a few sentences can still measure spontaneity and his ability to formulate his thoughts. At the same time they allow control over the competence tested and can be scored with a good deal of objectivity. Completion items, in which the student completes a sentence with one or two words, are only technically essays; essentially, they are a form of objective test and not a particularly fruitful or flexible form. If the essay task is to solve a numerical problem, specially designated spaces for equations and answers do not structure the essay. They offer no real guide to the student; their function is to make reading easier. Structured essays are discussed in greater detail in Section 11.2.

*Grading of essays by means of objective tests*   To avoid the difficult task of interpreting students' essays and the frustrating chore of reading them, the author has developed a testing technique that may be called *objective tests of essay answers* (57, Nedelsky). The central idea of the technique is simple and not entirely novel. It is based on the assumption that the meaning of the student's sentences is clearer to him than to anyone else. The procedure is as follows. The student writes a structured essay as a home assignment or as part of an examination. He is then asked, under examination conditions, to read his essay and comment on each part of it, choosing his comments from a prepared list of responses labeled A, B, C, and so forth. The final and usually the only product that has to be inspected is the objective-test answer sheet, which can be scored by a clerk or a machine. In doubtful cases, the student's essay may be read. The technique can be used only with those essays for which it is possible to prepare a detailed key, for only then is it possible to categorize acceptable essay answers and prepare appropriate sets of comments.

The technique described above has been tried on a small scale in a variety of courses at more than one college and has proved successful, in that the students' objective-test scores correlate almost perfectly with grades assigned to them by teachers who have read the essays. But the technique requires time and ingenuity on the part of the test-writer, and is at present probably more useful as a research tool in testing than for routine examinations.

## Open-book tests and study habits

Written tests, whether essay or objective, can vary with respect to the reference materials the student may use before or during the test. Open-book tests are more realistic than closed-book tests because in most real-life situations the student can consult a text. Also, open-book tests are less likely to test for straight memory of the book's content, an ability too often overemphasized. It is important, however, that the student taking an open-book objective test be given time to consult the text, perhaps an extra ninety seconds for each item. If only sixty to ninety seconds are allowed per item, consulting the text is usually unprofitable, and the test should be closed-book or the student advised to consult the book only rarely.

Giving the student material to read before the examination and perhaps allowing him to use it during the examination is a useful device for ensuring a common background of knowledge in a heterogeneous group. Test exercises in science always require knowledge, even those designed to test for understanding or learning ability. These abilities are more reliably measured if the majority of those taking the test have the requisite knowledge. Test exercises based on home reading assignments are also useful for measuring broad comprehension of reading because the assignments can be much longer than those given under examination conditions.

The form of the test may have an important influence on the student's study habits. The open-book test will make him emphasize the ability to use the text as reference, de-emphasize memory, and perhaps concentrate on understanding. When studying for an essay test, students usually work hard on some topics, skip others, and try to memorize whole sentences. In studying for an objective test, they spread their efforts more or less evenly over the material covered and memorize less. They spend more hours preparing for essay than for objective tests. Many of them, especially when fresh from high school, consider essay tests harder and fairer. They also feel that luck plays an important part in both tests—the luck of having studied the right chapters for the essay test and, especially, the luck in guessing on an objective test. A frank discussion of the nature and function of tests may have a salutary effect on students' habits of study.

## Validity

The degree to which the three requirements for validity—relevance, representation, and reliability—are met by essay and objective tests is discussed below.

*Relevance*   The essay form, because it requires a spontaneous response to a problem, effectively simulates most real-life or criterion situations. A major exception is voting, which in this country, at least formally, is a multiple-choice or simply true-false "test." We are, however, interested in problems that require an understanding of science. Creative or imaginative thinking by a research scientist or anyone else implies spontaneity; so does ability to persuade, for it requires formulation and organization of thought. However, the ordinary citizen will most commonly use his understanding of science to make better decisions on the *relative* value of assertions made by experts: politicians, the military, scientists, engineers, or salesmen and repairmen. Even in scientific research, it often seems that enumerating possible procedures is easier than choosing the most promising one. Situations in which the main difficulty is proper choice among stated or easily formulated possibilities are better simulated by objective than essay tests, both formally and because the tester has more control over the alternatives.

To turn to more specific abilities than the general competence of understanding science, the essay as compared to the objective form has higher relevance in tests of imaginative thinking and of the abilities to formulate and organize one's thoughts (objectives 3.4 and 3.32). The essay test is usually and perhaps even in principle less relevant to the other objectives primarily because of imperfect definition of task. It is nearly impossible, for instance, to design an open-ended essay exercise whose results can be unambiguously interpreted as measures of understanding. The essay is also sure to measure the ability to formulate and organize thoughts, and whatever other abilities various students feel obliged or inclined to exercise. The possession of a specific item of information is highly relevant in all tests, for without it the student may not be able to exhibit any other ability; but it is much less important in an objective item, for a test can contain many of these. Supplying information will almost invariably structure the essay and rob it of spontaneity. The best way to diminish the importance of specific information is to offer the students a choice of topics, even though such a step is certain to reduce the reliability of the scores. The usual argument that the student without the information relevant to an exercise ought to flunk anyhow is weak, as was shown in Section 8.3. It is especially weak when applied to essay tests, with their necessarily small sampling of information: students possessing equally important funds of information may fail or pass depending on the particular sampling. An accurate definition of the student's task is particularly important in testing for the ability to conform to scientific modes of thought (objective 3.31), for here even the path the student is to follow must be prescribed. On the other hand, when testing for at least one important aspect of understanding, the ability to interpret data, the student's path can be better controlled by an essay exercise, for in an objective exercise the student may reason backwards, from conclusions that are stated in the responses to data.

In conclusion, to make an exercise truly relevant to the abilities of imaginative thinking, organization, and formulation, the time allowance must be generous, for in real-life situations these are leisurely processes. Many students who are imaginative and can organize their thoughts may not do well if pressed for time. Examination stress is always a distorting factor but perhaps it is less important if the student can concentrate on a single point as he does on an objective item. Second, the effective relevance of an essay exercise depends crucially on the reader, for it is only what he can and does see in the essay that determines the student's grade.

*Representation*    Good representation requires not only that each essential constituent of the overall objective of the course be tested but that it play a role commensurate with its importance. Neither of these requirements is easy to satisfy without an accurate definition of the student's tasks. For the purposes of representation, objective tests are therefore tests of choice, except of course for those constituents to which they are irrelevant. Variety in students' mental processes—essentially uncontrolled, almost random variety—is an essential safety feature of a test designed to measure an understanding of science that can be used in post-academic life. Good representation can therefore be best achieved by variety in test forms. Whenever possible, the teacher should use both the essay and the objective exercises.

*Reliability*    Section 7.1 points out that the word *reliability* should be applied not to a test but to the students' scores. This distinction is especially important in dealing with essay tests. For the scores to be reliable they must be assigned objectively, differing only if the essays differ. The word *objectivity* has two fairly distinct meanings when applied to essay-reading. The reader is said to be objective or, more accurately, consistent if he sticks to a standard he has set for himself and does not allow the student's grade to be influenced by other circumstances, such as the student's bad handwriting or spelling, or the reader's fatigue after reading a number of essays, or his previous knowledge of the student. Objectivity also denotes a consensus of several readers. Ordinarily, essay-grading is not very objective by either standard. Scoring becomes much more objective if the student's name is removed from his paper before it is read. Both types of objectivity are also improved by the existence of a detailed "key" describing the various kinds of competence the student is expected to exhibit and specifying scores or grades for various student responses. With the aid of a key, reasonable agreement among readers can be established by discussing and grading several essays read by all readers. There are pitfalls, however. It is tempting to be satisfied with an agreement on the value of the easily identified but not necessarily important characteristics of an essay, such as units, arithmetic, and the knowledge of values of physical constants. Preparing a key for the abilities that the essay test can measure better than any other form—imaginative thinking and ability to organize and formulate one's thoughts—is extremely difficult. A key that is not relevant to the principal ability of an exercise can destroy the exercise's effective relevance. It is therefore better not to prepare a key than to prepare an essentially irrelevant one, even though reader reliability is thereby impaired.

If an essay exercise is scored objectively and the exercise is clearly understood by most students, the reliability of the exercise may be high. The reliability of the whole test, however, will depend on the sampling of the content and of abilities that the test measures. It is admittedly much more difficult to get good sampling with essays than with objective tests of the same length (in hours). In many situations, however, it is the usually low reader reliability that sets the upper limit to the reliability of the test (57). To sum up, the reliability of science essay scores is seldom high enough unless the test measures only a very clear-cut and narrow segment of knowledge, such as definitions of terms given in the text or solution of stereotyped problems. Such abilities can, however, be measured just as accurately and more conveniently by objective tests. The latter form therefore, as a rule, shows higher reliability for most objectives.

In the preceding paragraph the word *reliability* has its usual meaning of the overall or average precision with which scores are assigned to students. There are two decisions, however, that can more reliably be made on the basis of essay than objective tests. One of these is that a student who has received a satisfactory score could not be a failing student. For, after all, a completely ignorant student may get a passing score on an objective test; he is much less likely to do so on a science essay test. The other decision is that a student who has done very well has some unusually high talent. It should be emphasized, however, that the reliability of the decision against the student—that he is failing or that he is not unusually talented—is not high with the essay form.

### Summary on written tests

In the hands of expert test-designers *and* expert and conscientious readers, overall understanding of science can probably be more validly measured by means of essay than objective tests; but the large majority of science teachers will do better with objective tests prepared by themselves, especially if the essays will be read by assistants. The prevalent opinion that greater expertise is required to write an objective test of understanding than an equally adequate essay test is incorrect. That opinion is based primarily on the relative ease with which an inspector can find inadequacies and errors in an objective test. Detectable errors may embarrass the teacher, but they do lead him to improve his test. An essay topic usually contains no assertions and therefore no obvious errors; without reading a large number of students' papers, only an expert can judge its value as a test.

To ensure fair sampling the essay test should be longer (in hours) than the objective test. If it is to be read by a relatively untrained assistant, it should be much longer so that it will have adequate reliability. If the teacher himself writes and scores the test, he will save time by using essay tests for small classes and objective tests for large classes.

There are abilities for which a given form of written test has higher relevance than another form. For essays, they are imaginative thinking and the abilities to organize and formulate; for the objective form, the ability to abide by stated rules. Either form is unambiguous in testing for knowledge; both are ambiguous in testing for higher intellectual processes. Although one or the other form is preferable depending on the objective and local testing talent, either form can measure directly or indirectly any one of the science objectives. The important thing is to try to measure each major objective; the form of the test is secondary, except that the need for variety suggests the use of both forms.

Experimentation with forms of tests is not difficult and is in order for those who are now convinced that there is only one good form. Even if they do not change their opinion, they are likely to learn how to improve their favorite form. Correlation of the tests that are to be evaluated with a test of known high validity is the best procedure. Lacking a criterion test, anyone can easily calculate the reliabilities and intercorrelation of tests of different forms. If, for instance, the correlation between an essay test and an objective one is $r_{eo}$ and the reliabilities are respectively $r_e$ and $r_o$, and if $r_{eo}/\sqrt{r_e r_o}$ is not very different from unity, there is no reason to believe that the two tests measure different competences. The choice of the form then is a matter of taste and convenience.

## 10.3  PERFORMANCE TESTS (59)

A performance test is one that requires physical apparatus, whether or not the students have to handle the apparatus. Under *apparatus* are included tools, instruments, and materials. Performance tests are invariably more awkward and expensive to administer than written tests and should be used only when a written test would be inadequate. They are generally out of place in testing for a non-laboratory course even if it has lecture demonstrations. In the classification in Section 2.1, all laboratory objectives (L1, L2, and L3) require performance tests. The types of competence that are fostered by laboratory experience but, at least in theory, can be acquired without it, such as the knowledge of the structure of an ammeter or the ability to interpret written data, are classified under 1.23, instruments or experiments and conclusions, and under 2.13, understanding of experiments.

### Tests of products and of processes

The laboratory competence of a student may be inferred from an inspection of the product of his performance or from watching him at work. (In physics laboratories, the product will commonly be a written report or an arrangement of apparatus and meter readings. In chemistry, geology, and the biological sciences the product may be a manufactured object: a chemical, a polished or etched stone, or a slide for the microscope.) Inspecting the product is the better of the two methods because it is relatively objective, reliable, and convenient. It has, however, some shortcomings. If students work in groups, each student's individual contribution is hard to judge. Also, the finished product may not tell us the student's method of attack, his psychomotor skills, or the effort involved, and such knowledge is important for counseling and prognosis.

Watching a student at work can tell us what inspecting the product cannot, but the process is difficult and even risky. It requires many hours of observation; some behavior cannot be accurately observed; some students perform and learn badly when conscious of being watched; recording of observations is difficult; and uniform standards of grading are hard to apply. These difficulties largely disappear if the information obtained from watching is used not for grading but only for counseling.

### Performance tests given at examination time

Insofar as possible the student's final response, on which he is to be judged, should be in writing. Written responses can be evaluated at leisure; they make uniform standards of grading possible; they provide a permanent record; and they can usually be valid measurements of performance. A test of the student's ability merely to set up or adjust apparatus, however, need not be written to be valid. In this case the apparatus arrangement is the product and must be inspected. If the test requires both the ability to set up apparatus and the ability to perform a measurement, the students' written reports on the data obtained will usually show which students possess both abilities; they will not differentiate between students who have only one of the abilities and students who possess neither.

In one type of performance test requiring a written response, apparatus are already set up in such a way that the student can make a measurement (59, Kruglak). The student is asked to perform various tasks and record the results either in essays or by marking prepared responses. One possible task might be to name various instruments, read them, and give their functions. Another group of tasks might include some of the following: to give a possible function of the setup, diagram the setup, criticize it, estimate the probable accuracy of the measurement it would provide, make a specified measurement, and make a series of measurements and give both the result and the probable error. The student may also be asked to estimate, without using instruments, properties of materials and objects, for example, the electrical resistance of a wire, the focal length of a lens, the mass of an object (preferably an object that cannot be lifted but can be made to slide), the temperature of water, or the constant of a spring. A convenient arrangement for performance tests, if large groups of students are to be tested, is to have various setups numbered and distributed through the laboratory. Each student gets an examination booklet that tells him the order in which he is to use the setups. The tasks need not be the same for all students: one student may measure the length of cylinder 1, another of cylinder 2. A proctor should be available to adjust or replace mishandled apparatus or to reset measuring instruments.

Performance tests in which the student's response is in writing may be designed to test for a large variety of objectives. A test that requires the student to adjust and read a mercury barometer, and to record the reading, or to focus the image of an object on the screen and record the position of the screen, will measure certain laboratory skills. Imaginative thinking and certain kinds of understanding can be measured by a black-box test, that is, by a test in which the student identifies the invisible contents of a box. For example, the outside of the box may have two binding posts to which an electrical circuit inside the box is connected; the student is to identify the circuit elements. Intuitive thinking can be measured by asking the student to estimate, for instance, the temperature at a point of a wire from the temperatures at other points.

### Judging students' performances by their work in the laboratory

To test for the central objective of laboratory teaching, understanding the relation between physical reality and the physicist's description of it, the student must be required to spend several hours with apparatus. It is doubtful that such a length of time can be justified for the purposes of evaluation alone; evaluation opportunities must be incorporated into laboratory experiments used for teaching. Unfortunately, the conventional laboratory neither fosters the student's attainment of the central objective nor permits its measurement. Therefore at least one experiment per semester should be of a special kind. Since the experiment may take more than one laboratory period, it must be defended on the basis of teaching as well as testing. Such defense has been given in Chapter 6. Briefly, in such an experiment the student's goal is to acquire enough understanding of relevant phenomena to enable him to predict the outcome of a test experiment. The general and some of the specific characteristics of the test experiment are known to the student. The final step is an experimental verification of the prediction.

The experiment-predict-verify type of laboratory lends itself to a fairly accurate evaluation of the student's achievement. The aptness of the experimental design and the quality of its execution can be checked at several points. In those experiments in which the student is asked (as he usually should be) to choose his own apparatus, he should list the apparatus wanted and perhaps make a supplementary list after collecting some data. The appropriateness of the listed apparatus may be one basis for the grade. When the student is ready for the test experiment, the teacher gives him an exact specification of it. For instance, after the student, perhaps in partnership with another student, has experimented with various elements of electrical circuits, he is given a diagram of the test-experiment circuit for which the reading of one or more meters is specified. From this point on, the student works alone. His first task is to predict, from the data of his preliminary experimentation, the reading of the rest of the meters. The calculations leading to the predictions are made by each student under examination conditions and are handed in together with all relevant data. The data and calculations constitute a second basis for judging the student's performance. Next, the student sets up the test-experiment circuit, adjusts the rheostats under the instructor's supervision till specified meter readings are achieved, and records all the meter readings. An inspection of the circuit forms a third basis for judging the student's performance. The last basis for this judgment is the degree of agreement between the predicted and verification values. The grades for *this* part may be assigned as follows. If the predicted value is $X \pm \Delta X$, and the difference between the predicted and verification values is greater than $2 \Delta X$, the grade is F; if the difference lies between $\Delta X$ and $2 \Delta X$, the grade is D; and if the difference is less than $\Delta S$, the grade is C, B, or A depending on the magnitude of $\Delta X$. Ordinarily, the verification value itself should be the mean of several measurements.

It is worth noting that the calculations for prediction and the test-experiment arrangement of apparatus can easily be the product of the individual student and not of a partnership. These controllable data are usually enough for judging how active a role the student has played in the experiment as a whole. The laboratory session in which test experiments are performed may be a busy time for the instructor. Fortunately, students finish their preliminary experimentation and calculations for prediction one at a time, and checking their apparatus and recording test-experiment results takes only minutes. Therefore, in a class of twenty or so students, a student does not often have to wait for his turn.

# 11

# WRITING AND JUDGING
# TEST EXERCISES

Section 7.3 argued that teachers can and should write their own tests and that their tests, provided they are long enough, can be as valid as those prepared by experts. This chapter discusses rules and principles for writing better test exercises and for judging their worth. These rules and principles should enable the teacher to write shorter tests than he would otherwise have to, and to assay the value of commercially available ones. After a few general remarks that apply to all forms of tests, essay, oral, performance, and objective exercises will be taken up individually. The last section of the chapter refers to those sample exercises in Part II of this book that illustrate the various forms and characteristics of exercises discussed in this chapter.

## 11.1 GENERAL CONSIDERATIONS

The first requisite for writing a test for a course is a clear description of the subject matter and abilities that are the objectives of the course. In addition, the test-writer should not only know the relevant subject matter but have a more sophisticated understanding than his students of what is involved in solving a genuine scientific problem. He must also know the rough mean and the range of the students' knowledge, abilities, and general intelligence; he must even know their degree of preparation at least well enough to be able to judge how much novelty a particular test exercise will have for them. Finally, the exercise-writer must be familiar with the more common methods used by the students in solving various test problems. Experienced science teachers probably meet all these requirements. Section 9.3 argued that teachers can write valid tests if they use enough exercises: to make tests shorter, each exercise must be made to contribute more effectively to measuring the desired competence. The best and perhaps easiest way to make an exercise more effective is to make it measure just one rather precisely defined ability—the principal ability of the exercise. In the language of Section 8.3, the exercise should possess high relevance to one ability and low relevance to others, so that the one desired ability is much more likely to help the student do the exercise than any other ability. One-ability exercises have several advantages over those that mix abilities in indeterminate ratios. They make it possible to assign proper weights to various objectives, which increases the test's validity; to diagnose strengths and weaknesses of the students and of the course; and to shorten the test without reducing its reliability (41). The main job of this chapter is to help teachers write exercises testing for any desired ability in the list in Section 2.1 and, in particular, to show them how to judge what ability a given exercise measures so that they can criticize their own or commercially available tests.

### Sources of ideas for text exercises

Ideas for new test exercises can be obtained from content analysis, students' essays and reports, old tests, and published collections of exercises (some of these collections are listed in Section 15.1). As a teacher prepares for his class, he must decide what it is most important for his students to learn from the content to be presented. This decision will be easier and more comprehensive if the teacher is guided in his thinking by a list of objectives. Whether he is or not, it is while preparing for a lecture, discussion, or laboratory that ideas for items will most easily come to the teacher's mind and should be jotted down. Notes on test ideas are best taken down in the form of questions the students should be able to answer. The questions must of course be important, but it is not necessary at this time to decide on the form of the exercise (objective or essay) or on the ability to be tested (knowledge, understanding, or ability to learn). A more systematic but also more arduous way to attack problems of both teaching and testing is to go through a complete list of objectives and write down questions on each objective relevant to the material being studied.

Notes on the objective, knowledge, can be made conveniently by underlining various statements in the text or the laboratory manual and writing down problem numbers. Some of these statements and problems will suggest situations different from those in the text that can thus serve as bases for questions on understanding. Such situations should be briefly described in the notes. Some of them can be used as illustrative material for lectures and discussion and others saved for tests. The following year, the test situations can be used for lectures and the lecture situations for tests. Testing for the ability to learn requires new materials. Texts other than the course text and popular and semipopular articles may furnish passages suitable for testing reading ability. The passages themselves may be included in a test or, if they are long, given out a few weeks before the test. The same sources may suggest test exercises on disciplined, intuitive, or imaginative thinking. Ideas for exercises on the ability to follow prescribed rules can be obtained from materials containing assertions that students are likely to disbelieve; those on intuitive thinking, from problems that students cannot quite solve analytically; and those on imaginative thinking, from theories or experiments that are treated only sketchily in the source materials.

Students' questions and arguments in the discussion section and their written work—homework, laboratory reports, and essays—are excellent sources of test exercise ideas, for they reveal the degree of understanding the teacher may reasonably expect from his students, their more common misconceptions, and the phraseology they tend to use. Old tests are very good and widely used sources of new exercises: student essays can suggest both the correct and the wrong responses for objective items, and an objective item can be rewritten either by asking a different question about the same situation or merely by changing the responses. Some test-writers, including the author, write their exercises on understanding by modifying the situation in an old item on knowledge. For example, a standard physics problem on the Atwood machine can be modified by assuming that the machine as a whole is in motion, that the string is not weightless, or that the string is extensible. An objective item from a published collection can be made easier by making the wrong responses more obviously wrong; it can be made harder or subtler by making the wrong response more nearly right or the right response less exactly right.

After the test-writer, using the various sources described above, has made a collection of questions and topics, he should write brief correct answers and essay outlines. His next step may well be to sort this collection into groups. Into the essay group go the materials suitable for testing imaginative thinking and ability to organize and formulate one's thoughts; problems requiring intuitive thinking may be relegated to an oral test; those requiring apparatus, to a performance test; and what remains may be tentatively assigned to objective exercises.

### Ability measured by an exercise

The most important question about an exercise is what ability it measures, that is, to what ability it is most relevant. The first step in answering this question is to surmise students' mental processes as they work on the exercise. A very good method is for the test-writer to do the exercise himself. If the exercise is an essay, he should write it; if it is an objective item, he should argue to himself or still better to his colleagues that the right response is correct (or better than any of the wrong responses) and also that each of the wrong responses is incorrect. While working on the exercise and his arguments, the test-writer should keep track of his mental processes and not draw on any resources unavailable to the students. This limitation will confine him to certain methods and certain information only and permit him to discover which of the many qualifications that a rigorous solution requires are likely to occur to the students. Putting himself in the student's place should enable the test-writer to identify the principal ability measured by the exercise.

If a nearly complete solution of a problem can be obtained from one or two paragraphs of the text or if the problem is very much like those assigned as homework, the required ability is knowledge. Exercises on understanding should require no knowledge beyond that taught in the course; their main difficulty should lie in the novelty of the problem. Yet the novelty should not be so extreme as to call for highly imaginative thinking or great ingenuity; questions on understanding should be of about the same complexity and general structure as those the student has had to answer in the course. It should not be forgotten that the exercise is to test for an understanding of the *course* materials. At the same time, even the better student must be made to stop and reflect; the novel elements in a problem should not be so trivial that it can be solved by almost every student who can solve the most nearly analogous problem taught in the course. Exercises relevant to intuitive understanding, on the other hand, should be as analogous to course problems as possible, provided the students cannot solve the problems either analytically or by remembering one or two analogies. An analytical solution is precluded if the teacher allows only a short time for the exercise or, more surely, if it is beyond the students' competence.

Exercises that measure how well the student can learn—without the teacher's aid—require materials or situations that are quite new to him. (Exercises on imaginative thinking, discussed in the next paragraph, are a possible exception.) Since we are interested in the student's abilities to organize and formulate his thoughts primarily as an aid to learning, a test of these abilities will have higher relevance if it is based on new materials. The same is true of tests of the ability to conform to scientific modes of thought and, rather obviously, tests of reading ability. It is permissible, however, to base tests of the ability to learn on chapters in the course text and on other reading done outside class, provided the materials are not discussed or covered in lectures. In fact assigned readings have an advantage: they can be much longer than excerpts read under examination conditions. The students must clearly understand, however, that they are *sure* to be tested on the assigned readings, for we are interested in their ability to learn and not in their industry or docility.

A teacher should try to test his students only for the kind of imaginative thinking that is useful in learning science. The safest way to proceed is to base test exercises on the materials of the course. Questions on a theory discussed in the text may be as follows. What important facts still remain to be explained? How could the theory be modified to explain them? What new discoveries are likely to require important modifications of the theory or even its abandonment? While the ability to answer these questions is clearly useful in learning—including research, which is of course a type of learning—care should be taken that answers to them do not logically follow from the materials of the text. Otherwise, the exercise will test for understanding, not imaginative thinking. Exercises on knowledge, understanding, and ability to learn form a continuum, and the progression from the first to the last depends primarily on the degree of novelty the exercise has for the student.

As a rule, an exercise will require and therefore be relevant to several abilities; an exercise on understanding, for example, will require a knowledge of subject matter. To decide which ability is the principal one, it is necessary to estimate the degree of heterogeneity of the total group taking the test in each ability of potentially high relevance. The principal ability of the exercise is the relevant ability in which the members of the group differ most widely, for that ability will play the greatest role in determining the students' success with the exercise (32). An objective exercise seldom "requires" a given level of a specific ability: a student with little knowledge and much understanding, or vice versa, or with a modicum of each, may be able to do a given exercise. The lower the required level of an ability, the more easily it can be compensated for by another ability. If the exercise demands an ability at a much higher or much lower level than the average student has attained, the total group will be fairly homogeneous in that ability, and it is not likely to be the principal ability of the exercise. If the required level is too high, the separation of students into groups is obscured by chance factors; if the level is too low, it is obscured by chance factors and the use of other abilities. As a rule of thumb, from 15 to 85 percent of the class should have attained the level of the intended principal ability required to solve the exercise, with the mean for all the exercises at about 50 percent. Each of the intended auxiliary abilities should be possessed by at least 90 percent of the class. In items on understanding and ability to learn, the auxiliary abilities that should be watched are possession of information, knowledge of technical terms, and knowledge of mathematics. If it seems possible, for example, that as many as 20 percent of the students do not know the meaning of a necessary technical term, a definition of the term should be supplied; otherwise, the exercise may not measure understanding. The lower the level of understanding required, the more likely it is that the group will be equally heterogeneous in the principal and auxiliary abilities. It is desirable that the intended principal ability be very nearly necessary and sufficient for doing the exercise; it is essential that its possession help almost all students.

## 11.2   ESSAY EXERCISES (57)

The most difficult problem in writing essay exercises is how to make them unambiguous. The following procedure may lead to a partial solution of this problem. The exercise-writer starts with an open-ended essay exercise. He then tries to think of all the possible responses that a legitimate or semilegitimate interpretation of the task may produce; still better, he asks several instructors to write essays, perhaps only in outline, that are "off the point" yet defensible as being on the topic as stated. Next, the exercise-writer can rewrite the essay topic to rule out the irrelevant responses. Or, if this is difficult, as it usually is, he may instead structure the essay.

The procedure of structuring an essay can be illustrated by an example taken from the author's own experience. To find out whether students understood the role that the mechanical equivalent of heat played in establishing that heat is energy, they were asked an open-ended essay question: "Why was obtaining a numerical value for the mechanical equivalent of heat, MEH, considered important? Explain."

The acceptable answers to the question usually contained an explicit statement that MEH proved that heat is energy. Some explanations said that MEH gave a "conversion factor" between heat and mechanical energy; others, that it gave a "numerical relation between the calorie and the joule." Some of these responses, as was discovered by talking afterwards to the students, denoted excellent understanding of the role of MEH; others, no more than a description of the quantity, 4.2 joules/calorie. Still other explanations stated well and at length the value of quantitative expressions in physics. These explanations were irrelevant to the intended purpose of the exercise, but they were not irrelevant to the question as stated.

The following structured essay, essentially on the same topic, produced much more easily interpreted responses. "Starting with the definition of energy as the ability to do work and the premise that a hot body, such as hot steam, can, on cooling, do more work than a cold body, one may reach the conclusion that heat is a form of energy. Are any other premises necessary to make the conclusion valid? (Answer yes or no.) If your answer is yes, state the additional premises. Defend your statements."

It is true that the open-ended essay gave the students an opportunity to show that they knew not only what constituted a proof, which is the main purpose of the structured essay, but what "energy" and "work" mean and how well they could organize their thoughts. Unfortunately, the great majority of students seized these opportunities in such a random fashion as to make grading difficult. It seems more profitable to be satisfied with measuring fewer abilities more accurately.

The general procedure for structuring an essay may perhaps be this. The test-writer writes an essay, perhaps only in an outline form, on an open-ended topic. He then decides which parts of his essay are to be made known to the student and which left for the student to do. The final product, a structured essay, is in a sense a partly written, open-ended essay which the student is asked to finish. In the example above, the parts of the essay that have been written for the student are the definition of energy and the first of the following three facts: that heat is convertible into energy, that energy is convertible into heat, and that the conversion factor is the same for the two processess and is a constant. The student is expected to state the last two and to defend their relevance. With guidance on what is expected, most students will address themselves to the question and thus make it possible to grade the essay on the usual five-point scale. A grade of D may be given to those who state the second fact, C to those who state both the second and the third, and B or A to those who add good arguments. An open-ended essay, on the other hand, may identify most of the A students and some F students, but it may lump the rest together. Another convenient way to structure an essay is to give the student a completely written essay that contains errors of fact, logic, and organization and ask him to rewrite it. Here, too, the task is accurately defined and limited by what the student sees before him.

To ensure consistency, a key should be prepared for an essay exercise even if the test-writer is also the reader; a key *must* be prepared for readers other than the writer. It should specify the principal ability to be measured (such as knowledge of the main postulates of a theory, understanding of the relation among stated generalizations, or the ability to defend the value of a certain definition). It should also specify the factors that are to be considered and their relative values, or the range of values (such as that the mere recognition of a factor's relevance is worth one point and a complete argument for it, five points, or that if a given factor is not mentioned, the highest grade for the essay is C). It is even desirable to specify the most likely misinterpretations of the essay topic and assign point or letter-grade values to them. Since the number of semilegitimate interpretations is almost certain to be higher than can be foretold, a reader who runs across the same misinterpretation in several papers should add it to the key and, if he is not the only reader, inform the others. Finishing touches can best be made in the key after all the readers have read, graded, and discussed the same few papers.

It is highly recommended that the students' names not be known to the readers of the essays. Although knowing the author of the essay occasionally helps the reader interpret an ambiguous statement, in most such cases the points added or subtracted are based not on the real value of the essay but on the previous reputation of the student. It may actually be fairer—although manifestly reprehensible—to read the essays anonymously and give a few extra points to *all* students of good reputation.

**11.3**   ORAL TEST EXERCISES (56)

The use of class discussion as a form of oral test was discussed in Section 10.1. For more formal oral tests, the teacher might follow the European custom of giving the student written questions or topics and allowing him to reflect on them for a time, while other students are being quizzed. A key like the one for the readers of essays should be used by the examiner during an oral test. If the student fails to discuss a factor the key calls for, he may be quizzed about it; or if he merely mentions a factor, he may be asked to defend its relevance. The examiner should know the more common responses and be prepared to ask appropriate follow-up questions. The confessed practice of some examiners—having a single question in mind and then, after the student has made his first response, playing it by ear—will not yield good results, unless the examiner has a far better ear than most.

Students' arguments and justifications of their conclusions indicate that in most problems they use both the analytic and the intuitive approaches. They reason systematically and analytically, then skip a few analytical steps with an intuitive jump, then continue analytically, and so forth (2, Bruner). The magnitude of the jump varies from student to student. In an oral test of intuitive thinking, the examiner may first offer the student the opportunity to make an intuitive jump directly from data to a conclusion. If the student is unable to do that, the examiner should be prepared to offer judiciously chosen additional information, to narrow the gap to be jumped, so to speak. What the first bit of extra information should be, and perhaps the next one too, can and ought to be decided before the test. A few examples of oral tests of intuitive understanding are given in Part II.

**11.4**   PERFORMANCE EXERCISES (59)

Several kinds of performance test are described in Section 10.3; illustrative test exercises on laboratory objectives appear in Part II.

**11.5**   OBJECTIVE EXERCISES (58)

In preparing objective test exercises, many test-writers use intuitive thinking more often than analysis. Unfortunately, only the analytic approaches can be described. One way to prepare an objective exercise is to start with a question and write a complete answer to it with all the necessary qualifications that may occur to the better students. If it is possible to decide which qualification is most essential, it may be included in the correct or best response; the wrong responses will contain other, less essential qualifications. If several factors must be considered before the question can be answered correctly, the wrong responses may be those that occur to the students who are not aware of all the essential factors. Wrong responses may also be based on wrong formulas or on laws that do not apply directly to the problem; they should not be based on bad arithmetic. In general, deciding on the correct response is relatively easy; it is the wrong but attractive responses that are difficult to devise. As was indicated earlier, the best sources of wrong-response ideas are students' essays and homework. Last year's essay exercises can well be transformed into this year's objective exercises.

### Forms of objective exercises

Objective test exercises are usually of two general types or forms, multiple choice and master list. An item in the first consists of a stem—a question or incomplete sentence—and its own set of responses. In the master-list form, a set of responses (true or false, for instance) is common to several items. Since the relative correctness and attractiveness of the responses clearly depend on the question asked, the multiple-choice form affords better control over them and thus over the mental processes of the student. It is therefore the more flexible and useful form of objective exercises and allows a more precise definition of the objective being tested.

The advantages of the master-list form are that it is easier to prepare and requires less space, that the blind-guess score is lower if the master list is long, and that less time per item may be needed by the student. The first advantage is left to the conscience of the teacher; the second is slight because blind guessing is seldom a problem; but the third is real if the list of responses is easy to memorize or use. Short lists are easy for the student to memorize: true or false; larger, smaller, or equal; and the like. Even a long list, if it is homogeneous and comprehensive, is fairly easy to memorize. For example, many phenomena may be adequately explained on the basis of the limited number of postulates of the kinetic-molecular theory that are taught in introductory physics. The master list of responses may consist of all or practically all such postulates (strong molecular attraction, strong repulsion, molecules far apart, and high molecular speed) and their opposites. An item may then consist of the description of a phenomenon, such as a deviation from Boyle's law, for which the student is to pick the proper explanation. A long master list of responses may be used more easily if it is organized in some way. In a test on mechanics, for instance, all the laws that are taught may be listed alphabetically; the student is asked to pick the law that applies most directly to a particular phenomenon. The disadvantages of the master-list form are that the *kind* of question one can ask and therefore the kind of ability one can test within the form are quite limited and that even in very large lists there are usually few entries that are attractive to the student as responses to a particular item. The latter circumstance means that the student wastes his time reading rather obviously irrelevant responses and it effectively reduces the item to a multiple-choice question with few responses. The most popular master-list form, true or false, can test the student's competence only narrowly, because few important kinds of assertion in science can be accurately stated in a few lines: the assertions about real objects or phenomena, for instance, can seldom be precisely true. A slight refinement of the true-or-false items is to add a third response: "True if certain conditions are met, otherwise false."

Within the two main forms there is a great variety of possible exercises. The variation may be trivial or it may be important enough to affect the objective tested. For example, the stem of an item may be a question or an uncompleted sentence. The latter is easier to write briefly but the former is more directive: it gives the student a better idea of what responses to expect and a better opportunity to formulate his own tentative response. Another type of item asks a negative question: "Which of the following is *not* right?" Such items should be avoided as much as possible, for they make a tremendous demand on students' energy, time, and patience. An item may also have more than one right response. If the right responses exhibit enough coherence to constitute a single complex judgment, the ability to choose just one of the right responses may lack value, and the student should receive credit only if he marks all the right responses and no others. If, however, each right response can be chosen on its own merits, without regard to the other responses, the item is really a collection of true-or-false items and should be cast into that form to make things easier for the student and the scorer and to make the test more reliable. Similar considerations apply when the student cannot choose the right response to an item unless he knows the right response to the preceding item. A last example of a relatively unimportant variation is the use of separate answer sheets instead of the test booklet for the student's answers. Separate answer sheets are convenient for the scorer and the proctor (cheating is harder), but a nuisance for the student.

Of the more important variations, those likely to influence the objective being measured, two—matching and analogy—have been borrowed by scientists from tests in less well-articulated disciplines. Matching uses a master-list form in which the student is to establish one-to-one correspondence between the questions and responses. Matching exercises can often be worked rather like crossword puzzles. The student oscillates between two questions: "Which of these is the best response to a given question?" and "To which of the questions is this one the best response?" The ability to answer the second question has little, if any, relation to the understanding of science. Usually, nouns or other simple entities are matched with, say, physical quantities and their units. Even in such cases, the test is likely to be more reliable if the student is allowed to use a response more than once and some responses not at all.

An example of a physics analogy item is "An atom is to a molecule as

. . . ." The student is to choose a response that will complete the sentence. The right response may be "an electron is to an atom." However, the relation between an atom and a molecule is neither subtle nor vague enough to be described only by analogy. There are a few useful analogies, between water flow and electric currents and water waves and light waves, for instance, that can be used to test qualitative understanding of some concepts, but, in general, analogy items should be left to disciplines less precise than science.

It is useful to vary the degree and kind of correctness and wrongness of the responses to objective items. The "right" response may be a strictly correct answer to the question or it may merely be the best of those given. (In the former case, one can make sure the student knows that the response he chooses is really correct by adding as the last response, "None of the above responses is right.") The relative merits of the two kinds of right response are discussed under The best and the correct response later in this section. The degree and kind of wrongness of the wrong responses can also be varied. If the degree of wrongness varies, the reliability of the test may sometimes be improved if different weights are given to wrong responses. Thus the right response may be given five points, the least wrong, three points, and so on. It is more practical, and perhaps theoretically sounder, however, to divide the responses into only three categories, right, wrong, and very wrong or failing, and to assign them weights of $+1$, $0$, and $-1$. The *kind* of wrongness in wrong responses can be used to measure the student's disciplined thinking or habits of thought. For example, some wrong responses may be written to appeal to a student inclined to make rash judgments and others, to an overcautious student. These points come up again under Wrong responses later in this section and in connection with various sample items in Part II.

### Homogeneity of responses

Although students attack objective exercises in many ways, almost all of them involve the rejection of wrong responses. If, therefore, an exercise is to measure a specific ability, this ability must be the key not only to recognizing the right response but also to rejecting the wrong ones. This requires a certain homogeneity among the responses. Thus, if the exercise is to measure the ability to estimate the cogency of facts as evidence for a theory, the responses should all be factually correct; they should differ only in their value as evidence. If, on the contrary, the wrong responses contain false data that, if true, would have been good evidence, the exercise may contribute to measuring straight knowledge, but its validity and reliability in measuring the principal ability are reduced.

The "ability-homogeneity" of responses has other values transcending that of ensuring the purity of the ability measured. The main advantage of objective test exercises is that the problem can be defined for the student with a precision essay exercises cannot reach. The definition should start with the stem, the part that precedes the responses; the stem should be so suggestive or *directive* that it guides the student's thinking into proper channels and even enables him to anticipate the nature of the responses. Stems such as "Which of the following is true?" may produce tension and start some speculations in the student's mind—perhaps in connection with the preceding item—that are merely distracting. The very first response must further define the problem: after reading it, the better students should be able to formulate a response that resembles closely in form and substance the right response—which the first one may of course be. And when the student who has the relevant ability comes upon the right response (when there is only one), he should recognize it as correct and give only casual attention to the following responses. Thus the stem may well include hints as to the nature of the responses, such as: "All the following responses are factually correct. Choose the one that contains the best [or most convincing or best-established or most precise] evidence for the theory." Another example is: "None of the responses below is strictly correct [or quantitatively accurate or general enough or specific enough]. Choose the one that deviates least from correctness." If one of the parenthetical phrases is used, the stem is even more directive. Not just the stem, but every part of the exercise must contribute to the student's understanding of what the problem is and what kind of answer (its form, content, precision, and so on) is expected of him. The argument in this paragraph should make clear why the term "distracter" has been avoided here: it describes with damning aptness the wrong responses in many objective tests.

Homogeneity of responses also saves the student time and needless trouble. The time allowed for objective items is usually indecently short. Yet it is patently impossible to test the student's thinking ability without allowing him to think. If the student is to evaluate the cogency of evidence, he should be allowed to evaluate it, not be sidetracked into estimating the reliability of data or other matters. Nor should he have to be on the lookout for verbal traps. The "only's" and "never's" so frequently used to differentiate between right and wrong responses should be prominently displayed. If underlining such words ruins the exercise, chances are that it was not very good to begin with.

If all the responses are focused on the ability measured, this homogeneity helps define the problem, concentrate the student's attention on it, and reduce tension. If the *forms* of the right and the wrong responses—their length, qualifying words and phrases, technical level, and so on—are similar, this will help prevent successful guessing based on the auxiliary ability of test-sophistication (50). Ideally, responses should differ in only one respect —such as their cogency as evidence for a theory.

Inhomogeneities in the forms of responses are likely to lower the reliability of tests because they frequently enable students who lack the principal ability to identify the right response or to eliminate some of the wrong responses. Some clues that are known to many students are as follows. The right response is cautiously worded and qualified by such phrases as "usually," "approximately," "provided that," and "the available evidence." Or it might be the longest, most technical, or only response that repeats an important term from the stem. The right response is sometimes one of two "paired" responses, that is, responses that are more similar than any other two responses. (This may occur because the test-writer, in order to increase the discrimination between the A and B students, has made one response right and another nearly right.) The wrong responses, on the other hand, are made absolute by such phrases as "only," "always," "never," "precisely," "proves," and "without exception." In numerical responses, especially if given in round numbers, the largest and the smallest numbers are too often found in wrong responses.

### The best and the correct response

In science as in other disciplines, it is seldom possible to give a strictly correct answer to any but the most trivial or abstract question in a few lines. In order to decide how correct the best response should be, it must again be recalled that the main function of an objective item is to divide the students into two groups that differ on the *average* in a particular ability. The response marked right should appeal to those who have this ability. It is therefore at best nearly useless to increase the accuracy of the best response by adding qualifications that would not have been missed, except perhaps by a handful of students. For an obvious example, the relativistic and quantum-mechanical corrections or qualifications are usually out of place in a test in an introductory physics course. It is of course true that the absence of certain qualifications may disturb an exceptionally well-informed student. Disturbing him, however, is better than lowering the discriminating power of the exercise for the rest of the class. As qualifying phrases are added, two difficulties arise. First, many students become puzzled by the presence of the over-refined qualifications and bothered by their absence in succeeding items. Second, making the *formal* attractiveness of wrong and right responses approximately equal becomes more difficult: the poorer students soon learn that their best bet is to choose a response rich in qualifications. The optimum correctness of the best response must of course vary with the average caliber of the students: at the first-grade level, "Iron is heavier than water" is a better "best response" than "The density of iron is higher than that of water." We are thus reminded once more that the really effective test is tailor-made to fit a particular population.

In some exercises it is preferable not to have the best response correct even in the modest sense described above. (But the students should usually be warned if no response is correct.) If the right response is merely the best one of those included in the item, it may force the student to do more profound thinking. For example, the best response in the following exercise is A.

> Which of the following is the best definition of *potential energy?* (None of the definitions is strictly correct.)
> A. The energy that a body has because of its position.
> B. The energy that a body at rest possesses because of its position.
> C. The maximum energy that a body can acquire.
> D. The energy that a body possesses before it starts doing work.
> E. The energy that enables a body to do work.

If the right response were made more correct by including elastic potential energy, its form might easily become so like that in textbooks that the exercise could be worked by rote memory. As it stands, the exercise is likely to discriminate between those who understand the term *potential energy* and those who do not. It may be remarked in passing that the responses lack formal homogeneity because two of them, A and B, are "paired" by the phrase "because of its position."

Teachers are almost invariably unhappy about incorrect best responses even if they are shown good statistical evidence that the results of the exercise correlate highly with their own choices of good students. One argument against such responses is that since we have no accurate knowledge of the mental processes involved in a real-life or criterion situation, or even of those used in the test situation, we should hold firmly to the few similarities between the two situations that are under our control. Thus in almost any criterion situation it is a statement of the correct definition or law that is useful, and similarly correct statements should be used in test situations. There is a good deal of truth in this analysis, although it should be noted that choosing the best approximation concerns the scientist and the citizen more often than choosing between the correct and the wrong.

A less effective argument, shakily based on the incontestable truth that tests are valuable tools of instruction, maintains that tests should teach nothing but the truth. What the student should learn from a test, however, is not an isolated fact or generalization (and they would surely be isolated, for the test is only a few pages and a few hours long), but the objectives of the course. Another questionable argument runs as follows: "I told my students that 'the energy that a body possesses because of its position or configuration' is the only correct definition of potential energy. It is not fair to ask them to accept any other." A reply to this teacher would be that the only physics test that is truly fair to the students is one that reliably identifies students who understand physics. The question is rather whether the exercise is fair or kind to the teacher: he did not prepare his students to recognize degrees of wrongness, and he is forced to grant the justice of their complaints. Whatever the worth of the arguments for or against exercises with incorrect best responses, it should be clear that writing such exercises does require a steady hand.

## The wrong responses

The prevalent criterion for a wrong response seems to be that it should be wrong and yet plausible. As was indicated before, this requirement, although necessary, is not enough: if the student is asked to choose among conclusions from some data, the wrong responses should be wrong only in relation to the data. Of course, even if the wrong responses are homogeneous in this respect, degrees and kinds of wrongness are still possible. The *degree* of wrongness determines the difficulty of the item and sets the main discrimination line. If the degree is small and the wrong responses are nearly right, the item is difficult and will discriminate best between the A and B students. If the responses are crudely wrong, all but the F students may identify the right response by elimination or otherwise.

Although it is difficult and unnecessary to make a single exercise discriminate at several levels of ability, it is quite easy and useful to make it discriminate at two levels by having one (or more) of the wrong responses so wrong that only failing students will be attracted by it. Let us call this response an F response, and the right response, R response. Let the number of F responses a student chooses be called his F score, and similarly for R. The R-minus-F scores are almost always more reliable than the R scores; F scores, in turn, may discriminate more reliably between F students and passing students than *any* other scores. It should be noted that for students who try every exercise the reliability of the usual right-minus-wrong scores is identical with that of the R score. F scores are also useful for establishing absolute standards for passing performance, as is shown in Section 12.6.

The *kind* of wrongness in responses determines the auxiliary abilities that will help the student find the right response. If the wrongness is that of going beyond data, the rash or bold students will be more attracted to the wrong responses and get lower average scores than students who are overcautious. There are many other "polar" intellectual predilections or biases that make wrong responses, and sometimes the right response, unequally attractive to students who possess the principal ability in an equal degree. Two biases are "polar" if they are opposites that seldom occur in the same student. A play on various students' weaknesses and intellectual predilections to make wrong responses attractive to them is often justified and, in fact, can seldom be avoided. It is necessary, however, that the prevalent biases be sampled fairly. Such sampling is controlled primarily by the nature of the wrong responses and to a smaller degree, of the right response (if it deviates, as it usually must, from the strictly correct one).

Students' intellectual predilections may play an important role in their learning and perhaps even in their success in a field. It is therefore worth-while to detect biases by specially prepared exercises. For economy, these exercises may play a double role: the choice of the right response by a student may indicate the possession of an ability such as knowledge or understanding; the choice of a wrong response, on the other hand, may indicate a bias. It is good, though not always possible, to balance the wrong responses to a given item between a pair of polar biases: for instance, two responses may be designed to appeal to a student who is inclined to consider theoretical models true to reality, and two other wrong responses, to appeal to a student who distrusts theory. The two pairs of wrong responses should also be comparable in their degree of wrongness. The class as a whole may be taken as the norm; a biased student is then one who strongly and consistently deviates from the norm. Measures of intellectual predilections, however, should be used for counseling only; this use is discussed in Section 13.1.

Most science teachers tend to have their own strong biases. They are often inclined to be cautious rather than bold, to accept authority rather than challenge it, to revere facts and undervalue speculation. Since these biases may be more than intellectual predilections—they may add up to timidity—teachers need to make a special effort in their teaching and testing to be fair to the bold, adventurous, even fanciful student.

### Spontaneity

If the strongest argument for objective tests is that they can make clear to the student what is expected of him, the strongest argument for the essay test is that it calls for a spontaneously produced response. Since all criterion situations call for greater spontaneity than is required in the usual objective test, the objective test, if not supplemented by an essay test, must be modified to decrease this discrepancy in some of the exercises. For instance, objective exercises might be included in which the student reads the statement of the problem, decides on the right answer, and then searches for it among the prepared responses. Such a procedure can never be enforced but it can be made more profitable than any other, if the stem is very directive and the responses nonevocative and nonsuggestive. To illustrate: the student is asked to solve two simultaneous equations, $3x + 2y = 17$ and $x - y = 9$. If the responses were pairs of values of $x$ and $y$, some students would find it easier not to solve the equations but rather to substitute the pairs of values into the equations. If, on the other hand, the correct response is given nonevocatively as $x + y = 5$, and the wrong ones similarly, a solution of two simultaneous equations is the only way to the right answer, and solving the two given in the stem is by far the quickest way.

Numerical problems lend themselves well to nonevocative responses; numerical responses may be given in round figures or as ranges, 0 to 10,

11 to 20, and so forth. To make mathematical responses almost entirely nonevocative, each response may list just the second digit of a numerical answer, or the student may be asked to compute two quantities or two formulas and to choose among responses that are ratios of the two. In qualitative exercises, the analysis of each response, without first solving the problem of the exercise, may be made more of a chore than solving the problem. The following exercise, in which, to save space, only two responses are shown, may serve as an illustration.

> This exercise involves two steps. First, decide what law or generalization, in addition to laws of elasticity, is most directly useful in explaining the following fact. A brick can be pulled along a fairly smooth surface by means of a string; the string would break, however, if jerked sharply. Second, choose the one of the following phenomena for which this law also provides an explanation.
> A. A glass tube dropped from a height of ten feet breaks if it falls on a concrete sidewalk but will not break if it falls on soft ground.
> B. It is impossible to lift oneself by taking hold of one's own hair and giving it an upward jerk.

Most students will probably find that the most efficient way to deal with this exercise is to follow the directions, which suggest giving a spontaneous answer to the first question. (Directions to the students must of course always be scrupulously honest in indicating the easiest path to the right response.) The reader will note that the second part of the stem in the above exercise is not at all directive. This is the price we must pay for introducing spontaneity into objective exercises. A more elaborate method of combining the more advantageous aspects of the essay and objective exercises is outlined in Section 10.2.

## 11.6    SUMMARY OF THE CRITERIA FOR TEST EXERCISES, ESPECIALLY FOR OBJECTIVE ITEMS

An effective test must be tailor-made for a particular population. The mean and the range of the students' abilities should determine the optimum correctness of the best response, the optimum degree and kind of wrongness of the wrong responses, and the maximum allowable level of auxiliary abilities required for working the exercise. The level should be below that of the great majority of the students. The difficulty of the exercises should cluster around 50 percent and range from about 15 percent to about 85 percent.

The definition of the ability that is to be measured by an exercise should hold true for all the prevalent methods of solution used by students, including the method of eliminating wrong responses. The principal ability of the exercise should be as necessary and sufficient as possible for working the exercise. The various student biases that make certain kinds of wrong responses attractive to them should be sampled fairly by the test as a whole. Test exercises measuring a particular ability should exhibit as great variety as is consonant with the broadest definition of the ability. They can vary in content, form, type of analysis required, difficulty, and auxiliary abilities.

The situation on which an exercise is based should not be overly similar to the textbook situations even in tests of knowledge.

The stem of an exercise should contain a clear statement of the problem and even suggest the desired kind of solution. Responses should be homogeneous in the principal ability they require and in their form. It is possible to make an objective exercise evoke nearly spontaneous answers by making this process the easiest or fastest way to deal with the exercise.

### 11.7   REFERENCES TO ILLUSTRATIVE TEST EXERCISES

In the Introduction to Part II, test exercises that exemplify and illustrate various technical points discussed in this chapter are listed in the Index to Comments on Exercises.

# 12

## USES OF TESTS:
## ASSIGNING COURSE GRADES

Chapters 12 and 13 discuss the criteria a collection of test exercises must meet if it is to be used for assigning grades, admission, counseling, or as a tool for course improvement. The problem of designing a test is treated in these late chapters because they refer to types of items and forms of tests explained earlier. The two chapters also discuss interpretations of test results. This chapter deals with tests used for assigning grades.

### 12.1 COURSE CONTENT AND OBJECTIVES

Laying down general specifications for a test should ordinarily precede writing individual test questions. We shall assume that we have before us a collection of test exercises most of which have been clearly classified as to content and objectives. We shall also assume that, in accord with common practice, the main function of a certification or achievement test is to tell us how well the student understands science and thus what grade he deserves. The other functions of tests, to help the student profit directly from the experience of taking the test and to supply the teacher with more detailed information than is contained in the total score, are subsidiary. Consequently, the main criterion for the test will be that it adequately represent the competence of understanding science: it must properly weight and measure all the essential constituents of the course objectives.

#### Representation of desired competence

In designing a course test, it should be remembered that it will be only one of a battery of tests. During the quarter or semester information can be gathered on the student's competence from many sources (see Section 12.2): homework, laboratory, periodic examinations or quizzes, discussion, and the quarterly or final examination. Moreover, in a year's course, these will occur every quarter. Since every opportunity for estimating the student's competence may be viewed as a test, the available battery of tests given during a year's course is very large and can quite accurately represent the desired complex competence. Although the three quarterly grades are sometimes interpreted separately, more often they are reported as a pattern, without specifying the subject matter for which the individual grades stand. Even if it is known that the first grade is for mechanics, a student with grades C, C, and C is invariably assumed to have less competence in mechanics than one with grades C, A, and A. The universally accepted interdependence of quarterly grades allows us to parcel out some of our objectives among the three quarters. These objectives must, of course, be rather independent of content; in the list in Section 2.1, such objectives are the ability to learn and, to a lesser extent, an understanding of the nature and structure of a science.

As was pointed out in Sections 7.3, 8.4, and 9.1, the basic rule for making a valid test battery is to include in it measures of abilities that are important and of low intercorrelation. Science tests must therefore include exercises on knowledge, understanding, and ability to learn; exercises on laboratory objectives; and quantitative and qualitative exercises. Since the battery of tests is extensive, it should also include exercises on objectives 1.1, 1.2; 2.1, 2.2, 2.3; and 3.1, 3.2, 3.3; and the corresponding laboratory objectives, from Section 2.1. Systematic sampling or representation is better than random sampling; therefore, whenever the subject matter permits it, even finer subdivisions (see Section 2.1 for examples) should guide the test-writer.

The criteria for the content represented are the same as those for behavioral objectives—importance and low intercorrelation. For instance, the test battery must include exercises on science as a body of knowledge and on science as a process of inquiry. The paucity of data on the intercorrelations of tests covering different areas and topics makes further advice difficult, but perhaps the following types of content, provided of course that they are considered important, should be represented: highly mathematical and qualitative material; theories, experiments, empirical generalizations, and definitions; and technical, historical, and philosophical treatments.

The importance of variety in representing the general competence of understanding science can hardly be overemphasized: by varying test exercises in type of problem, content area, difficulty, and form, we may hope to force the student to use a variety of mental processes. Problems that require intuitive thinking should also be included in the total test battery, since intuitive thinking plays a part in the general competence. Care should be taken, however, that it is merely auxiliary and not the principal ability of an exercise, for we do not yet know enough about teaching and testing intuitive thinking to base course grades on it. Problems that require imaginative thinking should be treated similarly.

### Grades and the students' interest, effort, and progress

The prognostic meaning of a grade is ambiguous if it reflects not only the student's achievement but the effort the achievement cost him or the interest that motivated him. In the first place, the grade does not tell us what fraction of it was assigned for effort or interest, and in the second place, if two students have acquired equal competence, one through hard work and the other through intelligence, it is not easy to tell whose future is brighter. On the other hand, the prognosis is good for a student who entered a course poorly prepared and has caught up with the class, so a course grade may be modified on the basis of a student's progress. Unfortunately, progress is much more difficult to measure accurately than achievement. As a general rule, then, course grades should be based on the degree to which the major objectives of the course have been attained, provided of course that these objectives have been chosen for their prognostic value. This method will reward the student's rate of progress indirectly if the ability to learn is included among the objectives. A good way to take progress into account is to weight the very first examination less than the later ones. Such weighting is further justified because the results of the first test may depend strongly on the students' ability to adjust to a new course.

### Weighting of objectives

The primary criteria in weighting a topic or an objective in a test are how basic a part of science it is and, especially, how useful its mastery can be to the student. The time devoted to a topic in the course is not such a good criterion, for the time may depend more on the difficulty of the topic than on its importance. For pedagogical purposes, however, it may be wise to reflect the time spent on a topic in the composition of homework and weekly quizzes.

There are two common methods for increasing the weight of an important objective (or content) in a test: to increase the number of items testing for the objective or to increase the weight or number of points assigned to each item. Generally, the latter method should be used only to introduce a correction factor after the test has been designed and given (see Section 12.4). In designing a test, an important objective should, for reliability, be represented by many items rather than by a few heavily weighted ones.

*Weights given to various objectives by physics teachers*     In 1957–58, the American Association of Physics Teachers' Committee on Testing sent a questionnaire to 150 college teachers of introductory, non-calculus physics courses. The main question was: If a nationally standardized test were available, what objectives should it measure? Descriptions of objectives were illustrated by test exercises. Sixty teachers were good enough to spend the many hours necessary for a full reply. Although the classification of objectives in the questionnaire differs from the classification used in this book, the illustrations have made a fair translation possible. The results are presented in Tables 12.1 and 12.2. It should be noted that if, in the questionnaire, disciplined thinking had been included under ability to learn, as it is in the classification in Section 2.1, the ability to learn would probably have had a higher rating than that given the ability to read scientific literature in Table 12.1.

**Table 12.1    How sixty college physics teachers rate the importance of objectives to be measured by tests in their courses**

(The values are estimates: the terminology of the questionnaire differed from the terminology used in this table.)

|  | Essential | Quite Important | Of Some Importance | Unimportant |
|---|---|---|---|---|
| 1.  Knowledge | 81% | 13% | 6% | |
| 2.  Analytical understanding and disciplined thinking | 60% | 34% | 6% | |
| 3.  Ability to read scientific literature | 13% | 52% | 33% | 2% |

**Table 12.2    Average weights sixty college physics teachers would assign to subobjectives in a test measuring a given objective**

(The values are estimates: the terminology of the questionnaire differed from the terminology used in this table.)

|  |  | |
|---|---|---|
| | 1. Knowledge | |
| 1.1 | Information | 50 |
| 1.2 | Knowledge of relations | 50 |
| | | 100% |
| | 2. Analytical understanding of | |
| 2.1 | topics and principles | 40 |
| 2.2 | interrelations of principles | 30 |
| 2.3 | nature and structure of physics | 30 |
| | | 100% |
| | 3. Ability to learn | |
| 3.1 | Verbal symbolism | 40 |
| 3.2 | Nonverbal symbolism | 40 |
| 3.3 | Disciplined thinking | 20 |
| | | 100% |

## 12.2   COURSE TESTS

### Short quizzes, homework, and discussion

Homework and short quizzes given during the quarter usually, and quite properly, test for fairly detailed and topical knowledge in order to draw the student's attention to the necessity of studying each lesson in detail— learning facts, definitions, and generalizations, and solving routine problems. These tests (homework is included) probably represent and sample well the objective of knowledge. Indirectly they also test for reading ability, insofar as the students learn directly from a text. Weekly quizzes and homework should contain essays so that they will test the abilities to write clearly and concisely and to attack a complex problem, and other abilities that require spontaneous expression. The essays and occasional "thought" questions can measure some aspects of analytical understanding and perhaps disciplined thinking. Even a partial inclusion of these objectives in tests mainly devoted to knowledge is highly desirable because it gives the student a more comprehensive view of the aims of the course and a preview of the midquarterly and quarterly. Some weekly quizzes should be open-book, to remove from the teacher's path the temptation to test for memory of detail; the open-book test will measure instead the student's acquaintance with the text and his ability to use it efficiently as a reference. Open-book tests must, of course, allow time for the use of the books.

Section 10.1 suggested that students' arguments heard in the recitation section, laboratory, or outside of class can be used to evaluate their intuitive and imaginative thinking and their understanding of those subtler and quasi-philosophical points that do not find their way into more formal tests. Intuitive and imaginative thinking are hard to evaluate accurately, but oral tests can throw enough light on superior understanding to justify using their results to change students' grades. It is only fair, of course, that all the students be given a chance to speak; but for pedagogical reasons, discussed in Section 10.1, only good verbal performance should influence grades.

### Laboratory

The laboratory grade is usually assigned on the basis of the student's attainment of various laboratory objectives. A wider use of examinations involving apparatus would not only provide additional information about the students but might help advance a valuable testing technique. However, since such tests are expensive to administer, the teacher should ordinarily use a performance test that requires neither extra labor nor special equipment (see Section 10.3).

The laboratory report is correctly regarded by most students as a dull and unprofitable chore, and many of them do not hesitate to borrow from reports of the past twenty years the standardized paragraphs on the purpose, procedure, and conclusions of the experiment. The teacher knows this and regards report-*reading* as a chore. It would help if the student handed in reports on no more than one or two experiments during a quarter, but reports that are well thought out and carefully organized. The teacher can then afford to read the reports carefully enough to recognize the authorship and to evaluate the student's ability to organize and formulate his ideas. The knowledge and understanding the student acquires from other experiments can be surmised from very brief reports of their results and further tested by occasional written examinations.

The most important single basis of the laboratory grade should be the student's ability to design, perform, and interpret an experiment. As was shown in Section 10.3, testing for this ability can be easily and painlessly done by including in the quarter's work at least one experiment of the experiment-predict-verify type described in Section 6.4.

## Quarterly or semester examinations

When the suggestions on homework, weekly quizzes, and the laboratory given here are followed, the quarterly examinations will best round out the teacher's knowledge of the student if they are primarily devoted to testing analytical understanding; they should test the ability to learn by comparatively few exercises, and knowledge only indirectly, to the extent that it enters into testing for the other two main objectives. Because testing time is limited, the teacher should remember that, in a year's course, there are two other quarterlies. Exercises testing reading ability can be made fairly independent of content by supplying some of the required information, and they can therefore be parceled out among the three quarterlies: one quarterly may contain exercises on a passage of prose only, another on a passage illustrated with graphs, and the third on a passage containing tables. Because the quarterly has to test for a large number of topics, it should probably contain only objective exercises.

Starting with the weighting implied in Tables 12.1 and 12.2 and assuming that, during the quarter, knowledge has been tested extensively and the ability to learn to some extent, we arrive at the composition of a quarterly examination shown in Table 12.3. Objective 1.2 should be tested by those problems in the course text that have not been assigned or discussed and that differ sufficiently from assigned problems to require some understand-

Table 12.3  Suggested item distribution for a three-hour quarterly examination, one hour given in midquarter and two hours at the end. The objectives are numbered as in Section 2.1. Thus 1.1 stands for information, and so forth.

| Objective | 1.1 | 1.2 | 2.1 | 2.2 | 2.3 | 3.1 or 3.2 | 3.3 |
|---|---|---|---|---|---|---|---|
| Number of items (Total   100) | 0 | 10 | 30 | 20 | 20 | 15 | 5 |

ing. Conservatively, such problems are classified under knowledge. A time allowance—which, for a quarterly, might be three hours—may be considered sufficient if 90 percent or more of the students finish the test, that is, mark most of the items and especially the last five or ten items. The whole examination can be given at the end of the quarter, or a part of it can be given as a midquarterly.

### Tests prepared by outsiders

Although the main function of a course grade is prognosis, the prognosis will usually be made not by the teacher of the course but by teachers of succeeding courses or by teachers and administrators at other institutions. It is therefore essential that the meaning the teacher attaches to understanding science and to its constituents not differ widely from the generally accepted meaning. One of the best ways to correct one's idiosyncratic interpretations of various abilities is to have the grades assigned at least partially by some examiner who is not teaching the course (48). The teacher must of course inform the examiner, preferably before the course starts, what the content and objectives of the course are; he may also check the examiner's tests and veto the exercises requiring *information* not taught in the course; in other respects, however, he should change the tests as little as possible. The discipline suggested here is stringent: the teacher must learn to describe his objectives unambiguously and to abide by them in his teaching. But the rewards are commensurate. The main reward is that the students will view the teacher as a friend and helper, an ally against the common enemy, the examiner; in short, they will see him as a teacher. Apple-polishing will be abandoned and questions will be asked not to impress but to learn. Other advantages of tests prepared by outsiders are that they save the teacher's time and, if they supplement rather than entirely replace the teacher's own tests, contribute to variety.

Chapter 1 and Section 9.3 spoke warmly of teaching improvements that are likely to result from the teacher's involvement in testing. If the tests for a course are prepared by an examiner, the teacher's involvement in testing will be quite adequate if he states clearly the objectives of his course, illustrates them with exercises, works with the examiner in preparing a few items, and inspects critically the test results, paying special attention to item analysis. If, however, the teacher uses commercially available tests, he should supplement them with his own. Commercial tests provide variety, save time, and allow the teacher to check the students' achievements against those at comparable institutions. Before using such tests, the teacher must learn their objectives and content, perhaps by following the suggestions in Sections 11.1 and 11.5. From this point on, he can treat the tests as a part of his own battery of tests. This point is further discussed in Section 12.5.

## 12.3    TEST DIRECTIONS

A judicious arrangement of exercises and good directions to the student can increase a test's validity and relieve the student's tension. It is probably best to start with fairly easy exercises. If the test is short enough to prevent fatigue, the most difficult exercises should be put at the end so that the poorer student will have time to try all the questions within his capability; however, a long test—over two hours—should end with exercises of less than maximum difficulty (52). Within the test, items should be grouped to minimize mental jumps by the student. Items can be grouped according to their subject matter. Or they can be grouped according to their form: one or more than one correct answer; essay or objective; completion type, multiple choice, or master list. Objective items with more than one correct response should be grouped together, preferably as the last group of objective items. A point that is often overlooked is the desirability of a random distribution of right responses in objective items. It is very distracting for the student to see that he has marked, say, response A for every one of the first five or six items. Some students may then want to go back and check their answers; others will be on the lookout for similar "clues."

The most important rule for test directions is that they must be scrupulously honest: they should help the student get a higher score. The student should be told how the test will be scored and where he will find the easier exercises and the exercises with a particular content: subject-matter groups should have appropriate titles, such as Mechanics or Calorimetry. The only *form* that requires explicit identification is the objective item with more than one correct response. Ease of scoring is subordinate to ease and comfort for the test-taker. Separate answer sheets, machine-scored or not, are convenient and make proctoring easier (it is harder to see the neighbor's answers). They do, however, introduce a mental obstacle, and the student should be trained in their use before the examination. Even if answer sheets are used, the students should be allowed to mark up the test booklet.

### Directions for essays

If the student is admonished to be brief and neat and to formulate his thoughts clearly, he should be rewarded for neatness, brevity, and clarity and informed of the point value of each. Since directions of this sort are likely to be lengthy and essentially the same for several examinations, they may well be distributed in advance. Example: "Your definition, statements of laws, and other one- or two-sentence essays will be graded on their essential correctness (75 percent), clarity of formulation and grammar (10 percent), brevity (10 percent), and spelling and neatness of writing (5 percent). Your longer essays will be graded on their comprehensiveness—inclusion of relevant material (65 percent), cogency—exclusion of irrelevant material (10 percent), organization (15 percent), and brevity (10 percent).

The relevant material itself will be graded on essential correctness (50 percent), clarity of formulation and grammar (10 percent), and spelling and neatness (5 percent)." The directions should be discussed with the students and included in the key used by essay readers. On the test booklet, the student should be told, for each essay, the maximum number of points, approximate time allowance, and perhaps even reasonable length.

### Directions for objective tests

Directions for objective tests should contain complete information on scoring and advice on how to get the highest possible score. Example: "The average time allowance per item is two minutes; a reasonable range is between one and three minutes. Mark the response that you think is the best one even though you are not sure—there will be no penalties for guessing. Don't *skip* any item: mark it even if you have to guess. Just don't spend too much time on the doubtful items; come back to them later if you have the time. If, however, toward the end of the examination period you see that you cannot finish the test, don't hurry, for the last items are usually the hardest. The guess-score will be calculated for the remaining unmarked items and added to your score. (The guess-score is the score you would be most likely to get if you marked the items at random.)"

The scoring described in the above directions is probably the best one for objective items that have one best response (44, Gulliksen). If guessing is to be penalized, the penalties must be accurately described; a scoring formula is sufficient if it has been previously discussed. A direction to "avoid guessing," even for exercises on knowledge, seems ambiguous to many students, because there usually are few answers of which the average student is absolutely sure.

### Directions for exercises on novel material

Advice to avoid guessing is particularly out of place for exercises containing novel material. On the contrary, the student should be encouraged to make intelligent surmises and reassured that only a moderate background of information is expected of him. It is not advisable to use test directions for reminding the student that many exercises, especially those on understanding and ability to learn, contain elements of ambiguity and are thus open to more than one interpretation. A better place and time for discussing that point is in class a few days before the test and also after the corrected papers have been returned to the students.

If test exercises are based on a passage which the student is to read during the test, he should be told how to read the passage. Example: "The passage below deals with a theory of ionization. You have studied ionization in the chapter on batteries and cells, but some of the facts and generalizations in the passage will be new to you. The questions that follow the passage test your understanding of the new material—the arguments used by the author, the assumptions he makes, and his conclusions. Read the passage twice; first fairly rapidly, to get its general structure, and then more carefully, marking the more important and the more unfamiliar parts."

## 12.4   SCORING A TEST

In scoring a test the teacher must decide on the scales to be used for individual items, the corrections for guessing, and the weights to be assigned to various exercises.

### Scales for items

An item in an objective test has a clear-cut meaning. An item of an essay, on the other hand, may be a *part* of the essay—argument, conclusion, statement of a law; or it may be an *aspect*—organization, clarity, grammar. It is usually easy to identify the smallest independently scorable parts or items of an essay; it is harder, but still possible and desirable, to treat aspects as separate items. The following items of organization, for instance, may be scored separately: choice of the organizing principle, consistency, that is, keeping to the same organizing principle, organization of paragraphs, and organization within a paragraph. The rationale of itemizing an exercise is to allow the reader to grade the student on each item; its immediate goal is to reduce the scoring problem to simple scales. The simplest scale has only two points, right or wrong, good or bad; the next simplest scale is good, bad, and intermediate; and a very common scale has five points, A, B, C, D, and F. In general, simpler scales are preferable for the sake of ease and consistency (45). They require, however, that the exercise be itemized; it would be silly to mark a long essay simply as good or bad. If the essay is a numerical problem, features that can be scored on a two-point scale are: statements or names of the laws, equations, the order of magnitude, accuracy and precision of the answer, and units.

In scoring an objective item, each independent decision the student has made and recorded should also be scored separately. In a multiple-choice item with a single right answer, the correct decision is to mark the right response. If there are several correct responses, and their choice by a student indicates a single coherent judgment, the one correct decision a student can make is to mark all the correct responses and no others. If, however, as is frequently the case, each right response is independently correct and each wrong response is absolutely incorrect, the item is really a collection of true-or-false items and should be scored as such: each marked right response and each unmarked wrong response represents a correct decision. These items or decisions can be scored on a two-point scale: each correct decision may be given one point and each wrong decision none.

There are two kinds of objective item that deserve a three-point scale. The first is an item in which the student is asked to show when he is sure of the best response, say, by a second check mark (44, Lindquist). Each check mark against the right response can be scored $+1$, and each double check mark against a wrong response, $-1$. The second is an item containing one correct response worth $+1$ and one or more very wrong responses, each worth $-1$. This kind of item is discussed in Section 12.6.

### Corrections for students' guessing

As was stated in Section 12.3, a warning not to guess in objective items on understanding or ability to learn is undesirable, as are penalties for guessing, even in exercises on knowledge. If the warning is strictly observed by all students, the test will not differentiate between students to whom all responses to an item look equally good and students who know that some of the responses are wrong. Since the ability to recognize wrong statements in science is important, even though penalties for guessing may increase the test's reliability (44, Furst) they will decrease its validity. If, on the other hand, some students heed the warning and others do not, test scores become ambiguous. It is true that if no penalties for guessing are applied, students who have no time to finish the test will find it to their advantage to spend the last few minutes in random marking of the unfinished items. The best remedy for this is to allow enough time for the great majority of the students to finish the test; the second best is to increase the scores of those who have not finished the test by the guess-score for the unfinished part.

### Weighting of exercises or items

In weighting items (or, for that matter, tests) the following mathematically proven generalization should be kept in mind. If the number of items is large, say, thirty, and if they are highly intercorrelated as they would be in a test for one ability, such as knowledge, the choice of weighting is unimportant: students' ranks will be nearly the same for different sets of weights (40, Gulliksen). In particular, greater weights for more difficult exercises have little empirical justification. The simplest procedure for objective items scored on a two-point scale—merely to count the number of correct "decisions" that the student has made—is the best one, especially if the number of items (or decisions) devoted to an aspect of an objective corresponds to the importance of the aspect. Scores made on items graded on a three-point scale, $+1$, $0$, $-1$, can simply be added to the number of correct decisions.

If an exercise consists of several items testing for different abilities, differential weighting of the items is justified. Thus, if the organization of an essay or a paragraph within an essay is considered important, its three-point scale may be changed from 0, 1, 2 to 0, 2, 4 or 0, 3, 6. These changes correspond to weighting the "item" of organization by factors of 2 and 3, respectively. If the maximum sum of the points for all the items of a long exercise does not correspond to the importance of the exercise, the score can be multiplied by an appropriate factor before being added to the scores for other exercises.

The fewer scores there are to be combined and the lower their intercorrelations, the greater the effectiveness of differential weighting becomes: it is therefore efficient to divide a test into a few subtests of low intercorrelation. The following three types of exercise usually do not correlate highly even in a test for a single ability: (1) long open-ended essays, (2) numerical problems, and (3) qualitative objective items and highly structured or very short essays. Assigning a different weight to each such part is therefore justified. If, however, the number of recordable decisions in each part is already roughly proportional to its importance, unit weighting of the parts (simple addition of the scores) is in order.

## 12.5   WEIGHTING TESTS

At the end of the quarter, a teacher has usually gathered a good deal of information about his students. He then has the problem of translating it into letter grades. If, in all the tests given in a quarter, the number of decisions or items devoted to each major objective corresponds to the importance of that objective and if, further, most items have been scored by using fairly similar scales, such as 0, 1 or 0, 1, 2, no further weighting is necessary —all the scores may simply be added to produce a final score for each student. If these conditions are not satisfied, weighting individual tests is necessary in order to correct for discrepancies in the number of items, scales, and reliabilities.

### Theory of weighting

The validity and reliability of a battery of tests can be improved by judicious weighting of individual tests, especially if the tests are few and do not correlate highly. If a valid test that includes all the content and objectives of the course is available, there are straightforward though cumbersome statistical procedures for assigning such weights to various tests that the battery will have the highest validity possible. If these procedures are impractical, we must decide in some other way on the degree to which a given test should influence students' final grades. The main basis for this decision should be the importance of the objective measured by the test; a secondary basis, the precision of the test. A test will strongly influence students' grades if its standard deviation and the standard deviations of other tests in the battery with which it is highly correlated are large (40). Therefore our main control, once the tests are written, is in changing the standard deviations of their scores. If we want two tests to play equally important roles, we should make greater the standard deviation of the test that differs more from (correlates less highly with) other tests of the battery. Weighting according to importance and corrections for varying standard deviations and reliabilities can all be done at once by multiplying students' scores in each test by a given factor, explained below. (Corrections for varying intercorrelations are, for science tests, relatively unimportant.)

Suppose our battery consists of $N$ tests, with standard deviations $S_1$, $S_2, \ldots, S_N$; and reliabilities $r_1, r_2, \ldots, r_N$. Suppose further that the relative importance of the objectives measured by the tests is in the ratio of numbers $W_1 : W_2 : \ldots W_N$. (Assigning numbers to importance is difficult and unpleasant but unavoidable: not assigning weights would in effect be assigning unit weights.) The factor $F_i$ by which the score of each student in test $i$ should be multiplied is given by

$$F_i = \frac{W_i}{e_i}, \tag{12.1}$$

where $e_i = S_i\sqrt{1 - r_i}$ is the error of measurement. The weighted scores are then added to give the final composite score. (Formula 12.1 is not strictly accurate; it is simply the best available rule of thumb.) The contributions of various factors are as follows. If the scores of test $i$ are divided by $S_i$, of test $j$, by $S_j$, and so forth, and the scores thus obtained added, the tests will correlate approximately equally with the sum of the scores. The factor $S$ thus equalizes the effective weights of the tests. By dividing the scores further by $\sqrt{1 - r}$, greater effective weights are given to more reliable tests. Multiplications by $W$ increase the effective weights of tests for more important objectives.

*Approximate expressions for error of measurement*    If a student's score on a test is equal to the number of correct decisions he has made and recorded, formula 7.10 for the reliability can be used. If the total number of items or decisions in a test is large, say twenty-five or more, the error of measurement is then given approximately by

$$e = \sqrt{M(1 - M/K)}, \tag{12.2}$$

where $M$ is the mean score for the test and $K$ the perfect score. Even if the conditions under which formula 12.2 holds are not completely satisfied, it will usually give better approximations to $e$ than will omitting $e$ in calculating $F$, which is the same as considering $e$ to be the same for all tests. The value of $e$ can also be estimated from previous experience with similar tests. If test 1 and test 2 are similar, except for the numbers of items $n$, their errors of measurement are related as shown by formula 12.3.

$$\frac{e_1^2}{e_2^2} = \frac{n_1}{n_2} \tag{12.3}$$

If any two tests with errors of measurement $e_1$ and $e_2$ are added, the error of measurement $e$ of the combination test is given by $e^2 = e_1^2 + e_2^2$. If the scores of a test are multiplied by a factor $F$, its error of measurement increases by the same factor.

*Approximate values of* F    Most science tests are sufficiently highly correlated to make precise weighting unnecessary—whole number values are good enough. Thus, if we have $F_1 = 1$, $F_2 = 1.4$, $F_3 = 1.7$, $F_4 = 2.2$, and $F_5 = 2.8$, the first two may be said to equal 1; the next two, 2; and the last, 3. Time is saved if the scores on equally weighted tests are first added and the sum then multiplied by the appropriate value of $F$.

## Weighting of homework, examinations, and laboratory

If course tests are used for counseling and educational research, part-scores for knowledge, understanding, and ability to learn are essential. (The laboratory part-score is obtained routinely in all laboratory courses.) These four part-scores also have fairly low intercorrelations and thus require weighting.

The part-score for knowledge can be obtained by adding properly weighted homework and the relevant examination scores. If examination exercises have been weighted as described in Section 12.4, the scores for them can simply be added. The same procedure can be followed for homework exercises. Rough approximations in weighting are in order here, for the exercises are many and their intercorrelations are fairly high. Before the resulting two scores are added to give the score for knowledge, however, they should be weighted with some care, because their errors of measurement may differ widely, especially if the authorship of homework is in doubt. The weights can be calculated from formulas 12.1, 12.2, and 12.3.

Scores for understanding and ability to learn are easier to calculate because all or most of the relevant exercises come from examinations. The final score $X$ of a student can be obtained from equation 12.4,

$$X = F_k N_k + F_u N_u + F_a N_a + F_l N_l, \tag{12.4}$$

where $F$ is the weight factor, as in formula 12.1, $N$ is the student's score on a particular objective, and the subscripts $k$, $u$, $a$, and $l$ stand for knowledge, understanding, ability to learn, and laboratory objectives.

If part-scores for the behavioral objectives are not readily available, the following four sources of scores may be considered to constitute the test battery: homework, quizzes, the more important and longer tests here called the quarterlies, and the laboratory. Homework usually tests for knowledge only. If the advice in Section 12.2 is followed, however, the quizzes will test mostly for knowledge and the quarterlies, for understanding, but both kinds of test will also contain exercises on the ability to learn. The simplest procedure here is to assume that the quarterlies measure understanding and that the combined homework and quizzes measure knowledge, and to hope that the ability to learn is properly rewarded.

## 12.6   ASSIGNING LETTER GRADES

### Absolute standards

There are many methods for assigning grades. Three of the more widely used methods will be described and evaluated here. One method is to assign each letter grade to a predetermined fraction of the class, for example, the top 10 percent get A, usually without regard to possible variation in the quality of student or instruction from year to year. In some cases, in order to keep the standards more nearly constant, qualitative estimates of these variations are made, and the fractions changed accordingly. Another is to assign the grades on the basis of test scores expressed as a percentage of the maximum possible score; for example, 70 percent may be required for a C. In the interests of constant standards, these percentages may vary with the estimated difficulty of the test.

If the number of students who will get a given grade is fixed, each student must realize that his interests will be served approximately as well by his classmates' learning little as by his learning a good deal. The effect of the resulting pedagogical atmosphere on a sensitive student cannot be conducive to a wholehearted preoccupation with his studies; it may even influence his attitude toward learning and dissemination of knowledge in general. A disadvantage of basing grades on fixed percentages of the possible score is that the grades will have little meaning to those who have not seen the test used. In both methods of assigning grades discussed above, even if the standards are kept constant (that is, equivalent to some original standards), the question still remains whether the original standards were rational.

A third method of assigning grades is to base the score required for a given letter grade on the instructor's judgment of what represents adequate, good, or excellent achievement and not on a comparison of the student with his class or with any other particular group of students. In this sense, the standard used for determining the passing score is absolute, although it may well vary for the different schools using a given test. Thus some instructors, in setting up standards of satisfactory achievement, may take into account what can be expected from a typical student body under typical course conditions at their school. For other instructors "satisfactory completion of a one-year course in college physics," for example, may have a meaning that is independent of the school. In either case, the standard is absolute if it can be stated in terms of the knowledge and abilities a student must possess in order to get a given grade in the course.

Operationally, absolute standards require that a student's grade be assigned on the basis of his performance on a test without any regard to the performance of his classmates. For an objective test, decisions on passing and other scores should be made before the test is given. In scoring an essay, many teachers use absolute standards: they give an F for a bad essay without inquiring how many students have written bad essays. To apply absolute standards to objective tests, the scorer can use the technique described below, which has been found satisfactory for determining the minimum passing score (42, Nedelsky).

*Absolute standards for objective tests*    The responses of a multiple-choice item are first classified on a three-point scale as right, wrong, and grossly wrong or failing. We shall refer to these, respectively, as R responses, W responses, and F responses. F responses are those that even a barely passing or lowest D student should be able to reject as incorrect. Ordinarily, F responses should be specially designed; in any case, they should be such that most teachers will consider them the worst responses in the item. An item may have several F responses or none.

If a group of $n$ one-correct-response items has $r$ responses per item, of which $f$ are F responses, the students who reject all F responses and just guess among the rest will have scores with a mean, $m = n/(r - f)$, and the standard deviation $s$ given by

$$s^2 = \frac{n(r - f - 1)}{(r - f)^2}. \qquad (12.5)$$

The mean $M$ and $S^2$ for the whole test will be equal, respectively, to the sums of $m$ and $s^2$ for various groups of items. For each test, $M$ has to be calculated accurately, but the exact value of $S$ is not very important. A reasonable value, which may be checked by using formula 12.5, is $S = .45\sqrt{N}$, where $N$ is the total number of items in the test.

*The procedure for calculating* M    In each item of the test, the F responses should be crossed out. To the left of the item is written the reciprocal of the number, $n - f$, of the remaining responses. Thus, if we cross out one of five responses, E, for example, in the exercise below, we write $\frac{1}{4}$. The sum $M$ of all these fractions is the guess-score of a student who has just enough knowledge to reject all F responses.

> Light has wave characteristics. Which of the following is the best experimental evidence for this statement?
>     A. Light can be reflected by a mirror.
> R  B. Light forms dark and light bands on passing through a small opening.
>     C. A beam of white light can be broken into its component colors by a prism.
>     D. Light carries energy.
> F  E. Light operates a photoelectric cell.

(Response E is an F response because it states evidence *against* the wave theory; responses A, C, and D are at least consistent with the wave theory.)

The passing score, $P$, is found by the formula

$$P = M + kS, \qquad (12.6)$$

where $k$ can be determined as follows. If $k = 1$, 16 percent of the failing students will, by chance, get a score larger than $P$. If $k = 2$, the percentage of those passing through lucky guesses will be 2 percent. With $k$ slightly larger than 2, the formula is particularly simple. It is

$$P = M + \sqrt{N}, \qquad (12.6a)$$

where $N$ is the number of items in the test.

For identifying failing students, homework may be left out of account and the passing score on each major objective set equal to the sum of $P$'s on the relevant parts of tests. If an exercise is an essay, some numerical equivalent of the grade of D can be used as $P$ for that exercise. Since knowledge, understanding, ability to learn, and laboratory proficiency are quite distinct objectives, it is justifiable to require a passing score on each. This is, of course, a stricter requirement than the requirement that the student's total score be equal to the sum of passing scores.

Although the technique described in the preceding paragraphs can, theoretically, be extended to grades other than passing, in practice it is difficult to obtain reasonable agreement among teachers on the responses that the low C or the low B student should be able to reject. The possibility of agreement on F responses but not on D, C, or B responses is probably based on the relative ease with which teachers can identify failing and nonfailing students as compared to, say, D and C students. Therefore, after the failing students have been identified, we are reduced to using relative standards for assigning other letter grades.

## Relative standards

The most rational relative standard requires that the differences between the scores for the lowest C, B, and A be reliably large. Let us assume that the score for the lowest D is $X_D = M + \sqrt{N}$, calculated from formula 12.6a, and that the highest score of any student is $X_M$. (Because the class may contain a few exceptionally good students, whose performance should not affect the standards for the rest of the class, $X_M$ may be made equal to the lowest score made by the top 1 or 2 percent of the class.) The scores for the lowest C, B, and A may then be set equal to $X_M - \frac{3}{4}X_D$, $X_M - \frac{1}{2}X_D$, and $X_M - \frac{1}{4}X_D$, respectively. The normal curve is used here for determining the range of scores corresponding to a letter grade. This procedure is better than assigning some arbitrary percent of grades other than F because it makes all letter-grade differences equally reliable.

Defining scores as fractions of the maximum possible score—for instance, a passing score is 70 percent—has some merit if the tests used are *equated* (see Section 13.2). This procedure ensures that the same standards are maintained year after year, provided of course that the students do not profit from their familiarity with past tests. "Breaks" in the distribution of scores are almost always randomly distributed and are therefore unreliable as indexes of differences between the students below and above the break (46, Gulliksen). Perhaps the only argument for establishing the score just above the break as the lower limit for a letter grade is that correcting a small scoring error becomes less important because it is less likely to raise a student's letter grade.

### Scales for letter grades

Section 7.3 argued that few tests are valid or reliable enough to be used for assigning grades on the usual five-point scale and recommended reducing the scale to a three-point one. The grades may be H (for honors), S (for satisfactory), and F (for failing). F may retain its present meaning and H be made equivalent to the present B+ and above. Before a grading reform is achieved nationally, if it ever will be, H, S, and F can be used for the quarterly grades and A, B, C, D, and F for the yearly grades: H, S, and F may be assigned point values of 2, 1, and 0, respectively, added, and the sums interpreted as A, B, and so on. With a reduced scale of grading, it would also be easier to assign each student a reliable grade for each of the major objectives of the course.

*A multiple grade for a course* Perhaps the student's understanding of a science should be described by several grades rather than just one, for the proper weighting of the major objectives must depend on the use to which the combined score will be put. Deciding whether to admit a student to graduate school or hire him for a job may well require different relative emphases on the objectives. For example, one student may have only a modicum of knowledge but may have learned how to learn and to apply his knowledge, while another may have memorized a great deal of information but not know how to use it; this information, if it were available, might be used differently by graduate school admissions officers and prospective employers. Yet the two students may have similar enough total scores to have received the same letter grade. Can we meaningfully say that they have equal "mastery" or "understanding" of science? The absence of a word to describe the way in which the students are equal, in spite of the English language's magnificent store of ambiguous terms, strongly implies that the equality is a figment of a registrar's imagination.

# 13

# USES OF TESTS:
# DIAGNOSIS AND RESEARCH

This chapter discusses the diagnostic uses of tests for entrance, placement, and counseling, the role tests can play in course improvement, and research problems in testing.

## 13.1  DIAGNOSTIC TESTS

### College entrance tests (30)

Predicting success in college is difficult, and most entrance tests do not correlate better than .60 with college grades. There are three probable reasons for this low correlation. First, entrance tests are in substance tests of achievement through high school, achievement that varies in objectives and quality from school to school. The tests may therefore measure different abilities (see Section 11.1), and equal scores made by students from different schools are not likely to indicate equal promise. Second, most entrance tests fail to measure *directly* that most important single competence, the ability to learn, which includes, besides the intellectual ingredients described in Section 2.1, interest, industry, stamina, and perhaps a host of other characteristics. Third, success in science and success in the applied fields of, say, education or engineering require different patterns of abilities. Even in the same field, the required pattern or degree of abilities may differ from college to college.

The first two deficiencies of entrance tests are partially remedied if the entrance battery includes high school grades and recommendations, and if the type of training the school gives is taken into account. Although high school objectives are difficult to divine and although they undoubtedly vary from school to school, some ability to learn is almost certainly required. For this reason, high school grades are as a rule the best single predictor of success, especially, of course, in a curriculum that endorses the virtues that school grades reflect—memory and intellectual docility. The predictive power of grades is greatly increased if the school's grading standards and the success of their graduates in the college in question are taken into account (30, Bloom and Peters).

The difficulties of differential prognosis for various fields can be alleviated by using tests of interest and by validating entrance tests against the grades the students get in at least their freshman college courses. Tests of interest are probably best treated as placement tests and given to students who have already been admitted, for many high school students are—and should be—undecided on their fields of specialization (12).

Information available at college entrance includes scores on scholastic aptitude tests, an essay written under examination conditions, and high school grades and recommendations. In colleges of arts and sciences such information is generally enough to admit or reject more than half the applicants. The rest of the applicants present a more ambiguous picture because of unorthodox precollege educations or discrepancies between test results and high school grades, and may have to be interviewed or tested further. It is dangerous to neglect applicants of low average achievement, especially those who did exceptionally well in some one narrow area, even if the routine information has furnished the college with enough admissible applicants. High school grades, of course, indicate an ability to learn in particular learning situations only; such ability may include docility, lack of imagination, respect for an incompetent teacher, and other qualifications that a spirited and talented student may not possess. Finally, as Table 7.3 shows, even if the correlation between the entrance battery of tests (including high school records) and college success is as high as .65, 58 percent of the students will be misjudged and 12 percent misjudged seriously.

In combining entrance-test scores, as in combining certification tests, their weights should be determined first by the importance of what a test measures and only second by its precision. Perhaps the most important rule is not to give an infinite weight to any one test; for example, if an interviewer decides that a student with good entrance scores is "clearly inadmissible," the student should not be forthwith rejected but interviewed once more by someone who does not know the first interviewer's verdict. Personality tests may help here; even though their general validity is not high, they may identify students with serious emotional problems.

A rather unorthodox but defensible possibility is to validate college admission tests not against the grades in that college but against the grades of several similar but better colleges. Instead of identifying the students that will "fit into" the college, this procedure will identify those of generally higher academic promise. Since the level and kind of teaching usually adjust themselves to the student body, this validation will help avoid academic inbreeding and may raise teaching standards. Moreover, validity data for a *class* of colleges are usually available from the testing agency that prepares the entrance test.

### College placement tests

After the student is admitted to a college he should be given further tests whose results, added to entrance-test results, will help determine a good program of study. These tests may indicate courses from which the student is excused or for which he is given credit, and remedial courses he is to take in addition to the regular program. Because colleges differ in the courses they offer, placement tests should usually be prepared locally. Not all students need take placement tests. The entrance tests can usually be used to divide the students into three groups: those who are likely to need remedial courses, those who may be given advanced placement, and the rest. Placement tests should be given to the first two groups and to those other students who wish to take them for some good reason. It is quite unsound and uneconomical, although very common, to give identical placement tests to both the highest and lowest groups. First, as was shown in Section 11.1, what a test measures depends on the students' preparation. Secondly, exercises in a test that are too difficult or too easy for the group tested lower the test's reliability: differences among the members of the low group are obscured by their scores on difficult items and for the high group, by their scores on the easy items.

Remedial courses are intended to remove deficiencies in the students' high school training and prepare them for taking various introductory college courses. If the prerequisites to these courses are clearly stated, they should determine the essential features of the remedial courses and of the relevant placement tests.

An advanced-placement test covering a highly specialized course such as analytical mechanics may well be very similar to the course-certification tests because an acquaintance with the content of such a course is likely to be prerequisite to future work in the field. Therefore, adequate training in the subject cannot radically differ from that given in the course. Because even such courses, however, differ from college to college, the student who has received his training elsewhere is almost certain to possess some proficiency that the course tests do not measure. His scores on the tests will not do him full justice and should be interpreted with this in view. The situation is different in introductory courses. An introductory course can treat only a comparatively small sample of the total knowledge of a field. Two equally good introductory physics courses intended for the same kind of students, for instance, may have less than 50 percent of common content (14). The knowledge of the content of a particular course cannot therefore be expected of entering students. A test that may place the student out of an introductory course should therefore be based primarily on subject matter the student is likely to be familiar with. A compromise on the behavioral objectives of understanding and ability to learn, on the other hand, is probably not justified.

### Tests used for counseling

Section 12.5 showed that course grades can be more accurately assigned if part-scores indicating the student's attainment of various objectives are available. More generally, no rational and just action by a teacher can be based on tests that lump together in unknown quantities such heterogeneous elements as knowledge, understanding, talent, and predilection. Part-scores on behavioral objectives are clearly valuable in counseling: they enable the counselor to criticize not only the content the student has learned but what he can do with or within the content. The usual type of criticism, "You are weak in mechanics," and the suggested remedy, "Study harder," are little more than idle, ritual gestures.

Good counseling requires an acquaintance with the student. In college, science professors are not often in a position to know many beginning students well. On the other hand, college students themselves may in general be expected to have a fair enough idea of their own strengths and weaknesses to make self-diagnosis on the basis of part-scores useful, if the meaning of the part-scores is carefully explained in class. A few examples will illustrate the process of identifying a student's weaknesses and suggesting remedies on the basis of a multiple-choice objective test, the same test that is used to assign grades. Perhaps the most valuable part-scores in a science course are the R score (the number of right responses the student has chosen), the F score (the number of very wrong responses he has chosen), and the $R - F$ scores for knowledge, understanding, ability to learn, and the test as a whole.

For the sake of concreteness and simplicity, it is assumed that the test has fifty items on each major objective, knowledge, understanding, and learning ability, and that each item has one right response, two wrong responses, and one very wrong response. On the basis of this information and with the use of formula 12.6a, the barely passing R score, $P$, and the part-scores given in Table 13.1 can be calculated as follows:

$$M = (\tfrac{1}{3})\,(150) = 50; \qquad P = M + \sqrt{N} = 50 + \sqrt{150} = 62.$$

Jones, who does very well on knowledge, studies hard or has a good memory or both. Since he can get information out of the text, his low score on learning ability suggests that he is a slow thinker. His low F and R scores show that he finds it relatively easy to reject the really bad responses and relatively hard to assay the subtler differences among other responses. His low score on understanding shows that he finds it relatively difficult to attack a problem with novel features in it. Advice: let Jones be.

**Table 13.1    Diagnostic scores of four students**

The grade of F is assigned on the basis of the R score; other grades on the basis of R − F scores. Maximum possible R score is 150. The R score for the lowest D is 62. Maximum possible R − F scores in each of the three abilities is 50.

| | R − F part-scores | | | | | | |
| Student | Knowledge | Under-standing | Learning Ability | R score | F score | R − F | Grade |
|---|---|---|---|---|---|---|---|
| Jones | 45 | 20 | 20 | 90 | 5 | 85 | C |
| Smith | 20 | 30 | 35 | 115 | 30 | 85 | C |
| Perez | 45 | 35 | 15 | 120 | 25 | 95 | B |
| Brown | 15 | 15 | 15 | 60 | 15 | 45 | F |

Smith can learn and does well on novel problems despite his relatively small amount of knowledge. His high F score shows that he is almost entirely ignorant in some areas. Harder work and longer hours should be recommended; it may also be suggested that he make a summary of *every* assigned chapter. Smith can do better than C work.

Perez's main difficulty is probably his inability to read English rapidly. The high F score probably comes from misunderstandings. He should get an A the next quarter.

Brown obviously does not know any science. His uniformly bad showing indicates that the grade of F, assigned to him because his R score is below 62, is an accurate measure of his achievement, and his showing suggests that he should see an adviser who is familiar with Brown's whole academic career.

## 13.2    USES OF TESTS FOR COURSE IMPROVEMENT

The aim of this section is to explain how test results can be used to suggest or evaluate changes in a course. Changes may be indicated in the materials of instruction, for example, the text; in the subject matter; or in the method of teaching. First, however, we will review the use of tests themselves as a teaching device.

### Tests as a teaching device

Tests can acquaint the student with the objectives of the course and thus influence his study habits, and they can increase his understanding of science. They do the first well and the second badly. The student's opinion of what the course objectives are is strongly influenced by course tests (27). If the tests are devoted to knowledge, some students will dismiss as pious talk the teacher's protestations that he wants them to understand science or to acquire the ability to learn further; others will face the debilitating dilemma of directing their energies toward acquiring understanding *or* toward getting good grades; still others will equate acquisition of knowledge with scientific training. In all cases, the image of the science and the scientist is tarnished. It seems safer and more honest to test students for all the objectives the teacher considers and pronounces important, even if the conditions of learning are such that the teacher's direct help with some of the objectives is minimal and the student's own responsibility, maximal. Tests can also advance the student's understanding of science. If that is to be an important function of tests, they will have to be specially designed—at the expense of accurate measurement of student achievement—and will take up a considerable part of the instructional time. Unless that part is substantially larger than it is in most courses, modifying a test to enable the student to learn just a little more science from it while trying to maintain its measuring function seems an extravagant use of the teacher's time and talents. What a student can learn from test *results* was discussed under counseling.

### Use of tests in pedagogical research

Most college science teachers use tests only for assigning course grades. Reasonably accurate certification of achievement is necessary, for if the grades are unfairly assigned, the student's morale and thus his future learning may be seriously hurt, and some students may be misguided into changing their major or leaving college. Except for the possible damage to the student, however, certification is a less important function of testing than improvement of teaching and learning; it is more important that the student learn well than that the teacher know just how well. In most cases, tests that are used for assigning grades and counseling can also be used for experimental purposes, provided the tests measure the attainment of the major objectives and especially if a part-score for each major objective can be determined.

College science departments attach little prestige to good teaching and consequently allow very little time for related scholarly activity. Yet because of the almost complete lack of communication between departments of science and education (10), immediate progress in science teaching must be made by teachers themselves (see Section 1.4). Because science teachers are busy and likely to become busier, so that they will spend more time teaching and less in improving teaching, "conversation" about science teaching, enriched and made more lucid by evaluation concepts, will probably be the main path of progress. Some scientists, however—certainly those whose main interest is teaching—should find time to do modest research in teaching.

There are many unanswered questions in teaching science courses: there are also many questions that have been answered—mostly on the basis of tradition and folklore. There is little theoretical or empirical knowledge of how adolescents and young adults learn that is applicable to school situations in general. Any immediate hope thus lies in local experimentation, even if its conclusions are of limited validity, for experimentation is necessary just to keep teaching alive. What a teacher learns from his own experimentation may be of very little use to others, but it is likely to be of great help to the teacher who performs it. Because the greatest benefit from inexpert experimentation is likely to accrue to the experimenter himself, science teachers can afford to be bold and to do research on the problems of teaching that concern them most: they can test their most cherished beliefs or try to find solutions to their most vexing problems. It is true that finding definitive answers to important questions may require elaborate experimental designs, but often a teacher will be glad to settle for some empirical support of a hunch.

## Some published results of educational research

As every scientist knows, the first step in research is to find out what is already known. A few results of relevant educational research are summarized below.

1. Knowledge. Teaching knowledge, especially imparting information, is done about equally well by lecture, discussion, TV, and textbook, with the lecture perhaps holding a slight edge over the other methods (20). Knowledge unaccompanied by understanding is soon forgotten (7).

2. Understanding and ability to learn. Critical thinking, problem solving, reading with understanding, and other activities or abilities that involve higher mental processes are well taught through discussion or a seminar (19, 20). Understanding and ability to learn are more permanent acquisitions than knowledge (7). Discussion, especially of a fairly free kind, may arouse in the students a lasting interest in the subject matter (17).

3. Laboratory. Tests have been unable consistently to detect any learning that takes place in the conventional introductory physics laboratory beyond the ability to use instruments (59).

4. Educational experimentation. Almost invariably the experimental group, that is, the group taught by the method the teacher considers superior, learns more than or as much as the control group (4). This seems to indicate either that those few teachers who are willing to experiment have good judgment or that the teacher's enthusiasm strongly encourages learning; probably both are true.

5. Prognosis. The number of abilities that must be measured if a dependable prognosis of future success is to be made becomes larger as the student is more advanced and more intelligent. For highly intelligent adults, as many as twenty different factors or abilities may have to be taken into account (2). Prognostic tests of academic success in high school and beyond should measure knowledge, understanding, and ability to learn, but knowl-

edge is the least important of the three (8). The best single predictor of success in a course is the grades in previous courses with similar objectives and content (30).

6. Organization of learning. Factors that facilitate learning are accurate, detailed evaluation and continuity, sequence, and integration of the material taught. Continuity requires that the main ideas be repeated; sequence requires that the repetition take place in successively richer contexts; and integration requires that the ideas be organized into a coherent whole that makes sense to the student (20).

7. Transfer of training. Higher mental processes can be improved: students can be taught how to use their knowledge in situations that are new to them, and they can be taught how to learn. Before a general transfer of training can take place, the students must have acquired an understanding of the fundamental structure of the subject matter (objective 2.3); they must know in what abilities they are being trained; and they must understand the process of transfer (4).

None of the above generalizations enjoys the status of a law of nature, none is sure to have universal support, and none is entirely unambiguous; and, of course, the list is far from complete. Most educators, however, would probably consider those generalizations a good guide both to better teaching and testing and to further research. Further testing of the generalizations is in order, but a busy teacher will do well to follow Newton's rules of reasoning and take the generalizations pretty much for granted until he comes across contrary evidence or evidence that the generalizations do not apply under the conditions of learning in his course.

### Unsolved problems in teaching

There are a great many questions—theoretical and practical, general and specific—that could be answered at least partially by teachers interested in performing their own educational research. A sampling is given below.

The main theoretical question that can be asked about science courses in general is this: With ideal facilities (including personnel), what are the best objectives, content, and methods for a science course taken by students with a given academic past and future? For instance, what should be the content of the one science course that humanities majors can take? Should it include both biological and physical sciences, several physical (or biological) sciences, or only one science, and what is the optimum volume of content of the course? The corresponding practical question is, what is the best that can be done under specific local conditions? Another theoretical question is: Granted that a course tailored to a particular audience is best, in what way does students' learning decrease as the heterogeneity of the student body increases? Some of the corresponding practical questions are: How many different courses in introductory physics should be given in a college that offers majors from, say, engineering to humanities? In the different courses, could the lectures be the same? Should all the courses have laboratory? Other examples of practical questions are: Since the higher intellectual processes are taught better by discussion than lecture, what is the best procedure if the available personnel includes only one experienced teacher but several inexperienced assistants? In particular, what happens to students' learning if the professor reduces the number of lectures he gives and uses the time to train assistants? Does measurable improvement in the students' learning follow if the assistants are trained for a couple of hours a week by an experienced teacher? Can the students be taught to learn from books instead of lectures?

The last two questions are relatively easy to manage: an imaginative teacher can design an experiment that will give empirical data on the basis of which sound local decisions can be made and which may even be more widely useful. Other problems that do not require elaborate research setups are: selecting the best textbooks, demonstration apparatus, or other audio-visual aids; estimating the value of frequent short quizzes, reduced subject-matter coverage, or required attendance; and determining the real prerequisites to a course or the course's value as a prerequisite to the next course or, more generally, the contribution of the course to the later academic success of the student.

### Research design

First, let us lay the ghost of the unprejudiced, open-minded researcher who respectfully listens to nature and records all her gibberish. The tool of the modern researcher, whether in science or education, is increasingly more like an objective—perhaps even a true-false—test. The choice of such a tool shows that the researcher thinks he knows or assumes nearly all there is to know and that his mind is open no more than a crack; the crack is wide enough to admit a yes-or-no answer to his question and little else that is not striking or persistent. The reseacher in education must be prepared to hypothesize quite narrowly specified or qualified conclusions. The improvement produced by an innovation is more likely to be in the attainment of a particular objective by a particular group of students than in the attainment of all objectives by all students. It may be found, for instance, that only the poorer students learn better from a given textbook. Or it may be discovered that a shift from numerical problems to qualitative questions for homework does nothing except reduce the worst kinds of ignorance and confusion, as measured by the F scores discussed in Section 12.6. These discoveries might not seem earth shaking, but they would give us information that is not available now.

Qualified conclusions in evaluation research are supported by data that show that the innovation resulted in higher scores by *some* students on *part* of a test. To make such conclusions convincing, the relevant part of the test must be sufficiently long to have a small error of measurement. It is, however, impractical to make all part-scores highly reliable. A researcher must therefore prognosticate the nature and, if possible, even the degree of the most likely change in the students' learning and prepare a test that will reliably show the change, if it occurs. He must also be prepared for the possibility that a decrease in certain kinds of learning may accompany an increase in other kinds. Usually it is sufficient to show that the innovation did not produce a decrease in the overall learning. The evaluative instrument may therefore be a regular achievement test for all the important objectives of the course, supplemented by additional exercises on that aspect of competence expected to change most as a result of the innovation introduced into the course.

In the long run it saves time to give a good deal of thought to the research design before beginning the experiment. If, nevertheless, the results of the experiment are ambiguous because of faulty research design or unreliable tests, it is almost always possible to repeat the experiment and combine the new results with the previous ones. This procedure is explained and illustrated later in this section, under An example of research design.

### Controls

Research in teaching commonly starts with identifying a weak spot in a course. The weakness may be identified through a theoretical analysis of the course or through empirical data on students' achievement. The remedy is then hypothesized, introduced into the course, and the results studied. To evaluate an innovation—changing the text, substituting different demonstration apparatus, or dropping the laboratory—it is necessary to have controls. It is best to have parallel experimental and control groups that finish the course at the same time, to whom the same examination can be given. Last year's class can also be used as a control if equated tests are available. (How to equate tests is explained later in this section, under Comparison of groups that have not taken a common test.) All systematic differences between experimental and control groups, except of course the one that is the subject of the experiment, should be reduced; if they remain sizable they must be included in the description of the results. (Random differences, on the other hand, such as those that result from small samples of students or of items in the test, can be taken care of statistically.) For instance, a conclusion may read: The use of textbook X (by a teacher who prefers it to book Y) results in higher student scores on knowledge than the use of textbook Y (by a teacher who thinks the two books are equally good). The parenthetical qualification is unnecessary if the teachers exchange classes and books in the middle of the quarter. Research etiquette requires, however, that the remaining systematic difference—for instance, whether the enthusiastic teacher taught the first or the second half of the quarter—should be reported. Many professional educators also like to end their reports with an elegant truism, admitting the uniqueness of their experimental conditions and the lack of universal validity of their conclusions.

Although making the sponsor of an innovation change places with a presumably less prejudiced colleague, so that each teaches the experimental and the control group part of the time, introduces some control of the "enthusiasm variable," this control is ordinarily far from complete. If the results of the experiment are only to guide the enthusiast himself, however, he need not recheck the results unless his enthusiasm cools. Moreover, whether it is the innovation or the teacher's enthusiasm for it that has caused better learning, a group of students and very probably the teacher too *have* benefited from the experience. Educational research by a practicing teacher is only rarely, if ever, a waste of time.

The precision of an experiment is increased if the experimental and control groups are matched by using the scores not of all the students but only of properly selected ones (29). The selection is made on the basis of some previous records: high school or college grades, or entrance scores. If entrance scores are used, the mean entrance score of the two groups should be the same. A still better matching is achieved if each group is divided, on the basis of entrance scores, into high, middle, and low subgroups. The students should then be selected so that the *paired* high, middle, and low subgroups have the same mean score and the same number of students. It is not necessary to have the same number of students in the high, middle, and low subgroups; each subgroup should be as large as possible.

A different type of control is required for finding out how much the students have gained from a course. A common procedure is to use the same test both before and after the course, but this has its weaknesses: a test exercise is unlikely to be equally novel to the students before and after the course, and thus unlikely to measure the same ability. Also, a test on understanding and ability to learn must keep the auxiliary ability, knowledge, at the level of the great majority of the students. A pretest on these abilities must therefore cover only content familiar to the students entering the course. Such content, however, is usually too limited for a good course test. Yet if two different tests are used, absolute gain in competence is hard to determine. Fortunately, a teacher is usually interested in the relative gain for two differently taught courses. The *relative* gain can be measured by matching the two groups on the basis of a pretest and comparing their scores on a good course test.

*Comparison of groups that have not taken a common test*   It is sometimes necessary to compare the achievement of two groups that have taken different tests. If the two tests measure similar or highly correlated competences, it is possible to "equate" the scores made on the two tests (36). In general, this can be done only if both tests are administered to some one group that is a representative sample of the two groups to be compared. For instance, let us suppose that the present year's class is the experimental group, group 1, and is given test $X$, and that last year's class is the control group, group 2, and is given test $Y$. Tests $X$ and $Y$ can be equated by giving both of them to the class of year-before-last, group 3. To begin with, tests $X$ and $Y$ should be nearly parallel in objectives, content, and forms of exercises and, for group 3, they should have approximately equal means, $\overline{X}_3$ and $\overline{Y}_3$, and standard deviations, $\tilde{X}_3$ and $\tilde{Y}_3$. To equate the tests we transform the scores made by group 3 on one of them, say test $Y$, as follows:

$$Y_3' = aY_3 + b, \tag{13.1}$$

where

$$a = \frac{\tilde{X}_3}{\tilde{Y}_3} \text{ and } b = \overline{X}_3 - a\overline{Y}_3. \tag{13.2}$$

The transformed scores $Y_3'$ have exactly the same mean and standard deviation as scores $X_3$. The constants $a$ and $b$ can now be used to equate scores $Y_2$ of group 2 on test $Y$ to scores $X_1$ of group 1 on test $X$. All scores of group 2 are transformed as follows:

$$Y_2' = aY_2 + b. \tag{13.1a}$$

The values of $a$ and $b$ are given by equations 13.2 and are thus the same numerical values that have been used in equating the tests on group 3. If the score $Y_2'$ of a student in group 2 is equal to the score $X_1$ of a student in group 1, the two students may be presumed to have done equally well. This presumption is of course subject to error; the error in comparing the means, $\overline{Y}_2'$ and $\overline{X}_1$, however, is much smaller. If tests $X$ and $Y$ are parallel, their reliabilities are equal to their correlation, and the error incurred in using equated tests is of the same order of magnitude as that incurred in giving the same test to the groups to be compared. In most experiments we are interested only in the differences of the means $M_2$ and $M_1$ given by

$$M_2 - M_1 = \overline{Y}_2' - \overline{X}_1 = a\overline{Y}_2 + b - \overline{X}_1. \tag{13.3}$$

Therefore, as a rule, transforming individual students' scores is unnecessary. All we need are the values of $a$, $b$, $\overline{X}_1$, and $\overline{Y}_2$.

### An example of research design

Question: What happens to students' learning if some chapters in the text are assigned but not covered in lectures? We may hypothesize that the students will have less knowledge in areas not covered in the lectures and that perhaps their ability to read will improve more than under the usual arrangements. A possible research design may be to lecture on all the text chapters, but to allow only half the class to attend any one lecture. At the end of the quarter, each half-class will have heard approximately the same number of lectures but on different topics. The class should be divided into halves, at random if the class is quite large, or matched. The matching can be done on whatever information is available; if, for example, the experiment is to take place in the second quarter, first-quarter grades can be used for the matching. Each half should attend groups of consecutive lectures on coherent units—a chapter in the text or a group of chapters. It may also be advisable to instruct all students in the techniques of reading the text.

Tests given at various intervals during the quarter may be on knowledge and the quarterly may be primarily on understanding. All these tests should have part-scores based on content: one score for the content of the lectures heard by one half of the class and another score on the content of the lectures heard by the other half. Each group will thus have two mean scores on knowledge and two mean scores on understanding. Let the mean score and standard deviation of the knowledge scores of one group ($n_1 = 50$ students) be $M_1 = 100$ and $S_1 = 20$; and of the other group ($n_2 = 40$ students), on the same content, be $M_2 = 94$ and $S_2 = 18$. Then (by equations 7.8 and 7.9):

$$S^2{}_{M_1-M_2} = \left[ \frac{(20)^2}{40} + \frac{(18)^2}{50} \right] \frac{(50 + 40)}{(50 + 40 - 2)} = 16.9;$$

$$S_{M_1-M_2} = \sqrt{16.9} = 4.11; \text{ and}$$

$$z = \frac{100 - 94}{4.11} = 1.46.$$

The probability that a value as large as 1.46 occurred by chance, because one of the groups happened to consist of more able students or students who had better luck in guessing on the test, is about .15 or 15 percent. Thus there is a fairly strong indication that group 1—the group that has heard the relevant lectures—acquired more knowledge of a particular part of the content than the other group. If analogous results are found with the other half of the content, the probability that both results occurred by chance is only $(.15) (.15) = .02$. It may then be reasonably concluded that, under the conditions of the experiment, lectures are superior to mere text reading as a source of knowledge. Similar comparisons can be made with scores on understanding and on combined scores of knowledge plus understanding. If the groups are matched, separate comparisons of learning by superior students and by inferior students can also be made.

To test the influence of text reading without lectures on the ability to read with understanding, we need a different research design, because the ability to read is usually less dependent on content than are knowledge or understanding, and because the two groups have had the same amount of training in that ability. The experimental group may now be the whole class and the control group last year's class, if the latter was taught throughout by the lecture method. The two groups may then be given reading tests equated on the class-before-last or on a class in a similar course at a comparable institution; or, more conveniently, the groups may be given two equated published tests if such are available. From this point on the procedure is the standard one: the standard deviation of the difference of the two means is calculated by equation 7.8 and the level of significance of the difference, by equation 7.9. For more precise or more detailed results, the groups can be matched.

If the experimental group, as compared to the control group, is superior in some abilities and inferior in others, the overall relative value of the two methods of instruction may have to depend on the teacher's opinion of the relative importance of various objectives; in the example described in the preceding paragraphs, on his opinion of the relative importance of reading ability, knowledge, and understanding.

Sometimes the experimental difference between the mean scores of the experimental and control groups is too small to be dependable and yet too large to be disregarded. A value, $z = 1.3$ or larger, for example, will occur by chance 20 percent of the time. In such a case, the experiment can be repeated at a later time. If the value of the new $z$ is still positive, say, 1.2, and thus significant at the 23 percent level, the combined results of the two experiments may be considered significant at the 4.6 percent level (obtained by multiplying the two probabilities .20 and .23)—a very respectable level indeed. If the experiment cannot be repeated, a difference significant at the 20 percent level should not be dismissed. After all, this number indicates that the odds are four to one in favor of one of the methods; unless the favored method is inconvenient or distasteful, the teacher should use it, even if some of his best friends are statisticians.

### 13.3   IMPROVEMENT OF TESTING

In various chapters it has been suggested that, for a teacher, the main criterion for a test is its prognostic value, and that a test should provide a reliable part-score on each important objective. If we agree in addition that a test should be short, we have laid down guidelines for research in test improvement.

#### Prognostic tests

The predictive powers of a test can be determined directly only by following the progress of students who have taken the test. (An indirect way is to correlate the test with another test whose predictive power is known.) The scores on the test should be correlated with the success of the students in the next quarter of the course, in the next course, in the undergraduate college, in the graduate school, or in professional work. If the correlations are to lead to an improvement in teaching or testing, it is necessary to know both what content and what kinds of competence the test measures.

We must therefore ask what the predictive powers are of tests of knowledge, analytical or intuitive understanding, and the ability to learn. Several investigators have attacked the problem of prediction in reverse: they have tried to find in the pasts of successful men some indexes that could have been used for prediction. The results are interesting but they offer little guidance to the teacher: a very successful scientist seems often to have been an only child and to have studied beyond the requirements. One of the difficulties in the time-reversal prediction studies is the lack of detailed information on the abilities the successful man exhibited while still a student. His course grades, for instance, were probably based mostly on knowledge and thus not very good for prediction.

### Tests for "pure" abilities

In Section 8.6 a method was described for estimating the relevance of an exercise to an ability. From the study of exercises of high relevance, such as those in Part II of this book, the teacher can learn to write or choose exercises that measure primarily one ability. There are now no good recipes for writing such exercises, and anyone who develops a good set of rules or even prepares a test covering only one ability will have rendered valuable service to testing and therefore to teaching.

### Development of new tests

Tests of intuitive, disciplined, and imaginative thinking and of understanding of experiment, as these terms are defined in Section 2.2, are yet to be developed. Essay, oral, and performance tests also need study and improvement. Finally, a test of the competence of understanding physics, or any other science, that will be considered valid by a large panel of judges is badly needed. Such a test, even if long and clumsy, can be used for much needed validation of shorter and more convenient tests.

### Other problems in testing

It seems highly desirable that absolute standards be used for assigning grades to students. *All* students with an excellent understanding of science, not simply the top 10 or 15 percent of the class, should be so certified. Similarly, all those without an adequate understanding should be refused a passing grade. A reasonably good technique, described in Section 12.6, has been developed for determining the failing score on an objective test, but no such technique is available for defining excellence. That some second-raters now get top ranking is less unfortunate than that talent is allowed to languish in obscurity.

In conclusion, let us remember that this chapter outlines only a few of the problems in teaching and testing that can and should be attacked. If such problems are to be solved, science teachers—individually or in groups—must engage in educational research.

# 14

# TOPIC INDEX
# AND ANNOTATED BIBLIOGRAPHIES

Section 14.1 contains arguments for systematizing references to other writings under a topic index. Section 14.2 explains how the topic index of Section 14.3 can be used. The following sections are annotated bibliographies: Section 14.4, of books on teaching and testing; Section 14.5, of recommended texts in the physical sciences; Section 14.6, of sources of scientists' original writings suitable for introductory courses; and Section 14.7, of books on the nature and structure of science. Section 14.8 lists books that may form an inexpensive library for a science teacher.

## 14.1 REFERENCES TO THE LITERATURE IN EDUCATION

The preceding chapters offered opinions on how introductory science should be taught, especially how one can learn to teach it. The reader of this book may find the opinions sensible, either immediately or after reading the arguments for them, which, as a rule, make an appeal to his own experience. If not, perhaps he will be convinced by the authorities and empirical evidence cited in this chapter.

Finding empirical support for assertions in the natural sciences, especially in physics, is pleasant and unambiguous. One can usually find a "classical" experiment, an experiment that everybody who is anybody has found entirely persuasive. Who can deny the conclusiveness of the Joule-Thompson porous plug experiment on intermolecular forces? Even its title, if one can suppress an unworthy giggle, is as sonorous as James Joyce's *Anna Livia Plurabelle*. The persuasiveness of physics experiments rests on the high degree of accuracy with which they can be described and repeated and on the coherence of physics generalizations. Experiments in education, on the other hand, defy accurate description or repetition. Any reasonably good description of the students, of how the teacher acted, and of the educational outcomes would require an impractically long report. In the usual

**200**

brief article, the assertion that the lecture method was used leaves open the question of how good the lectures were, and the assertion that the students' understanding was measured requires for its verification that the reader know the students' background and be prepared to inspect and analyze the measuring devices.

Of course, even a physics experiment cannot be fully described. Innumerable factors are not even mentioned because they are considered negligible or irrelevant, and many parts of the apparatus are merely named or shown in a drawing. To be really persuaded by Joule-Thompson's conclusions one must be a physicist with years of experience and versed in physics literature. Even more is required from a reader of a report on educational research, for there is much less agreement on what is negligible or irrelevant than in physics. In fact, the effect of admittedly relevant factors is often reported as uncontrolled. To be persuaded that, for instance, ability to learn can be taught, the author had to read a very large number of reports and several books on learning theory, and then supplement what he had read with information from his own experience. The opinion that the ability can be taught has thus been derived not from one classical experiment but from years of experimentation seen in the light of psychological theories. In the end it appears reasonably certain that training can be transferred even at that general level and that other generalizations now widely accepted by psychologists and educators are well enough supported by empirical evidence to offer the best available guide to teaching.

As was pointed out in earlier chapters, the main strategy of this book is not to tell teachers how to teach but to show them how they can learn to teach. Nevertheless it seems uneconomical for every teacher to try to rediscover the better established generalizations; he should build on the knowledge of others. However, few teachers would probably be willing to steep themselves extensively in psychological and educational research papers; instead, references are given here to hard-cover books written by recognized authorities. The books almost invariably refer to original papers; a persistent reader can therefore look these up.

There are additional difficulties, however, for the "recognized authorities" are recognized by other psychologists and educators, not by science teachers. College science teachers, especially, have little respect for departments of education, for the lore that these departments have accumulated, or for their methods of research. Possible reasons for this lack of respect are discussed in Section 1.1; here it should merely be repeated that, at present, educational and psychological literatures are the *only* available sources of empirical data and theory on teaching and testing. The teacher who takes his teaching seriously must learn from that source or conduct his own research or both. Learning by doing is possible, but a teacher can profit from observing his own teaching and its outcome only if the observations are *planned* to be informative. If they are not, he may still improve but perhaps at the expense of his students and almost certainly at the expense of thousands of wasted man-hours—his own and the students'.

## 14.2  ORGANIZATION OF THIS CHAPTER

In Section 14.3, references to chapters and sections in this book and to other writings are given in the form of questions that thoughtful teachers may have asked themselves. The section can be used in two ways, as a reference and as an index. For example, in Section 3.6 the following is asserted: "As a matter of fact, however, there is little doubt that it is possible to help students attain every one of the three major objectives (4)." The parenthetical "4" stands for references (4). Looking up (4) in Section 14.3, we see that the references relate to the question, "Can the ability to use knowledge in new situations and the ability to learn be taught?" (The first of these abilities is objective 2 and the second is objective 3.) Reference (4) tells us that this question is discussed in Sections 3.3, 3.6, 9.2, and 13.2 of this book and in various books listed by the name of the author, such as Bruner, Cronbach, and so forth. For most books, page references are also given. The title and the publisher of "Bruner" (and of all other books) is given in Section 14.4, where the books are arranged alphabetically by author. The cited sections and books will generally (but not invariably) support the assertion by statement, argument, or empirical evidence. Thus in Bruner (page 6), we find the following sentence: ". . . it is indeed a fact that . . . learning properly under optimum conditions leads one to 'learn how to learn.'"

A reader can also start with Section 14.3, decide which of its questions interest him, and look up the references. The use of the section as an index— a question rather than a topic index—has the advantage that the references listed under a question often have a somewhat closer relevance to that question than to the particular assertion in this book that leads the reader to the references. If the reader has the time and the patience to read all the references under a given number, he will find that the opinions of the authors—almost always supported by references to empirical studies—add up to a fair agreement with the assertion. To make easier the use of Section 14.3 as an index, the individual questions are classified under two general headings, Teaching and Testing, and their subdivisions. Thus, under Teaching are the following general questions: What is teachable? What is worth teaching? How is science now taught? How should science be taught?

The remaining sections are annotated bibliographies.

## 14.3  TOPIC OR QUESTION INDEX

Treatment of the topics relevant to a given question in this section can be found in the cited sections of this book and in other writings. These are given by the author and page. Unless another section is indicated, the author's full name, title of the book, and publisher are given in Section 14.4.

**Teaching**
### What is teachable?

1. What is meant by an "ability"?
   SECTION 2.2.
   ACE, p. 5; Anastasi and Foley, p. 492; Boguslavsky, p. 287; Cronbach (1960), Ch. 9; Freeman, p. 60; Lindquist (1955), p. 648; Vernon, p. 130.
2. How many identifiable—separately measurable—abilities are there that constitute a complex competence such as science understanding?
   SECTIONS 2.2, 2.3, 3.2, 9.2, 11.3, 13.2, and 13.3.
   Anastasi and Foley, pp. 457, 476; Bruner, p. 13; Cronbach (1960), Ch. 9; Cronbach (1963), p. 223; Getzels; Pinard, p. 11; Smith, p. 12; Torrance; Vernon, pp. 132, 144, 146. (See also references under 18 and 35.)
3. Are there any abilities that are essentially unchangeable?
   SECTIONS 2.3, 9.2, and 13.2.
   ACE, p. 5; Anastasi, p. 492; Anastasi and Foley, pp. 224, 238; Maddox, p. 166.
4. Can the ability to use knowledge in new situations and the ability to learn be taught?
   SECTIONS 3.2, 3.3, 3.6, 4.2, 6.2, 9.2, and 13.2.
   Bruner, pp. 6, 12; Cronbach (1963), Ch. 10; Dressel (1954), pp. 73, 238, 292; Henry (1946), p. 15; Henry (1960), p. 45; Judd, p. 195; Sanford, Ch. 8; Schwab, p. 67.
5. Can disciplined, imaginative, and intuitive thinking, and attitudes be taught?
   SECTIONS 2.2, 2.3, 5.3, and 9.2.
   Anastasi, p. 515; Boguslavsky, p. 291; Bruner, pp. 15, 29, 59, 64; Cooper, p. 52; Cronbach (1963), Ch. 10; Dressel (1954), p. 284; Dressel (1961), p. 74; Getzels; Henry (1960), p. 47; Krauskopf, p. 71; Roe; Sanford, Ch. 8; Torrance.

### What is worth teaching?

6. Lists of objectives of teaching.
   SECTIONS 2.1 and 2.3.
   Bloom (1956); Brandwein, pp. 95, 105, 390, 420; Carleton; Commission; Connecticut; Dressel (1961), p. 39; Dressel and Mayhew, p. 4; Gerberich, p. 16; Henry (1946), p. 104; Henshaw, p. 133; Ortega y Gasset, pp. 101–15; President's Committee, p. 34.

7. What are the more permanent learnings that students get from a science course?
   SECTIONS 1.2, 3.3, 8.3, and 13.2.
   Brandwein, p. 365; Bruner, p. 24; Freeman, p. 400; Furst, p. 48; Henry (1946), p. 15; Judd, p. 197; Lindquist (1955), p. 22; Sanford, Ch. 8; Tyler, p. 76.

8. What can students learn from a science course that will be of use to them in the future?
   SECTIONS 3.5, 8.1, 9.2, and 13.2.
   Anastasi, pp. 489, 504; Bruner, pp. 13, 17; Carleton; Connecticut; Cronbach (1960), p. 381; Cronbach (1963), Ch. 10; Freeman, p. 400; Froelich, p. 149; Henry (1946), pp. 43, 104; Judd, pp. 189, 197; Ortega y Gasset, pp. 101–15; Remmers, p. 215; Ross, p. 418; Sanford, Ch. 8; Thorndike, p. 251; Torrance; Wrightstone, p. 10.

### How is science now taught?

9. What image of science and scientists do students have?
   SECTION 5.1.
   Brandwein, Ch. 21; Friedenberg.

10. Do teachers understand teaching?
    SECTIONS 1.1 and 13.2.
    Friedenberg; Henry (1946), p. 25; Judd, p. 189; Williams, pp. 19, 22, 41.

11. What abilities are now taught and used as a basis for grading?
    SECTIONS 1.1, 3.1, 3.6, 6.3, 9.2, and 13.2.
    Brandwein, p. 464; Bruner, p. 66; Commission; Cronbach (1963), Ch. 10; Henry (1946), p. 25; Judd, pp. 6, 197; Lindquist (1955), p. 122; Nedelsky (1949) and (1958); Schwab, p. 39; Williams, p. 40.

12. Are students' talents being recognized? Do students find science courses rewarding?
    SECTIONS 1.4, 3.1, 4.2, 5.2, and 13.1.
    Anastasi and Foley, p. 605; Brandwein, p. 450; Bruner, p. 77; Friedenberg; Judd, pp. 6, 197; Williams, p. 25.

### What improvements in science teaching are being made or contemplated?

13. Improvements in high school science courses.
    SECTION 1.4.
    AAAS; CBAC, Chem. Study, and PSSC in Section 14.5.

14. Improvements in college science courses.
    SECTIONS 1.4 and 13.1.
    AAAS; Carleton; Commission; Connecticut.

15. Should teachers do educational research?
    SECTIONS 1.4, 13.2, 13.3.
    Commission.

## How should science be taught?

16. What should be the overall goal of a student's first course in a science?
    CHAPTERS 3 and 4.
    Bruner, p. 9; Henry (1960); Krauskopf, p. 74; Ortega y Gasset, pp. 101–15; Rogers, *Preface* (Section 14.5); Torrance.
17. How important is the students' motivation? How can it be increased?
    SECTIONS 2.3, 4.2, and 13.2; Chapter 5.
    Boguslavsky, pp. 288, 291; Bruner, pp. 31, 50; Cronbach (1963), pp. 494, 535; Dressel (1961), p. 59; Friedenberg; Krauskopf, p. 71; Roe; Sanford, Ch. 8. (See also references under 27.)
18. Should each separate ability, for example, the ability to interpret data or the ability to learn from a text, be consciously and specifically taught?
    SECTIONS 2.3, 3.2, 3.6, 4.2, 7.2, and 9.2; Chapters 5 and 6.
    Anastasi and Foley, pp. 484, 512; Cronbach (1963), Ch. 10; Dressel (1954), pp. 269, 292; Dressel (1961), p. 72; Furst, p. 5; Henry (1946), pp. 21, 136; Judd, pp. 6, 15; Remmers, pp. 31, 113; Ross, p. 115; Sanford, Ch. 8; Thorndike, p. 66; Tyler, p. 11.
19. Should the students in a school or college science course be specifically trained in reading and study habits?
    SECTIONS 4.2 and 13.2.
    Judd, p. 189.
20. What abilities are best taught by lecture? By discussion? In the laboratory? Through homework assignments?
    SECTIONS 1.2, 3.6, 4.1, 4.2, 6.1, 13.1, and 13.2; Chapter 5.
    Axelrod; Bloom (1946); Dressel (1954), p. 292; Dressel (1961), p. 335; French, p. 197; Krauskopf, p. 71; Nedelsky (1958); Sanford, Ch. 8; Schwab, p. 54; Tyler, p. 87.
21. How should the subject-matter content be chosen?
    SECTIONS 1.2 and 4.2; Chapter 6.
    Cronbach (1963), Ch. 10; Krauskopf, p. 71; Rogers, *Preface* (Section 14.5); Ross, p. 4.
22. How important is integrative content (the history, philosophy, and nature and structure of science)?
    SECTIONS 3.6 and 4.1; Chapter 6.
    Boguslavsky, p. 291; Brandwein, p. 272; Bruner, pp. 11, 24, 31, 52; Dressel (1961), p. 59; Furst, p. 2; Remmers, p. 114; Schwab, p. 110.
23. Should the students understand the teacher's objectives, method of teaching, and evaluative standards and procedures?

SECTION 4.2.

Henry (1946), pp. 42, 136.

24. How should teaching aids, for example, slides, be used?

SECTION 4.2.

Boguslavsky, p. 289; Commission; Dressel (1961), p. 340; Smirnov, *Summary.*

25. Should students be segregated according to ability?

Boguslavsky, p. 287; Levin, p. 4; Lindquist (1955), p. 17.

## Testing

How can tests be used to improve teaching and learning?

26. How useful is evaluation in solving educational problems?

CHAPTER 1.

ACE, p. 12; Boguslavsky, p. 294; Commission; Gerberich, p. 1; Hotyat, pp. 313, 321; Levin, p. 4; Lindquist (1955), Chs. 1 and 2; Nedelsky (1949); Ross, p. 21.

27. Do tests motivate students and direct their efforts?

SECTIONS 9.2 and 13.2.

Anastasi, p. 457; Bloom (1946); Bruner, p. 30; Cronbach (1960), p. 398; Dressel (1954), p. 229; Henry (1946), pp. 25, 136; Judd, p. 6; Lindquist (1955), pp. 41, 514; Schwab, p. 63; Smith, p. 14; Thorndike, p. 66.

28. How can test results be used in counseling students?

SECTION 13.1.

Lindquist (1955), Ch. 3; Nedelsky (1954); Nedelsky (Section 14.5); Smith, p. 10.

29. How can test results be used to suggest specific improvements in teaching (for example, the selection of a better text)?

SECTION 13.2.

Lindquist (1958); Walker.

30. How can tests be used for student selection and placement?

SECTIONS 13.1 and 13.2.

ACE, Chs. 2 and 3; Bloom (1946); Bloom and Peters; Bruner, p. 11; Cronbach and Gleser, pp. 1, 8, 68; Dressel (1961), p. 314; Freeman, p. 357; Henry (1960), p. 51; Lindquist (1955), Ch. 4; Skard, p. 4.

What does a given test measure?

31. What abilities can be measured by tests?

SECTIONS 2.3 and 9.2.

Anastasi, p. 489; Dressel (1954), p. 284; Freeman, p. 377; Froelich and Hoyt, p. 149; Holton; Pinard, p. 74.

32. How can one tell what a test measures and how accurately (validity)?

SECTIONS 2.2, 7.1, 7.3, 8.3, and 11.1.

Anastasi, pp. 166, 492; Bloom (1946); Cronbach (1960), pp. 348–56; Gulliksen, Chs. 9 and 11; Lindquist (1955), p. 253 and Ch. 16; Ross, p. 114; Vernon, p. 228; Walker. (See also references under 37.)

33. What are the students' mental processes as they work on a test question?
SECTIONS 2.2, 8.3, and 11.5.
Bloom and Broder, pp. 2, 8; Sarason.

34. Can objective tests measure higher mental processes?
SECTION 9.2; Chapter 6.
Anastasi, p. 515; Cronbach (1960), pp. 370–74; Freeman, p. 400; Froelich and Hoyt, p. 149; Furst, p. 100; Gerberich, p. 137; Lindquist (1955), p. 212; Tyler, p. 27. (See also references under 58.)

35. To what extent do two given tests measure the same ability (correlation)?
SECTIONS 7.2 and 8.6.
Anastasi, p. 132; Furst, p. 49; Gulliksen, p. 13; Judd, pp. 11, 135; Thorndike, p. 519.

36. How can the scores on two tests be compared or equated?
SECTION 13.2.
Gulliksen, p. 299; Lindquist (1955), pp. 576, 750.

37. How trustworthy is a student's score on a test (reliability)?
SECTIONS 7.1, 7.3, and 8.5.
Anastasi, p. 109; Cronbach (1960), pp. 126–32; Furst, p. 321; Gulliksen, Ch. 3 and p. 207; Lindquist (1955), Ch. 15; Remmers and Gage, p. 142; Thorndike, p. 125; Walker, p. 302.

38. How important is high reliability?
SECTIONS 8.5 and 9.3.
Cronbach (1960), pp. 126–27; Lindquist (1955), p. 607; Ross, p. 416. (See also references under 32.)

How should a student's grade for a course be determined?

39. What are the general criteria for assigning grades?
SECTIONS 7.3, 8.1, and 9.1; Chapter 3.
Anastasi, p. 489; Cronbach (1960), p. 17; Thorndike, p. 456. (See also references under 8 and 27.)

40. How can proper weight be assigned to examination, recitation, laboratory, and homework?
SECTIONS 8.4, 12.4, and 12.5.
Cronbach (1960), pp. 339–41; Gulliksen, pp. 336–42; Lindquist (1955), pp. 169, 776; Thorndike, p. 519.

41. Should a test have a separate part devoted to measuring knowledge, another part to measuring understanding, and so forth?

SECTIONS 8.3 and 11.1.

Anastasi, p. 167; Lindquist (1955), pp. 137, 286, 318, 647; Remmers, p. 31; Smith, p. 36.

42. Should a student's grade depend on his performance relative to the rest of the class (grading on a curve *vs.* absolute standards)?

SECTION 12.6.

Boguslavsky, p. 287; Dressel (1961), p. 243; Gulliksen, p. 262; Lindquist (1955), p. 26; Nedelsky (1954).

43. Should the number of letter grades be reduced, say, from A, B, C, D, and F to only three?

SECTIONS 7.3, 8.5, and 12.6.

44. Should guessing be corrected for?

SECTIONS 8.5, 12.3, and 12.4.

Bruner, p. 66; Cronbach (1960), pp. 49–51; Furst, p. 145; Gulliksen, p. 250; Lindquist (1955), pp. 268, 365; Nedelsky (1954). (See also references under 37.)

45. Should answers other than the right one be given some credit?

SECTIONS 7.3, 8.5, 12.4, and 12.6.

Furst, p. 157; Gulliksen, p. 246; Lindquist (1955), p. 369; Nedelsky (1954).

46. In assigning grades should breaks in the distribution be used?

SECTION 12.6.

Gulliksen, p. 266.

### Should teachers construct their own tests?

47. What can a teacher learn from *preparing* tests?

SECTIONS 1.2 and 9.3.

ACE, p. 12; Gerberich, p. 1.

48. What are the advantages of the teacher's own tests? What are the advantages of those prepared by an outside agency?

SECTIONS 9.3 and 12.2.

ACE, p. 44; Bloom (1946); Boguslavsky, p. 287; Cronbach (1960), pp. 394–400; Dressel (1961), p. 250; Lindquist (1955), pp. 37, 65, 138; Ross, p. 56; Thorndike, p. 270; Tyler, p. 71; Wrightstone, p. 11.

49. Can teachers construct valid tests measuring higher mental processes, such as tests on the ability to learn?

SECTION 9.3.

Gerberich, pp. 1, 5; Lindquist (1955), p. 120.

50. How does one design test questions measuring a particular ability, for example, understanding?

SECTIONS 8.3 and 11.5.

Anastasi, p. 167; Furst, p. 112; Henry, (1946), pp. 46, 64; Lindquist (1955), Ch. 7.

51. What directions should the students taking a test be given?
    SECTION 12.3.
    Dressel (1961), p. 235; Lindquist (1955), pp. 255, 524; Thorndike, p. 73.
52. How difficult should the test questions be? Should the more difficult questions be put at the end of the test?
    SECTIONS 7.3, 7.4, 8.5, and 12.3.
    Gulliksen, p. 374; Lindquist (1955), pp. 178, 309.
53. How much time should the students be allowed on a test?
    SECTION 7.3.
    ACE, p. 54; Cronbach (1960), pp. 47, 221–23; Furst, p. 318; Gulliksen, p. 203; Lindquist (1955), p. 334; Vernon, pp. 132, 165.
54. How can test questions be improved (item analysis)?
    SECTION 7.4; Chapter 11.
    Anastasi, p. 164; Borko; Gulliksen, p. 363; Jaspen; Lindquist (1955), p. 305.

## What are the virtues and defects of various forms of tests?

55. What are the relative advantages of various forms of tests, such as essay *vs.* objective?
    CHAPTER 10.
    Judd, p. 185; Lindquist (1955), p. 204; Nedelsky (1953); Ross, p. 166; Thorndike, p. 42; Vernon, pp. 223, 228; Whyte.
56. What are the strengths and weaknesses of formal and informal oral tests? How can the weaknesses be diminished?
    SECTIONS 10.1 and 11.3.
    Dressel (1961), p. 268; Hartog.
57. What are the strengths and weaknesses of essay tests? How can the weaknesses be diminished?
    SECTIONS 10.2, 11.2, and 11.5.
    Cronbach (1960), p. 65; Gulliksen, p. 211; Hoffman, p. 49; Lindquist (1955), Ch. 13; Nedelsky (1953); Ross, p. 195.
58. What are the strengths and weaknesses of all objective tests and of their varieties, for example, multiple-choice tests?
    SECTIONS 8.1, 10.2, and 11.5.
    Barzun, p. 139; Hoffman; Lindquist (1955), p. 209; Whyte.
59. What are the strengths and weaknesses of performance (or laboratory) tests?
    SECTIONS 3.6, 10.3, and 13.2; Chapter 6.
    Kruglak; Lindquist (1955), Ch. 12; Nedelsky (1958).

## 14.4 ANNOTATED BIBLIOGRAPHY OF BOOKS ON TEACHING AND TESTING

Almost all the references cited in Section 14.3 are listed below, alphabetically by author; the rest of the references are listed in Sections 14.5 to 14.7.

AAAS (American Association for the Advancement of Science), "Report on Broad Improvement in Science Education." *Science Education News*, 1961.

ACE (American Council on Education), *College Testing*. Washington, D.C.: 1959. A very general, nonmathematical analysis of evaluation theory and of uses of tests in college. More useful to the administrator than the teacher but for both, a good introduction to testing.

Anastasi, A., *Psychological Testing*. Macmillan, 1957. A scholarly, well-organized, and very well-written text on the theory and application of measurement and evaluation. It contains criticisms of published tests. Most useful to a psychology major but can be read with profit by counselors and teachers, even though the field covered is much broader than educational testing and some knowledge of elementary statistics is presupposed. (The last two statements apply, unless otherwise noted, to the following books on this list: Cronbach (1960), Freeman, Furst, Lindquist, Remmers and Gage, Ross, Thorndike, Vernon.) The second (1961) edition reviews tests that have appeared since 1957 and has an interesting discussion of decision theory. Otherwise, the book's usefulness, compared with the 1957 edition, has increased for psychology students and decreased for the teacher.

Anastasi, A., and J. P. Foley, Jr., *Differential Psychology*. Macmillan, 1949. A fascinating and usually objective analysis of human differences in intelligence, talent, attitudes, and even genius, as functions of age, sex, occupation, and so forth. The reader will be glad to know, for example, that scientists, though not as bright as poets and philosophers, are reasonably masculine, cheerful, modest, and sociable.

Axelrod, J., et al., *Teaching by Discussion in the College Program*. Univ. of Chicago Press, 1949.

Barzun, J., *The House of Intellect*. Harper Torchbooks, 1962. Professor Barzun writes: "Taking an objective test is simply pointing. It calls for the least effort of mind above that of keeping awake: recognition" (page 139). If Professor Barzun used a typewriter in writing the above sentences, he also had only to recognize the right key and point or push. But surely he thought before or during typing: pointing may require thought. He is right, however, in saying that objective tests make it easier for the students to get by without learning to write.

Bloom, B. S., *The Relationship Between Educational Objectives and Examinations*. Department of Photographic Reproductions, Univ. of Chicago Libraries, 1946.

———, "Thought Processes in Lectures and Discussions." *Journal of General Education*, **7**, 160 (1953).

—— (Ed.), *Taxonomy of Educational Objectives* (*Handbook I: Cognitive Domain*). Longmans, Green, 1956.    The book divides cognitive—as distinct from attitude, value, or interest—objectives of *all* teaching into six categories. This attempt at universality is premature and too facile but nevertheless welcome, for such attempts often reveal problems and suggest questions that might be missed. Many educators have found the taxonomy conducive to more precise communication.

Bloom, B. S., and L. J. Broder, *Problem-solving Processes of College Students.* Univ. of Chicago Press, 1950.

Bloom, B. S., and F. R. Peters, *The Use of Academic Prediction Scales for Selecting College Entrants.* Free Press, 1961.    Prediction of college grades from high school grades is greatly improved if the latter are weighted on the basis of previous correlation between the grades of a given high school and a given college.

Boguslavsky, G. W., "Educational Research in the Soviet Union." *The School Review,* **66,** 283 (1958).    In the Soviet Union, empirical studies of correlation between teaching method and success on tests are unknown. Educational research is basic: on motivation, perception, long-term retention, and transfer.

Borko, H. (Ed.), *Computer Application in the Behavioral Sciences.* Prentice-Hall, 1962.

Brandwein, P. F., F. G. Watson, and P. E. Blackwood, *Teaching High School Science: A Book of Methods.* Harcourt, Brace & World, 1958.    A comprehensive analysis of the major problems of science teaching. The book is addressed to the high school teacher but much of it, especially the following chapters, could be read with profit by the college teacher: Chapter 2, on the way of the scientist; 13 and 14, on chemistry and physics courses; and 21, especially the part on the pupil's image of science and scientists.

Bruner, J. S., *The Process of Education.* Harvard Univ. Press, 1960.    A short, highly readable account of the main currents of thought at a ten-day conference of scientists, and other scholars and educators, who met in 1959 "to discuss how education in science might be improved in our primary and secondary schools." Highly recommended.

Buros, O. K., *The Fifth Mental Measurement Yearbook.* Highland Park, N.J.: Gryphon Press, 1959.    The most comprehensive reference to testing. It contains critical reviews of published tests and books on testing. It is so admirably indexed that even a novice can easily find references to the kind of test he needs. (The sixth yearbook is in preparation.)

——, *Tests in Print.* Gryphon Press, 1961.

Carleton Conference, "Improving the Quality and Effectiveness of Introductory Physics Courses: Report of a Conference Sponsored by the American Association of Physics Teachers." *American Journal of Physics,* **25,** 417 (1957).

Commission on College Physics, "Progress Report." *American Journal of Physics,* **30,** 665 (1962).

Connecticut Conference, "Laboratory Instruction in General College Physics: Report of the Committee on Conclusions." *American Journal of Physics,* **25,** 436 (1957).

Cooper, R. M. (Ed.), *The Two Ends of a Log.* Univ. of Minnesota Press, 1959.

Cronbach, L. J., *Essentials of Psychological Testing,* 2nd edition. Harper, 1960. One of the standard texts. Clearly written. Has a good elementary discussion of factor analysis.

————, *Educational Psychology,* 2nd edition. Harcourt, Brace & World, 1963. Chapter 10 on transfer of training is especially recommended and can be read in an hour.

Cronbach, L. J., and G. C. Gleser, *Psychological Tests and Personnel Decisions.* Univ. of Illinois Press, 1957.    A book for the specialist. Some of its ideas are provocative or even provoking, such as the essentially correct but brutal concept of the "pay off" as criterion for a test, which requires that test-users assign additive numerical values to money, learning, and perhaps happiness.

*Daedalus.*    The quarterly of the American Academy of Arts and Sciences is the most intellectual, nonspecialized American periodical. Each issue is devoted to the discussion of one general topic by a great variety of contributors, each eminent in some one field. Issue 88 (Winter, 1959) discusses education in the age of science.

Dressel, P. L .(Ed.), *Evaluation in General Education.* Wm. C. Brown Co., 1954. An analytical report of several empirical studies.

————, *et al., Evaluation in Higher Education.* Houghton Mifflin, 1961.

Dressel, P. L., and L. B. Mayhew (Eds.), *Science Reasoning and Understanding.* Wm. C. Brown Co., 1954.    The discussions of how excerpts from physical or biological science literature can be used in teaching and testing various abilities are of particular interest. Contains a large bibliography on science in general education.

Freeman, F. S., *Theory and Practice of Psychological Testing.* Holt, 1955. The first two chapters are recommended as a clear exposition of the principles of psychological testing.

French, S. S., *Accent on Teaching.* Harper, 1954.

Friedenberg, E. Z., "Why Students Leave Science." *Commentary,* **31,** 144 (1961). A report, written with elegance and humor, on a brilliantly designed empirical study of the reasons why *good* science students leave science for other fields. The conclusions are convincing and damning of the prevalent methods of teaching college science. Fascinating and depressing reading. (This report with fuller data is now published in book form: C. Nordstrom and E. Z. Friedenberg, *Why Successful Students of the Natural Sciences Abandon Careers in Science.* Brooklyn College, 1961.)

Froelich, C. S., and K. B. Hoyt, *Guidance Testing,* 3rd edition. Chicago: Science Research Associates, 1954.

Furst, E. J., *Construction of Evaluative Instruments.* Longmans, Green, 1958. A simple but careful treatment of the fundamental problems of evaluation and test construction.

Garrett, H. E., *Testing For Teachers.* American Book, 1959.    A simple and clear guide for the school teacher's use of published tests.

Gerberich, J. R., *Specimen Objective Test Items: A Guide to Achievement Test Construction.* Longmans, Green, 1956.    A guide to teachers on how to write test items, illustrated by items from many fields and many educational levels. Contains an extensive and well-organized bibliography.

Getzels, J. W., and P. W. Jackson, *Creativity and Intelligence*. Wiley, 1962.

Goheen, J. W., and S. Kavruck, *Selected References on Test Construction, Mental Test Theory, and Statistics*. U.S. Government Printing Office, 1950. Especially useful to one who wants to do research in teaching or testing.

Guilford, J. P., et al., *Studies in Aptitudes of High-Level Personnel*. Reports from the Psychological Laboratory, Univ. of Southern California, 1950–54.

Gulliksen, J., *Theory of Mental Tests*. Wiley, 1950.    A theoretical-mathematical text that is classic in lucidity, logic, and organization. The treatment is in the best sense mathematical: *all* assumptions are stated, and thus the content and the realm of applicability of every formula are clear. The reader must be at home with algebra and familiar with the concepts of elementary statistics. College teachers of science will probably find this book the most congenial exposition of the subject. The first fifty-seven pages give a superb introduction to the fundamentals of statistics.

Harris, C. W. (Ed.), *Encyclopedia of Educational Research*, 3rd edition. Macmillan, 1960.

Hartog, P., and E. C. Rhodes, *An Examination of Examinations*. London: Macmillan, 1935.    A classic, documented study of essay and oral tests. As a treatise on the anarchy that is associated with such tests even in the hands of experts, the book is an excellent antidote to B. Hoffman's *Tyranny of [objective] Testing* (which is reviewed below).

Henry, N. B. (Ed.), *The Measurement of Understanding*. The 45th Yearbook of the National Society for the Study of Education, Part I, Univ. of Chicago Press, 1946.    Examples of test questions measuring various aspects of understanding in science and other fields at school and college levels. The theory chapters are clear and addressed to school teachers.

———, *Rethinking Science Education*. The 59th Yearbook of the National Society for the Study of Education, Part I, Univ. of Chicago Press, 1960.

Henshaw, C., "A Critical Analysis of the Natural Sciences in General Education," in R. D. Miller (Ed.), *General Education at Mid-Century*. Florida State Univ., 1950.

Hoffman, B., *The Tyranny of Testing*. Crowell-Collier, 1962.    Despite its title, the book is not a much needed criticism of testing but only criticism of a particular form—the objective. The main objection seems to be that an objective item is often ambiguous and penalizes a talented student who could, but is not allowed to, defend his choice of response. This objection seems especially valid if the item cannot be answered by following an algorithm or a sanctioned recipe, that is, if it is designed to measure understanding. Although a test as a whole is much less likely than a single item to penalize a particular kind of subtle mind, the correlation between students' scores and their ability is of course far from perfect; in particular, there are no existing objective tests that can identify the brilliant and the imaginative. To identify these students, an essay test read by a "wise examiner who knew his subject well" would have been preferred. One may agree, especially if the examiner is willing to read many essays. But where this kind of reader can be found—whether among overworked high school science teachers or bored graduate assistants in the college—the book does not say. It does suggest a way to improve objective tests: they are to be censored by a committee of scholars. Presumably the committee would certify that the right answer was in agreement with the latest research findings and thus proof against the subtlest attack. The resulting items would probably be as clean—and as valuable—as a whistle. The following is an example of criticism (much shortened) of a physics item. Item:

Potassium metal loses electrons when struck by light (the photoelectric effect) more readily than lithium metal because

A. the potassium atom contains more protons than does that of lithium.
B. the valence electron of potassium is farther from the nucleus than is that of lithium.
C. potassium occurs above lithium in the electro-chemical series.
D. the potassium atom contains more electrons than does that of lithium.
E. the potassium nucleus is larger than that of lithium.

The desired answer is B. But D is a "more profound answer" because it gives a reason for B. By the same token, A "cuts deeper" than D.

Our comment: Presumably an even more thoughtful student would have preferred an answer that gives a reason for A. But nobody knows the reason for A. The proposed committee on "un-American testing" might as well include as the most profound response to all questions in science, "nobody really knows."

Holton, G., "Testing and Self-discovery." *University College Quarterly* (Michigan State Univ.), **9**, 329 (1963).

Hotyat, F. A., "Education Research in French-speaking Countries of Europe." *The School Review*, **66**, 313 (1958).    In French-speaking countries interest in empirical studies is growing among educators and governmental agencies.

Jackson, R. W. B., and A. J. Phillips, *Prediction Efficiencies by Deciles for Various Degrees of Relationship*. Res. #11, Department of Education, Univ. of Toronto.

Jaspen, N. "Self-scoring Item Analysis Procedure for the IBM, 1620." *Educational and Psychological Measurement*, **22**, 595 (1962).

Judd, C. H., *et al.*, *Education as Cultivation of the Higher Mental Processes*. Macmillan, 1936.

Krauskopf, K. B., "A Critical Analysis of the Natural Sciences in General Education," in *General Education at Mid-Century*. Florida State Univ., 1950.

Kruglak, H., and C. N. Wall, *Laboratory Performance Tests for General Physics*. Western Michigan Univ., 1959.    The book presents pertinent elements of evaluation theory, describes in complete, practical detail many performance tests, and gives a critical review of published research.

Levin, D., *Soviet Education Today*. London: Staples Press, 1959.    In the Soviet Union, intelligence testing is in complete disrepute: "There is no such thing as fixed innate ability which is unchangeable." Teachers themselves, not psychological counselors, are asked to deal with "difficult" children. (See also Boguslavsky above.)

Lindquist, E. F. (Ed.), *Educational Measurement*. Washington, D.C.: American Council on Education, 1955.    The best general reference book, with each chapter an independent essay. The content is very uneven in difficulty: Part

I, "The Functions of Measurement in Education," can—and should—be read by all teachers; Part II, "The Construction of Achievement Tests," is practical and useful but harder; and Part III, "Measurement Theory," is scholarly, but many sections are aimed at the graduate student in the field. The science teacher who works through the book will find his labor rewarded.

————, *Design and Analysis of Experiments in Psychology and Education.* Houghton Mifflin, 1958.    Strictly for a trained researcher.

Maddox, H., "Nature-Nurture Balance Sheets." *British Journal of Educational Psychology,* **27,** 166 (1957).

Miles, V. W., "Bibliography With Annotations for Science in General Education at the College Level." *Science Education,* **35,** 159 (1951).

Mills, L. C., and R. M. Dean, *Problem-solving Method in Science Teaching.* Bureau of Publications, Columbia Univ., 1960.

Nedelsky, L., "Formulation of Objectives of Teaching in the Physical Sciences." *American Journal of Physics,* **17,** 345 (1949).

————, "Evaluation of Essays by Objective Tests." *Journal of General Education,* **7,** 209 (1953).

————, "Absolute Grading Standards for Objective Tests." *Educational and Psychological Measurement,* **14,** 3 (1954).

————, "Introductory Physics Laboratory." *American Journal of Physics,* **26,** 51 (1958).

Obourn, E. S., *Analysis of Research in the Teaching of Science.* U.S. Government Printing Office, 1958.

Ortega y Gasset, J., *El libro de las misiones.* Madrid: Espasa-Calpe, S. A., 1959. This paperback contains a brilliant essay on the function of the university and teaching of science.

Pinard, A., *et al., Tests differentiels d'intelligence.* Editions Institut de Psychologie, Université de Montreal, 1954.    A short report (in French) on empirical evidence for several kinds of "intelligence" among university professors and advanced students. The authors believe that the *kind* of intelligence one possesses may be as important as its level or degree.

President's Committee on Education Beyond the High School, *Second Report to the President.* U.S. Government Printing Office, 1957.

Psychological Corporation, The, *Test Service Bulletins.* Psychological Corporation, 304 East 45th St., New York 17, N.Y.    Test service bulletins, available free of charge, discuss measurement processes and concepts, for example, reliability, authoritatively and nontechnically. Other test publishers listed in Section 15.5, especially ETS, provide useful literature and advice.

Remmers, H. H., and N. L. Gage, *Educational Measurement and Evaluation.* Harper, 1955.    The book is easy to read. Recommended chapters are 2, "Nature of Achievement," 3, "Achievement Testing," and 8, "The Nature of Mental Abilities."

Roe, A., *The Making of a Scientist.* Dodd, Mead, 1953.    The scientist develops from a boy who "found that there was a way in which he, personally, could find things out for himself, and that there could be things that mattered to him."

Ross, C. C., *Measurement in Today's Schools,* revised by J. C. Stanley, 3rd edition. Prentice-Hall, 1954.    Not an up-to-date book even in the most recent revision, but Chapter 1, "Measurement in the Modern World," and, to a lesser extent, Chapter 2, "The Historical Development of Measurement in Education," are highly readable and interesting.

Sanford, N. (Ed.), *The American College.* Wiley, 1962.    Chapter 8, "Procedures and Techniques of Teaching: A Survey of Experimental Studies," by W. J. McKeachie, gives a clear, convincing, and well-documented account of what is known of the relation between teaching method and students' learning. Highly recommended.

Sarason, I., "Test Anxiety and Intellectual Performance of College Students." *Journal of Educational Psychology,* **52**, 201 (1961).

Schultze, W., "Educational Research in the Federal Republic of Germany." *The School Review,* **66**, 298 (1958).    In Germany, American education is regarded as pragmatic and positivistic. Interest in empirical studies is recent but growing.

Schwab, J. J., and P. F. Brandwein, *The Teaching of Science.* Harvard Univ. Press, 1962.    Schwab's essay is an eloquent and convincing argument for teaching science as a process of inquiry and against the prevalent "rhetoric of conclusions."

Skard, O., *et al., Development and Application of Tests for University Students in Norway.* Washington, D.C.: American Psychological Association, 1954.

Smirnov, S. S. (Ed.), *Voprosy psilhologiy pamyati* (*Problems of Psychology of Memory*). Moscow: Academy of Pedagogical Sciences, 1958.    A collection of empirical studies (in Russian) of the complementary roles of words and nonverbal "signals"—pictures, apparatus, or simple requests to visualize.

Smith, E. R., and R. W. Tyler, *Appraising and Recording Student Progress.* McGraw-Hill, 1942.    Chapter 2, "Aspects of Thinking," and the test samples are recommended. These are excellent examples of exercises measuring the higher mental processes. The tests are too complex for achievement testing but excellent for diagnosis.

Thorndike, R. L., and E. Hagen, *Measurement and Evaluation in Psychology and Education.* Wiley, 1955.    A simply and carefully worded book. It contains analyses of published tests, extensive bibliographies, and lists of test publishers with descriptions of the services they provide.

Thurber, W. A., and A. T. Collette, *Teaching Science in Today's Secondary Schools,* 2nd edition. Allyn and Bacon, 1964.

Torrance, E. P., *Guiding Creative Talent.* Prentice-Hall, 1962.

Tyler, R. W., *Constructing Achievement Tests.* Ohio State Univ., 1934.    This is a book of only 110 pages. It contains reports of classical experiments and clearly stated principles of evaluation, especially in science, by perhaps the best-known pioneer in the field.

Vernon, P. E., *The Measurement of Abilities.* Univ. of London Press, 1956. The book is short, lucid, literate, and somewhat intemperate. Recommended are Chapters 7, 9, 10, and 12.

Walker, H. M., and J. Lev, *Statistical Inference.* Holt, 1953.

Whyte, W. H., Jr., *The Organization Man.* Anchor, 1957.

Williams, G., *Some of My Best Friends Are Professors.* Abelard-Schuman, 1958. A sensible, easy to read, and somewhat wordy book of bitter and well-substantiated criticism of college teaching. "Good teaching counts for nothing at all in the major universities" (page 205). "In general, the best research and the worst teaching in the university are done in the science departments" (page 217).

Williamson, E. G. (Ed.), *Trends in Student Personnel Work*. Univ. of Minnesota Press, 1949.

Wrightstone, J. W., *et al.*, *Evaluation in Modern Education*. American Book, 1956.

**14.5  ANNOTATED BIBLIOGRAPHY OF PHYSICAL SCIENCES TEXTBOOKS**

This section includes reviews of a sample of textbooks in the physical sciences at the introductory level. In their treatment of subject matter these textbooks make explicit and extensive use—as integrative content—of the nature and structure of science, in particular, of science as a process of inquiry.

CBAC (Chemical Bond Approach Committee), *Chemical Systems*. McGraw-Hill, 1964.

Chem. Study (Chemical Education Material Study), *Chemistry: An Experimental Science*. W. H. Freeman & Co., 1963.

Both books are high school texts in theoretical chemistry: they attempt to explain chemical phenomena in terms of electrons-plus-nuclei molecular models, that is, in terms of physics. For a theoretical understanding of these complex phenomena, the student needs almost as much physics as is given in a year's course in physics. The books solve the insoluble problem of a one-year course in theoretical chemistry—without a physics prerequisite—by introducing physics concepts, theories, and laws too briefly for real understanding. Yet this half-digested physics is used as the basic explanatory material. As a result, the student must find it difficult to decide what he is expected to understand and what to take on authority and merely remember —one of the most dangerous ambiguities in a science text. To make room for physics—and to allow time for understanding—a theoretical chemistry text must choose phenomena sparingly and primarily for their illustrative value. These texts, however, strive to be encyclopedic in the variety of elements, compounds, and reactions. More wisely, they are theoretical rather than merely descriptive and classificatory, and they do attempt to show some aspects of the nature and structure of science. The only aspect which both texts treat extensively, however, is the relation between theoretical models and phenomena: little is done on criteria for definitions or classifications, and there is little reference to the complexity of phenomena from which an empirical generalization must be wrested by an imaginative scientist. The distinction between models and phenomena, though stated forcefully, is not maintained in the actual treatment of material. In this respect the chemistry texts share the faults of PSSC *Physics*. (See review below.)

Although the grand and commendable design of the CBAC text is to start with physics, develop models, and then use them to explain chemical phenomena, the design has been carried out only half-heartedly. Not only is the preliminary physics too sketchy for the models to carry conviction, but the models are not really used much. After many pages of describing a model made up of spherical electron clouds, fitted as compactly as possible to form molecules, and an orbital model, the text makes a cursory attempt to show a relation between the models and the structural formulas, and from then on depends mostly on the formulas. The text does make very clear the tentativeness of scientific models, clearer than this is done in the PSSC *Physics*.

The Chem. Study text, as compared to the one by CBAC, spends less time in developing models and more on their use. It accomplishes this by postponing a good deal of physics till later. The price of the postponement is the limitation of the earlier discussion to *what* happens to the models in chemical reactions at the expense of *why*. The advantages are that the usefulness of the models is made clear, that chemistry proper is introduced early, and that physics is discussed at leisure and much more thoroughly than in the CBAC text. On the other hand, the Chem. Study text is less able to hold onto its own stated distinction between a concept or theory and an empirical generalization; for example, the text refers to the number of atoms in a molecule as an "experimental fact" but later suddenly becomes overcautious and says that condensed steam from a salt solution "*behaves* like pure water." (Italics added.)

All in all, Chem. Study seems clearer, more thorough, and more convincing than the CBAC text. What really counts, however, is how much students learn; a careful evaluative study is needed to provide empirical evidence on the relative value of the two books.

The authors of both books should be congratulated for their courageous and imaginative attempt to get away from the dreary annotated-handbook form of the standard chemistry text. With all their faults, the books are superior to any other introductory chemistry text for either high school or college teaching.

Conant, J. B. (Ed.), *Harvard Case Histories in Experimental Science*. Harvard Univ. Press, 1957.

Einstein, A., and L. Infeld, *The Evolution of Physics*. Simon and Schuster, 1938. A nonmathematical treatment of the mechanical (Newtonian) and field theories of physical phenomena. It is addressed to a thoughtful reader without formal training in physics. The book is easy to read—the style is informal—but less easy to understand: it requires hard thinking. In the hands of a good teacher who knows physics, the book would be a good text for high school or college.

Holton, G., *Introduction to Concepts and Theories in Physical Science*. Addison-Wesley, 1952.    One of the best college physics texts (it treats chemistry and astronomy only where these play an important role in the growth of physics). The book has three chapters, "On Structure and Method in Physical Science," and ideas from these chapters are utilized in the rest of the text.

Holton, G., and D. H. D. Roller, *Foundations of Modern Physical Science*. Addison-Wesley, 1958.    This book differs from *Holton* in that it has better historical cohesiveness, the addition of nuclear physics, and a less thorough treatment of some topics.

Nedelsky, L., *The Physical Sciences*. McGraw-Hill, 1945.    This book is a study guide for Krauskopf's *Fundamentals of Physical Science*. The latter provides the material in physics, chemistry, astronomy, and geology, and the study guide contains discussions of the relevant aspects of the nature and structure of science, suggestions on how to study, and comprehensive tests. *Krauskopf* is intended for college; with the study guide it can be used in high school.

Physical Sciences Staff, Univ. of Chicago, *Selected Studies in the Physical Sciences for Physical Sciences 105–108*. Univ. of Chicago Press, 1960.    A college physics and chemistry text consisting primarily of selections from original papers, from Galileo to Chadwick's *The Existence of a Neutron*, and of excerpts from some modern texts. Years of experimentation and argument have gone into selecting and editing material that would be of cardinal importance in understanding modern science, truly authentic, and at the same time readable by an average freshman.

PSSC (Physical Science Study Committee), *Physics*. Heath, 1960.    The book, intended for high school use, succeeds superbly in describing the modern view of matter and radiation and in convincing the student that the description is true to nature. The description is more accurate and more sophisticated than that of the standard college text. Pedagogically, a firmer distinction between theoretical models and observable phenomena and between evidence and proof would have been preferable. For example, "at this point we cannot *prove* [that light is a wave] but in the next chapter [we shall]," and "the *evidence* is that molecules of hydrogen gas are *definitely* $H_2$ molecules." (Italics and words in brackets added.) The book would have been improved by less dependence on mathematical representation and more emphasis on understanding of phenomena. Finally, the process of inquiry aspect of physics suffers because the book slights the difficulty scientists have found in inventing fruitful concepts (Newton's m and F is an example) and deciding just what to measure. "Measurement is *the* means by which we make progress" is much too strong a statement. (Italics added.)

The book is highly recommended for college use and for those high school students who are at ease with mathematics. The first six chapters contain formidable formal apparatus that will constitute a nearly impenetrable barrier to the majority of high school youngsters: perhaps these chapters can be treated lightly. The profit obtainable from the book under review will be greatest for future physical scientists, less for other college candidates, and least for those who don't intend to go to college.

Besides the textbook, the following associated materials are available: Science Study Series catalogue and inexpensive paperbacks, for example, *Gravity,* by G. Gamow, from Doubleday and Co., Garden City, New York; films, from Modern Learning Aids, 3 East 54th Street, New York 22, N.Y.; and laboratory apparatus, from Macalaster Scientific Corporation, 253 Norfolk Street, Cambridge 39, Mass.

Rogers, E. M., *Physics for the Inquiring Mind*. Princeton Univ. Press, 1960. A superb work by a sound physicist and talented teacher; it makes possible a real understanding of every major topic treated, both in relation to raw phenomena and to the manmade discipline of physics. It is an excellent text for college students. It is even better for teachers and should be required reading for all high school and most college teachers of physics.

*Scientific American.*    Authoritative, carefully prepared—scientifically, pedagogically, and journalistically—articles on the newest developments in science. Available as offprints (at 20¢ each) from W. H. Freeman and Co., 660 Market Street, San Francisco 4, Calif.

Taylor, L. W., *Physics, the Pioneer Science.* Dover, 1959.    A college physics text that has become a classic and a forerunner of texts that treat physics both as a body of knowledge and as a process of inquiry.


## 14.6  BOOKS CONTAINING ORIGINAL SCIENTIFIC WRITINGS

These books are suitable for introductory courses in the physical sciences.

Knedler, J. W., Jr., *Masterworks in Science.* Doubleday, 1947.

Knickerbocker, W. S. (Ed.), *Classics of Modern Science.* Knopf, 1927.

Leicester, H. M., and H. S. Klickstein, *A Source Book in Chemistry: 1400–1900.* McGraw-Hill, 1952.

Magie, W. F., *A Source Book in Physics.* McGraw-Hill, 1935.

Mather, K. F., and S. L. Mason, *Source Book in Geology.* McGraw-Hill, 1939.

Schwartz, G., and P. Bishop (Eds.), *Moments of Discovery.* Basic Books, 1958.

*Selected Studies in the Physical Sciences for Physical Sciences 105–108.* Univ. of Chicago Press, 1960. (See review in Section 14.5.)

Shamos, M. H. (Ed.), *Great Experiments in Physics.* Holt, Rinehart and Winston, 1962.

Shapley, H., and H. E. Howarth, *A Source Book in Astronomy.* McGraw-Hill, 1929.

Shapley, H., H. Wright, and S. Rapport, *Readings in the Physical Sciences.* Appleton, 1948.


## 14.7  BOOKS ON THE NATURE AND STRUCTURE OF SCIENCE (SCIENCE AS A PROCESS OF INQUIRY, HISTORY OF SCIENCE, PHILOSOPHY OF SCIENCE)

These books are not very technical, yet sound.

Born, M., *The Restless Universe.* Dover, 1951.

Bragg, Sir W., *Concerning the Nature of Things.* Dover, 1954.

Bronowski, J., *The Common Sense of Science.* Harvard Univ. Press, 1953.

Brown, H. S., *The Challenge of Man's Future.* Viking Press, 1954.

Butterfield, H., *The Origins of Modern Science: 1300–1800.* Macmillan, 1951.

Campbell, N. R., *What Is Science?* Methuen, 1921; also Dover.

Cohen, I. B., *The Birth of a New Physics.* A Science Study Series paperback, Doubleday, 1960.

Cohen, M. R., and E. Nagel, *An Introduction to Logic and Scientific Method.* Harcourt, Brace & World, 1934.

Conant, J. B. (Ed.), *Harvard Case Histories of Experimental Science.* Harvard Univ. Press, 1957.

————, *On Understanding Science*. New American Library, 1951.

————, *Science and Common Sense*. Yale Univ. Press, 1951.

de Salla Price, D. J., *Science Since Babylon*. Yale Univ. Press, 1961.

Eddington, Sir A. S., *The Nature of the Physical World*. Cambridge Univ. Press, 1953.

Forbes, R. J., and E. J. Dijksterhuis, *A History of Science and Technology*. Penguin, 1963.

Hall, A. R., *The Scientific Revolution 1500–1800*. Beacon Press, 1956.

Koestler, A., *The Watershed: A Biography of Johannes Kepler*. Anchor, 1960.

Leicester, H. M., *The Historical Background in Chemistry*. Wiley, 1956.

Madden, E. H., *The Structure of Scientific Thought*. Houghton Mifflin, 1960.

Obler, P. C., and H. A. Estrin (Eds.), *The New Scientist: Essays on the Methods and Values of Modern Science*. Anchor, 1962.

Oppenheimer, J. R., *Science and the Common Understanding*. Simon and Schuster, 1957.

Pannekoek, A., *History of Astronomy*. London: Allen and Unwin, 1961.

Platt, J. R., *The Excitement of Science*. Houghton Mifflin, 1962.

Snow, C. P., *The Two Cultures and the Scientific Revolution*. Cambridge Univ. Press, 1959.

Toulmin, S. E., *The Philosophy of Science: An Introduction*. New York: Hutchinson, 1953.

————, and J. Goodfield, *The Architecture of Matter*. London: Hutchinson, 1962.

Whittaker, E., *From Euclid to Eddington*. Dover, 1958.    This book is a little harder than the others but is worth the extra trouble.

Wilson, M., and D. I. Duveen, *Lives in Science*. Simon and Schuster, 1957.

### 14.8    A SMALL LIBRARY FOR A SCIENCE TEACHER

The books listed below would make a good start toward a reference library for a college or high school teacher. They are all accurate, highly readable, and relatively inexpensive. (The prices are, of course, subject to change.)

From Section 14.4:

Brandwein, P. F., *et al.*, *Teaching High School Science: A Book of Methods* ($7.50).

Bruner, J. S., *The Process of Education* ($2.75).

Dressel, P. L., and L. B. Mayhew, *Science Reasoning and Understanding* ($3.75).

Furst, E. J., *Construction of Evaluative Instruments* ($4.75).

From Section 14.5:

Rogers, E. M., *Physics for the Inquiring Mind* ($8.50).

*Scientific American* offprints (20¢ each).

From Section 14.6:

*Selected Studies in the Physical Sciences* ($4.30).

From Section 14.7:

Obler, P. C., and H. A. Estrin (Eds.), *The New Scientist* ($1.25).

Oppenheimer, J. R., *Science and the Common Understanding* ($2.75).

Whittaker, E., *From Euclid to Eddington* ($1.35).

# 15

# AN ANNOTATED BIBLIOGRAPHY
# OF A SAMPLE OF TESTS

This chapter lists and criticizes some published high school and college tests, with recommendations for their use. Section 15.1 lists sources of test exercises and items that teachers can use to supplement their own or published tests. Section 15.2 deals with certification or course-grade tests in physics, chemistry, and general science; Section 15.3, with entrance and placement tests. Recommendations for certification tests in high school and college chemistry and physics, and for entrance tests to college and to chemistry and physics graduate schools are contained in Section 15.4. Section 15.5 lists test publishers.

This compilation is intended to be representative of what is readily available or widely known, not exhaustive. For a more complete overview of published tests the reader should see books on testing listed in Section 14.4, especially Buros' *Yearbooks* and *Tests in Print*.

## 15.1 SOURCES OF TEST ITEMS OR ITEM IDEAS

Most texts on testing listed in Section 14.4 under Books on Teaching and Testing have illustrative test items. The following contain a large number of items: Bloom (1956); Gerberich; Kruglak; Nedelsky (Section 14.5); and Smith and Tyler.

The following sources are not listed in Section 14.4; they are essentially collections of items.

Dressel, P. L., and C. H. Nelson, *Questions and Problems in Science: Test Items Folio No. 1.* Princeton: Educational Testing Service, 1956 ($27.50).
Several thousand test items in the biological and physical sciences at advanced secondary and college levels. Not all items are technically good enough to be put in a test, but most would make an excellent starting point or could be used with minor modifications.

Znamemsky, P. A., *Sbornik voprosov i zadach po fisike*. Leningrad: Uchpedgiz, 1957.    Contains 1,300 test questions and problems (in Russian) in high school physics that are suitable for U.S. college-level physics.

## 15.2   CERTIFICATION, ACHIEVEMENT, OR COURSE-GRADE TESTS

The tests reviewed in this section have been obtained by writing to all the publishers listed in Buros' *Tests in Print*, 1961, for tests in the physical sciences that high school and college teachers could use as one basis for course grades. Most of the tests have been reviewed in Buros' *Yearbooks*. The tests are listed by the principal ability they measure: it is assumed that the students who take the tests have had the usual school or college courses. For students in unusual courses, the tests may measure very different abilities. With these students, the most important consideration is the degree of novelty the exercises present (see Section 9.1). Under each ability, the tests are classified by subject matter. The name of the publisher is given in abbreviated form in capitals. In Section 15.5, test publishers are listed alphabetically. The reliability of the test, if available, is given in two forms: $r$ is the reliability of the test in its present form, and $R$ is the reliability the test would have if lengthened (or shortened) to one hour. $R$ is the better measure of the relative technical excellence of tests; it has been computed from equation 7.13, which can be written as follows:

$$R = \frac{r}{r + t(1 - r)},$$

where $t$ is the length of the test in hours. Neither $r$ nor $R$, however, is a good measure of the technical excellence of a test (see Section 7.1). Exercises in the reviewed tests are objective and mostly multiple choice, unless otherwise indicated.

### Tests that measure only knowledge

These tests measure objective 1.1, information, and 1.2, knowledge of relations, and primarily information.

#### Chemistry

ACORN, 1958. *National Achievement Tests: General Chemistry Test, Form A.* High school and college, 120 items, 40 minutes.    Almost entirely information. Ability to read rapidly may strongly influence students' scores.

BEM, 1940. *Kirkpatrick Chemistry Test: Form A.* High school. Test I: 104 items, 40 minutes. Test II: 165 items, 40 minutes. $r = .83$; $R = .88$ (per hour).

ERB, 1957. *Cooperative Chemistry Test: Form ERB-RY.* High school, 74 items, 80 minutes.

ETB, 1962. *Midwest High School Achievement Examinations: Form E, Chemistry.* 95 items, 60 minutes.

INDIANA. *Chemistry Tests.* High school. First semester: 103 items, 40 minutes. Second semester: 100 items, 50 minutes. Some items in both tests require short written answers.

OHIO, 1961 and 1962. *Chemistry: District-State Scholarship Tests.* Preliminary: 111 items, 60 minutes. Final: 145 items, 60 minutes.

———, 1961 and 1962. *Chemistry: Every Pupil Tests.* High school. First semester: 90 items, 40 minutes. Second semester: 74 items, 40 minutes.

*Physics*

ACORN, 1958. *National Achievement Tests: General Physics Test, Form A.* High school and college, 130 items, 40 minutes.    Almost entirely information. Subject matter is more appropriate to high school than college. Ability to read rapidly may strongly influence students' scores.

BEM, 1934. *Fullmer-Schrammel Physics Test: Form A.* High school. Test I: 100 items, 40 minutes. Test II: 126 items, 40 minutes. $r = .85$; $R = .90$ (per hour).    Almost entirely information.

ERB, 1957. *Cooperative Physics Test: Form ERB-RY.* High school, 92 items, 80 minutes.    The test has a few items based on a reading passage; these measure the ability to understand short sentences and to locate them in the passage.

ETB, 1962. *Midwest High School Achievement Examination: Form E, Physics.* 122 items, 60 minutes.

INDIANA. *Physics Tests.* High school. First semester: 98 items, 40 minutes. $r = .90$; $R = .93$ (per hour). Second semester: 75 items, 50 minutes.

OHIO, 1961 and 1962. *Physics: District-State Scholarship Tests.* Preliminary: 103 items, 60 minutes. Final: 80 items, 60 minutes.

———, 1961 and 1962. *Physics: Every Pupil Tests.* High school. First semester: 70 items, 40 minutes. Second semester: 80 items, 40 minutes. In each test, 10 items require written answers.

*More than one subject*

BEM, 1941. *McDougal General Science Test: Form A.* High school. Test I: 170 items, 40 minutes. Test II: 160 items, 40 minutes. $r = .90$; $R = .93$ (per hour).

BEM, 1962. *Every Pupil Scholarship Tests: General Science.* High school, 90 items, 40 minutes.

HARCOURT, 1962. *Metropolitan Achievement Tests, High School Science Tests: Forms AM and BM.* 122 items, 55 minutes. $r = .91$ (estimated); $R = .92$ (per hour). The content is natural sciences. The two forms are accurately equated. The manual gives norms for comparing a student's achievement with that of his peers.

## Tests that measure primarily knowledge

Unless otherwise mentioned, these tests measure objectives 2, understanding, and 3, ability to learn, to a very small degree.

*Chemistry*

ACS, 1954. *General Chemistry: Form K.* College, 105 items, 105 minutes. $r = .94$; $R = .90$ (per hour).

ACS, 1959. *High School Chemistry: Form 1959.* 100 items, 80 minutes. $r = .95$; $R = .94$ (per hour).

PERCENTAGE OF ITEMS DEVOTED TO A GIVEN ABILITY

| Ability | ACS, 1959 | ACS, 1954 |
|---|---|---|
| Information (objective 1.1) | 45% | 20% |
| Knowledge of relations (objective 1.2) | 50% | 60% |
| Understanding of concepts and principles (objective 2.1) | 5% | 20% |

The estimate of items on understanding is probably overgenerous: neither test allows quite enough time for thinking.

BEM, 1962. *Every Pupil Scholarship Tests: Chemistry.* High school, 100 items, 40 minutes.

ETS, 1950. *Cooperative Chemistry Test: Form Z.* High school, 81 items, 40 minutes.    Some items may measure understanding if more time is allowed.

HARCOURT, 1950. *Anderson Chemistry Test: Form AM.* High school, 80 items, 40 minutes. $r = .92$; $R = .94$ (per hour).    About 15 percent of the items on the test will test understanding if the students have time to think; the rest of the items are on knowledge. Present time allowance is inadequate for testing understanding. The test can be used at the college level to supplement other tests.

QUEENSLAND, 1956. *Junior Chemistry Test: Form A.* After two years of high school chemistry, 60 items, 35 minutes. $r = .91$; $R = .95$ (per hour). Some items require short written answers.

*Physics*

BEM, 1962. *Every Pupil Scholarship Test: Physics.* High school, 100 items, 40 minutes.    The test has a few items on understanding.

ETS, 1950. *Cooperative Physics Test: Form Z.* High school, 77 items, 40 minutes.

HARCOURT, 1950. *Dunning Physics Test: Form AM.* High school, 75 items, 45 minutes. $r = .88$; $R = .91$ (per hour).    On the test, 30 percent of the items are devoted to information, 45 percent to knowledge of relations, and 25 percent to understanding of concepts and principles. The estimated percentage of items on understanding is based on the assumption that the students have time to think; the recommended time is too short for that. The test can be used at the college level to supplement other tests.

QUEENSLAND. *Junior Physics Tests: Form B.* After two years of high school physics, 55 items, 40 minutes. $r = .84$; $R = .89$ (per hour).    Some items require short written answers.

*More than one subject*

CALIFORNIA, 1954. *California Tests in Social and Related Sciences: Form AA, Test 5, Physical Science.* Grades 9–12, 45 items, 40 minutes. $r = .81$; $R = .87$ (per hour).    With the recommended time, the test measures knowledge only; if more time is allowed, a few items may measure understanding.

CALIFORNIA, 1959. *Survey Test in Physical Science: Form 1*. Grade 9: 45 items, 40 minutes. $r = .81$; $R = .86$ (per hour).    The form is multiple choice but the formulation of the responses makes the test essentially a collection of true-or-false items. (Each response is likely to be evaluated by the student for its truth or falsity rather than for its relevance to the question.) Many items ask for two responses. The number of independent decisions the student is asked to make is thus quite large. With a greater time allowance, some items will measure understanding.

ETB, 1962. *Midwest High School Achievement Examinations: Form E*. Science VII: 86 items, 60 minutes. Science VIII: 132 items, 60 minutes.    The content of both tests corresponds to most general science courses; the items are qualitative (that is, nonmathematical). The science VIII test has a section on "Methods and Meanings of Science." In this section, the right answers resemble assertions from a fairly dogmatic and unsophisticated book. The students who have been taught such information will be tested on knowledge, but at least on knowledge of science as a process of inquiry. Other students, if allowed more time for thinking, will be tested for some understanding.

ETS, 1955. *Cooperative General Achievement Tests, Test II: National Sciences, Form YZ*. End of twelfth grade or entering college freshmen, 60 items, 40 minutes. $r = .88$; $R = .92$ (per hour).    The content is qualitative items in the biological and physical sciences. Ability to understand a passage will be measured if more time is allowed.

## Tests measuring more than academic knowledge

ACE. *Tests of General Educational Development* (GED): *Interpretation of Reading Materials in the Natural Sciences*. High school and college.

ETS, 1957. *Sequential Tests of Educational Progress* (STEP): *Science, Forms 4A, 3A, 2A, 1A*. For grades 4–6, 7–9, 10–12, and 13–14, respectively. 60 items, 70 minutes (two parts of 35 minutes each). The two forms for grades 4–6 and 7–9 have reliabilities of $r = .90$ and $R = .89$. Forms 1A and 2A have reliabilities of $r = .80$ and $R = .77$ (per hour).    Most questions are based on "real life" situations. For example: "How can the productivity of a given farm be increased?" or "What can one do about a possibly impure water supply?" Some items may measure knowledge and understanding of science as a process of inquiry. Almost all situations are too rich and complex to be worked by a recipe. But many complexities can be traced—or so it may seem to the student—not to science but to practicality, economy, safety, and, notably, to the length of the descriptions. Thus understanding, as measured by the tests, partakes of the prudential arts. These cannot be greatly improved in a science course, except perhaps in the lower grades, and may therefore be qualitatively different from objective 2, understanding, which implies relatively formal reasoning within quite specific subject matter. The principal abilities measured by the tests are therefore somewhat ambiguous; the tests probably measure knowledge of science and certain aspects of general—not liberal—education, and general ability or intelligence. The *content* of science knowledge corresponds to objectives 1.2, knowledge of relations; 2.2, interrelationships of principles; and 2.3, nature and structure of science. Some understanding of this content is also measured but, because of complexities outside of science, only as an auxiliary ability. The subject matter is the biological and physical sciences.

The problems of the tests may be similar to those discussed in elementary schools and high schools but not to college science problems. Empirical validity studies are still to be done, but the validity of the tests as a measure of progress in science probably decreases steadily as one goes from the fourth to the fourteenth grade and is low at the college level. Nevertheless, even at the college level, STEP, added to any of the tests reviewed or to the usual homemade tests, will contribute to validity if only because of increased variety.

ETS, 1959. *Tests of the Physical Sciences Study Committee (PSSC).* To be given at various times during the PSSC high school course in physics, 10 tests, 35 items, 45 minutes each.    These tests are for a high school physics course based on a particular text, PSSC's *Physics.* The principal abilities measured by the tests, if given to the students of the course, are probably the ability to work with mathematical representations of physical generalizations and the knowledge of these generalizations (objective 1.2, knowledge of relations). The acquisition of these abilities at the required level will depend for many, perhaps most, students on their understanding of individual topics and principles taught in the course (objective 2.1), especially if the students do not know what the tests are like. Thus understanding is tested indirectly by the majority of exercises. Direct testing of it is much less common because the situations on which exercises are based usually have a close resemblance to those in the text. Weighting knowledge more than understanding is also furthered by the time element. The eighty seconds per item allowance is adequate if the student recognizes the problem as quite like those he has practiced on, but it is, for most items in the tests, too short if he finds the problem so novel that he must spend some time in deciding what principles are applicable and how to apply them. The ability to learn (objective 3) is measured indirectly—insofar as the students have to learn from the text. Learning from the text is more likely to be important in those schools in which the text's treatment of physics is more sophisticated than the teacher's understanding of physics—not an unusual situation, perhaps.

The tests should be a valid measure of the ability to major in physics as it is now taught in our colleges and a good predictor of academic success in other exact sciences. The competence measured by the tests would probably be of little value to a student outside the mathematical sciences and would soon be lost to him because he would not use it. It is possible to classify types of understanding of many physical generalizations and their relation to phenomena into intuitive or nonverbalizable, qualitative or verbalizable, and formal and mathematical. The PSSC tests deal almost entirely with the last type. Many situations are stripped of all physical content, except that expressed by a simple algebraic equation or graph, and it is often possible to substitute "apple" or even "glurg" for "electron" or "photon" without changing the problem or its solution. The abstractions of college physics are a major obstacle to many students; a student with high scores on the PSSC tests need not fear that obstacle. He may also be assured of good grades in college physics courses, for these are like the PSSC tests in that they shy away from the uncouth phenomena of physical reality and preoccupy themselves with highly idealized, highly abstract representations.

The PSSC tests are intellectually tough—considerably harder than most college physics tests—and high scores on them must be limited to bright students. The tests should therefore be at least as good predictors of academic success in any field as, say, the quantitative part of the Scholastic Aptitude Tests. But besides being too abstract and mathematical for future majors in fields other than the exact sciences, the tests measure very inadequately what is perhaps the heart of understanding physics as one of the liberal arts—the interrelationship of principles and the nature and structure of the science (objectives 2.2 and 2.3). The PSSC course and text (see Section 14.5, Physical Sciences Textbooks), however, do not share the limitations of the tests.

Technically the tests are excellent, and the right answer is always unambiguously right, a univocity that is usually restricted to highly formalized exercises. Teachers of college and the more advanced high school physics courses could profitably supplement their own tests with PSSC tests if these were made available. If the tests were given to the students of courses other than the PSSC course, the tests' center of gravity should markedly shift from knowledge to understanding, provided some quite parochial items were eliminated. Although these tests are criticized here for their narrow range of objectives, the range is certainly much wider than that of most tests covering introductory physics courses, either homemade or bought. In fact, the criticism of the PSSC tests may have been too severe: it has been influenced by the feeling that it is unfortunate to have devoted so much talent, thought, and energy to building that sharp and shiny but overspecialized tool—a Phillips screwdriver of a test.

ETS, 1961. *Test on Understanding Science: Form X.* High school, 60 items, 40 minutes. $r = .76$; $R = .83$ (per hour).    The test, known as TOUS, measures primarily knowledge—both information and knowledge of relations—and some understanding. The subject matter, however, is quite different from that of most tests: it concerns procedures scientists employ in their work and the relation of science and scientists to society. Thus it corresponds to the *content* of objectives 2.2, interrelationshp of principles, and 2.3, nature and structure of science. The test is more *about* science than of it. On a good number of items a student with an "enlightened" point of view—one who thinks highly of scientists—will have an advantage. The measure of this attitude, however, is not too dependable. Because the tester's image of the scientist, if not exactly stereotyped, is one that is now generally accepted and widely quoted on this side of the Iron Curtain, it is comparatively easy to imitate. The imitators would be tested for objective 3.3, disciplined thinking.

Unfortunately the test is available for research purposes only; it would form a valuable addition to high school achievement batteries.

ETS, 1961. *The Graduate Records Examinations: The Area Tests, Natural Science, Form JGRI.* Sophomore through graduate school, 75 items, 70 minutes.

This is a very good test of general or liberal education in the natural sciences at an advanced level. The range of behavioral objectives tested is broad: one third of the items measure objective 1.2, knowledge of relations; another third, 2.1, understanding of concepts and principles; and the remaining third are divided among 1.1, information, 2.2, interrelationships of principles, and 3.1 and 3.2, ability to read verbal and nonverbal material. A more liberal time allowance would favor understanding; the recommended time allowance favors those with technical terminology at their finger tips. (The corresponding tests in the social sciences and humanities are also recommended.)

SRA. *The Iowa Tests of Educational Development* (ITED): *Test 6, The Ability to Interpret Reading Materials in the Natural Sciences.* Grades 9–13.

## 15.3  ENTRANCE AND PLACEMENT TESTS

ETS. *American Council on Education Psychological Examination for College Freshmen* (ACE).

ETS. *College Entrance Examination Board Scholastic Aptitude Test* (SAT).

ETS. *Cooperative School and College Ability Tests* (SCAT). Grades 4–14. (ETS recommends using SCAT–STEP combination.)

PS, 1956. *College Qualification Test* (CQT): *Form A.* 200 items, 80 minutes. $r = .95; R = .93$ (per hour).

The tests above fall roughly into two types: the quite abstract tests of mental abilities or intelligence and those that include more specific school-learned abilities. To the former type belong ACE and SAT, and to the latter, CQT and SCAT. The differences among the tests, however, don't seem to be great, and all the tests intercorrelate highly. Recommending one of the tests as the best is made more difficult by great variations in their powers to predict success in different types of college. The present tendency is toward tests including school-learned materials or abilities; therefore one such test, CQT, is reviewed below.

The CQT test is available in three separate booklets: *Verbal,* 75 items, 15 minutes; *Numerical,* 50 items, 35 minutes; and *Information,* 75 items, 30 minutes. The *Information* test measures knowledge (mostly information) of natural sciences and social studies, with a subscore in each of the two areas.

The manual that accompanies the test gives detailed information on norms and on correlations with college grade-point averages, by sex, region, and the type of college—whether public, private, or junior. The correlations or validity coefficients vary from .34 to .73, with a rough median of about .57. This figure is respectably high for an eighty-minute test. Nevertheless it is clear that the test is not a good predictor for some institutions.

## College placement tests

ETS. *College Entrance Examination Board* (CEEB) *Advanced Placement Examinations.* For high school seniors who have taken college-level courses. Chemistry: 3 hours. Physics: 3 hours.    Each test covers the content of the usual one-year college course in the subject. The form is partly objective and partly essay. About 80 percent of either test is devoted to knowledge, with the main emphasis on 1.2, knowledge of relations. The physics test has a large number of items on information but compensates for this by taking a fairly good sample of objectives 2.1, understanding of concepts, 2.3, nature and structure of physics, and 3.1 and 3.2, ability to read verbal and nonverbal material. The chemistry test does not go beyond objective 2.1 but compensates for this by fewer items on information. The college to which the student applies has access to the already graded test essays, CEEB descriptions of the course the student took, and the school's recommendations. On the basis of such material, colleges can grant credit at least as confidently as they now do to transfer students from an average college.

### Entrance to graduate schools (college seniors and graduate students)

ETS. *The Graduate Record Examinations (GRE) Aptitude Test.* 150 minutes.
PS. *Miller Analogies Test.* 50 minutes.

These two tests measure general scholastic ability.

ETS, 1959. *The Graduate Record Examinations Advanced Tests. Chemistry, Form HGR:* 160 items, 3 hours. *Geology, Form KGR:* 200 items, 3 hours. *Physics, Form KGR:* 1962. 100 items, 3 hours.    The geology test is devoted almost entirely to information; it requires no mathematics—not even arithmetic—no physics, and no chemistry. It should be a closed-book test because with a bit of tutoring and a handbook almost any college student should be able to get a high score. A fossil of a test!

About one third of the items in the chemistry and physics tests measure objective 2.1, understanding of concepts and principles; the rest measure 1.2, knowledge of relations. The tests should be useful as a partial measure of achievement at about the end of the sophomore year. It is difficult to see how they can measure readiness for graduate work, except the readiness simply to take more courses—an ability that is well enough measured by undergraduate course grades. Presumably, graduate students should have some potential for research. At a minimum, they should have some understanding of the nature and structure of science, especially as a process of inquiry, and an ability to extract and clearly state information from their experiments and from texts and journals. None of these abilities is measured by either test. A hopeful sign is a considerable improvement of the physics test over its previous form—a sizable shift from items on knowledge toward items on understanding. But there is still a long road ahead, and the prognosis is not very hopeful. Those who train graduate students in science are not acquainted with theoretical pedagogy or evaluation and can't be bothered to learn: little is known about training intelligent adults. Those who know something of these disciplines usually don't know enough science and would find it very difficult to learn enough.

## 15.4  RECOMMENDATIONS

### Recommendations on achievement tests

Tests in college or high school chemistry or physics are not satisfactory: the published tests measure knowledge primarily and slight or entirely disregard the objectives of understanding and ability to learn. It is, however, possible to assemble a reasonably satisfactory course test by using more than one published test and by adding certain items. Two of the tests cited below, CEEB and TOUS, both published by ETS, are now available only under certain circumstances: CEEB for college-level high school courses and TOUS for educational research. But if there is a demand for the tests, the publisher may make equivalent tests more generally available.

All four batteries recommended below should include items on understanding, especially on the nature and structure of the science. Sources listed in Section 15.1 contain items on understanding of concepts and occasional items on interrelationship of principles. Items on the nature and structure of science will have to be written by the teacher. He may find items in Part II of this book helpful.

All four batteries should also include appropriate passages from either of the following tests:

ACE, *Interpretation of Reading Materials in the Natural Sciences.*
SRA, *Iowa Tests of Educational Development: Test 6, Ability to Interpret Reading Materials in the Natural Sciences.*

For a high school chemistry battery add the following:

ETS, *Test on Understanding Science* (TOUS).
HARCOURT, *Anderson Chemistry Test.*    Time allowance per item should be increased; some information items may be omitted.

For a high school physics battery add the following:

ETS, *Test on Understanding Science* (TOUS).
HARCOURT, *Dunning Physics Test.*    Time allowance per item should be increased; some information items may be omitted.

For a college chemistry battery add either of the following:

ACS, *General Chemistry.*    Time allowance per item should be increased.
ETS, *College Entrance Examinations Board (CEEB) Advanced Placement Examinations: Chemistry.*

For a college physics battery add the following:

ETS, *College Entrance Examinations Board (CEEB) Advanced Placement Examinations: Physics.*

### Recommendations on entrance tests

*Entrance to college*    The ability to learn from a textbook is required in all college courses. College entrance tests should therefore measure the ability to read textbook material, in addition to general scholastic ability and the ability to write a short essay. The student may be asked to read passages or chapters of standard texts in the humanities and the social, biological, and physical sciences; and he may then be examined on his understanding of what he has read. In the physical sciences, the tests may well include problems similar to those in the text. If the tests require deep understanding of the written material, the material need not be read under examination conditions. As to the choice of the available entrance tests, a somewhat heterodox suggestion has been discussed in Section 13.1.

*Entrance to graduate school*   The battery of entrance tests to graduate schools should measure readiness for scholarly work. It may include three *Graduate Record Examinations:* the aptitude test, the area test in the natural sciences, and the advanced test in the student's major. These tests should be supplemented with measures of objective 2.3, understanding of the nature and structure of science, and objectives 3.1, 3.2, and 3.32, ability to extract and clearly state the main ideas of texts and articles. All of these objectives can be conveniently measured by asking the student to read an article and a chapter in the *kind* of text that he will be using in his graduate courses and examining him on this material. Appropriate articles in physics can be found in the *American Journal of Physics,* and in all sciences in *Science* and *Scientific American.* The student should criticize the author's conclusions, method of argument, assumptions, and criteria for theory, experiment, and definition; and he should perhaps be able to suggest the next step in research.

Most tests should be open book, for it is usually not necessary that the chapter or article be read under examination conditions. They may be objective, essay, or oral, but a combination of these is best. With the now available testing techniques, readiness for scholarly work has to be measured by ambiguous test questions (see Section 9.2). If the college is sensitive to public criticism it may start with essay examinations, whose faults are easier to sweep under the rug labeled "wise and scholarly readers." Essay examinations have also the genuine advantages of testing for the ability to write and for imaginativeness and creativity.

The preparation of the test and interpretation of its results will take some faculty time, but it will not take so much time as is now wasted on the students who are not ready for graduate work. What is perhaps more important, the suggested supplementary tests are fairly direct. They probe into the student's readiness for graduate work—not into how well he did in his undergraduate days; they may therefore spot the unorthodox or rebellious but talented student. Understanding of science and good grades in courses are by no means perfectly correlated; in fact, the time and energy devoted to getting an A is, in many a course, spent at the expense of real learning. It is left to the reader's imagination what happens to the student who becomes genuinely interested in a topic, digs into literature on it, and thus spends a month instead of the scheduled one day. Such students are becoming rarer but fortunately they still exist.

The suggested supplement to published tests should at some time be empirically validated. This requires that some record of the student's performance on all entrance tests be kept and compared to his later achievement in scholarship and research.

## 15.5  PUBLISHERS OF THE REVIEWED TESTS

ACE. American Council on Education, 1785 Massachusetts Ave., N.W., Washington 6, D.C.

ACORN Publishing Co., Inc. Rockville Centre, Long Island, N.Y.

ACS. American Chemical Society, Examinations Committee, Division of Chemical Education, Univ. of South Florida, Tampa 4, Fla.

BEM. Bureau of Educational Measurements, Kansas State Teachers College, Emporia, Kans.

CALIFORNIA Test Bureau, Del Monte Research Park, Monterey, Calif.

ERB. Educational Records Bureau, 21 Audubon Ave., New York 32, N.Y.

ETB. Educational Test Bureau, Oak St. and Washington Ave., S.E., Minneapolis 14, Minn.

ETS. Educational Testing Service, Princeton, N.J.

HARCOURT, Brace & World, Inc., 757 Third Avenue, New York 17, N.Y.

INDIANA State High School Testing Service for Indiana, Purdue Univ., Lafayette, Ind.

OHIO Scholarship Tests, Dept. of Education, State of Ohio, Columbus 15, Ohio.

PC. The Psychological Corporation, 304 East 45th St., New York 17, N.Y.

QUEENSLAND. University of Queensland Press, St. Lucia, Brisbane, Australia.

SRA. Science Research Associates, Inc., 259 East Erie Street, Chicago, Ill.

# PART TWO
# SAMPLE EXERCISES
# WITH COMMENTS

Part II contains a large number of test exercises designed to measure various aspects of understanding science. The number of exercises is large for three reasons: first, to make clear, primarily by example, the meaning of the terms used in Part I to describe various types of competence, for example, understanding of experiment (the totality of the exercises testing for a given competence may be regarded as a tentative operational definition of the competence); second, to elucidate and exemplify the criteria, for example, homogeneity of responses, for good test exercises that were discussed in Part I, especially in Chapter 11; and, finally, to illustrate various test forms, for example, multiple choice, and to analyze their appropriateness to different situations in some detail.

**How to locate desired exercises**

Most readers interested in constructing good tests will find it profitable to read Part I first. The arrangement and content of Part II is such, however, that it can be read by itself with only occasional references to Part I, provided the reader has read Chapter 2. To this end and in accordance with the purposes stated in the preceding paragraph, an index to the nature of comments made on various exercises is given on page 238. As can be seen from the Table of Contents, test exercises are classified by the ability they measure; subject matter, which is mostly physics and some chemistry, is merely sampled. Part II is divided into four chapters: "Tests for Knowledge," "Tests for Understanding" (analytical and intuitive), "Tests for Ability to Learn," and "Tests for Laboratory and Performance Abilities." Laboratory and performance abilities include knowledge, understanding (analytical and intuitive), and ability to learn. Within each chapter are classifications of objectives and subclassifications concerning content. For example, under ability 2, understanding, is objective 2.1, understanding of concepts and principles, and under that, content 2.12, theories. The first exercise within this content is numbered 2.12-1, the second, 2.12-2, and so forth. These exercises are designed to measure understanding of theories.

A strong word of caution is necessary. The ability measured by an exercise depends on the preparation of the student, especially on the degree of novelty the exercise has for him. Most of the exercises of Part II will probably measure the ability under which they are classified if given to the students of a one-year, non-calculus, college-level course in physics. But the reader should apply the following approximate rule. An exercise probably measures knowledge if the student can find an answer to it in one or two paragraphs of the course textbook or his lecture notes, or if the exercise is very much like a homework assignment. It probably measures understanding if the situation on which the exercise is based could have been, but was *not*, used as illustrative material in the course. Finally, if an exercise is to measure ability to learn, it has to be based on material new to the student.

## Types of exercises

Most of the illustrative exercises have been written by the author, and almost all have been used in examinations in a variety of courses at the University of Chicago. They appear in this book in essentially the form in which they were actually used. All the exercises have correlated positively with the major ability under which they are classified and thus all have helped determine the relevant part-scores. On the other hand, the exercises possess various technical faults. To have improved them would have weakened the empirical assurance that they do measure the appropriate ability; instead, both their bad and good qualities will be used to illustrate the criteria for good tests. The majority of the exercises are of the "objective," that is, prepared-answer, type. Although objective exercises have some disadvantages, they do, because they exhibit both the question and the responses, point much more clearly than essay exercises to the competence they are designed to measure and are easier to analyze and discuss. Moreover the technique of objective tests is both less well known and easier to master than the technique of equally valid essays.

### INDEX TO COMMENTS ON EXERCISES

Column II lists exercises not individually but by groups. Thus the entry 1.1 stands for all the exercises under objective 1.1. Occasionally the more relevant exercises are shown in parentheses. Column I describes the nature or content of the comment made on one or more exercises in the group listed in column II. Column III gives the sections and chapters of Part I of this book in which the general theory underlying the comment is developed.

| I | II | III |
|---|---|---|
| CONTENT OF COMMENTS | EXERCISE NUMBER | PART I |
| *Competence measurable by the exercise.* Evidence or argument that the exercise does test for the specified competence; description of abilities and knowledge, other than the desired competence, that the student needs for working the exercise. | Comments on all exercises deal with this point. | §§ 2.2 and 8.3; Ch. 11 |
| *Importance of competence.* Argument that the competence tested by the exercise is an important objective of introductory physics courses. | Comments on almost all exercises deal with this point. | Chs. 3, 4, 5, and 6; §§ 9.2, 12.1, and 13.2 |

| I | II | III |
|---|---|---|
| CONTENT OF COMMENTS | EXERCISE NUMBER | PART I |
| *Method of attack.* Description of methods a student may use in working the exercise. | 1.1, 1.21, 1.23, I2, 3.12, and 3.21 | §§ 2.2, 8.3, and 11.5 |
| *Directiveness of exercise.* Analysis of how much of an exercise the student must read before he can be sure of what is expected of him. | 1.1, 1.21, 2.11, 2.13, 2.2, and 2.32 (16–22) | § 11.5 |
| *Homogeneity of responses.* Analysis of the relation between the degree of desired competence possessed by the student and the relative attractiveness to him of the right and wrong responses. | 1.1, 1.22, 2.11, 2.12, and 2.32 (16–22) | § 11.5 |
| *Types of responses.* Analysis of various types of responses, especially their degree of correctness. | 1.1, 1.21, 1.22, 1.23, 2.11, 2.12, 2.13, 2.14, 2.2, 2.31, 2.32 (1–7 and 16–22) | Ch. 11 (especially § 11.5); §§ 12.4 and 12.6 |
| *Formal clues.* Discussion of clues, having little to do with understanding of physics, that a student may follow in working the exercise. | 1.1, 1.21, 1.22, 1.24, 2.31, 2.32 (1–7 and 16–22), and 3.12 | Ch. 11 (especially § 11.5) |
| *Item analysis.* Statistical data on the relative attractiveness of responses to a particular group of students. | 1.1 | § 7.4 |
| *Time allowance.* Suggested time allowance for the exercise. | 1.1, 2.2, 3.12, 3.22, 3.32, L1, and L2.2 | § 7.3 |
| *Improvement of exercise.* Suggestions for writing or improving the exercise. | 1.1, 1.22, 1.23, 2.11, 2.12, 2.13, 2.2, 3.12, and L2.1 | § 7.4; Ch. 11 |
| *Criticism of the form of the exercise.* Multiple choice, master list, essay, essay-objective, and performance | 1.1, 1.21, 1.22, 1.23, 1.24, 2.11, 2.12, 2.13, 2.2, 2.32 (8–15), 3.11, 3.12, 3.13, 3.21, 3.32, and L3.4 | Chs. 10 and 11 |

# 16

## TESTS FOR KNOWLEDGE

**ABILITY 1, KNOWLEDGE**

*For a discussion of this ability see page* 21.

**Objective 1.1, Information**

**Content 1.11, Knowledge of laws and principles (verbal and mathematical)**

1.11-1  A beam of beta-rays is passed between a pair of powerful magnets as shown. What will happen to the beam at point *P?*

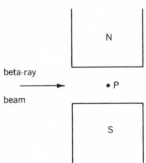

A. It will continue in a straight line but at a reduced speed.

B. It will curve toward the North pole.

C. It will curve toward the South pole.

D. It will curve out of the plane of the paper.

**Content 1.12, Knowledge of theories**

1.12-1  According to the photon theory of light, the color of light is determined by the
A. speed of photons.
B. number of photons crossing a unit area per second.
C. shape of photons.
D. energy of photons.
E. state of polarization of photons.

**Content 1.13, Knowledge of facts (generalizations of narrow scope)**

1.13-1  The period of a simple pendulum vibrating with a small amplitude is
A. proportional to the amplitude.
B. proportional to the mass of the bob.

**239**

       C. inversely proportional to the maximum speed of the bob.

       D. proportional to the acceleration.

       E. independent of the amplitude.

## Content 1.14, Knowledge of definitions of physical quantities, technical terms, and units

1.14-1   The subject matter of mechanics is

       A. the study of motion of bodies.

       B. the study of motion of solid bodies.

       C. the study of motion of solid bodies under the influence of forces.

       D. the study of motion of solid bodies as parts of a mechanism.

       E. the study of motion of parts of machines and mechanisms.

## Content 1.15, Knowledge of history

1.15-1   Newton announced the law of universal gravitation

       A. after his own measurements convinced him that planets move in ellipses.

       B. after careful laboratory measurements of the gravitational forces between bodies.

       C. after he found that it agreed with recorded observations.

       D. as a basic assumption requiring no testing by observation.

## Comments on exercises 1.1

The preceding five items measure the student's store of information. The content of the correct responses is assumed to be explicitly given in the text (or lecture), and most students are expected to identify the correct response through straightforward recall. The wording of the responses, however, should differ from that in the text, because the student's knowledge of science is more important than the memory of particular phrases. This precaution discourages cramming and encourages students to express ideas in their own words. A time allowance of forty seconds per item seems reasonable.

Item 1.11-1 tests for a knowledge of Lorentz force, knowledge that the force on a moving charge is at right angles to its velocity and to the magnetic field. (The sense of the direction of the force was not tested for because its knowledge was considered too impermanent to be of value in the introductory course in which the test was used.) The auxiliary knowledge of the direction of the magnetic field and of the fact that beta-rays are charged is assumed to be possessed by the majority of students. The item is fairly directive: the students who possess the desired knowledge can anticipate the right answer as they read the question. Such anticipation is desirable because it saves students' time and introduces an element of spontaneity similar to that evoked by essay exercises. The responses are homogeneous in the ability tested, for each of them specifies a direction, and the wrong responses are wrong only because they specify wrong directions. Thus the relative attractiveness of the right and wrong responses depends on the knowledge tested, and the item is essentially valid.

Technically, however, the item has two faults. First, it is not accurately directive: the student, after reading the stem, may try to establish the sense of the direction and thus waste his time. Second, the responses are not formally homogeneous: the first three specify the sense, but the last one does not. It may therefore be attractive to some students merely because a response that combines two senses seems a safer choice. Another formal inhomogeneity is the occurrence of the word *curve* in three responses, the differences being in the kind of curve. Students soon learn to expect the right response among such "paired" or grouped responses—responses that form a group because they use the same concept with comparatively minor variations. In this item the remedy is simple: group the wrong responses about the concept of straight line motion with the variation of higher, lower, and same speed; and combine responses B and C into "It will curve toward one of the poles."

The problem of improving item 1.11-1 can be attacked more systematically. Since we want to test for the knowledge of direction, several plausible directions should be provided, preferably of varying degrees of correctness. For example, the directions may be specified to be at right angles to both the velocity of the charge and the magnetic field, at right angles to one or the other, and at right angles to neither. By not specifying the sign of the charge, it should also be made clear to the student that he is not to worry about the sense of the direction.

The following item satisfies these conditions and, as the item analysis shows, was quite successful. The item analysis figures should be interpreted as usual: 5 percent of the high scorers and 23 percent of the low scorers

1.11-1a   A charged particle $Q$ is moving northeast in the space between two magnets. What is the direction of the force on the particle?

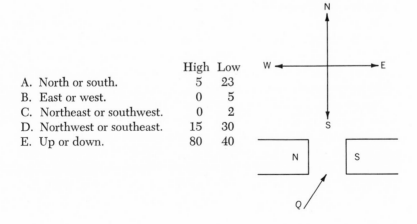

|                              | High | Low |
|------------------------------|------|-----|
| A. North or south.           | 5    | 23  |
| B. East or west.             | 0    | 5   |
| C. Northeast or southwest.   | 0    | 2   |
| D. Northwest or southeast.   | 15   | 30  |
| E. Up or down.               | 80   | 40  |

chose response A, and so forth. In this particular case the class was small, only ninety students, and the high scorers were all the students above the median on the total score for the test. The test was mostly on knowledge.

Item 1.12-1 is very directive: the right response can be surmised from the stem alone. Response C is bad enough to qualify as an F response, for even D students should be able to reject it. Students choosing it should be penalized: for example, response D may be given 1 point; response C, −1; and the rest, zero.

Item 1.13-1 tests for knowledge of a generalization that is narrow and can be derived from grander generalizations. The generalization is therefore listed under Facts. It is expected that the great majority of students will remember the generalization as such and not derive it. The item is faulty because nondirective. The student is in effect asked to make several mutually independent decisions. He should be rewarded for each correct decision. The easiest way to do this is to recast the item into several true-or-false items. Or, if the main interest is in the amplitude-period relation, the item can be rewritten with appropriate homogeneous responses, for example, as follows:

1.13-1a  If the amplitude of a simple pendulum is increased from 5° to 10°, what will happen to its period?
   A. It will be more than doubled.
   B. It will be approximately doubled.
   C. It will increase by about 50 percent.
   D. It will increase by about 25 percent.
   E. It will increase by much less than 25 percent.

The wording of the correct response in item 1.14-1 should not be the same as that of the text used for the course. Item 1.15-1 requires a knowledge of a historical sequence rather than of an event. If the sequence has not been taught as such, the item may be classified under 2.32.

### Objective 1.2, Knowledge of relations

This is the knowledge of the relations or patterns studied in the course; it is more complex and functional than information. The ability to organize the materials of the course should help most students retain these relations. It is important to notice, however, that these relations or patterns should be tested in nearly the same contexts as they appear in the course. If the context or the situation were sufficiently novel, not the memory of the relation but the ability to discern it would be tested. Such an ability belongs not under the heading of knowledge but of understanding. The phrase *sufficiently novel* is of necessity ambiguous; often it is a matter of opinion whether to classify an item under 1.2 or 2.1.

Content 1.21, Knowledge of the relations between empirical generalizations (laws of nature) and specific phenomena

The generalizations are those taught in the course.

1.21-1  Two identical balls $X$ and $Y$ are suspended by strings from the top of a box as shown. What may be said about their potential energies due to gravity *relative to the bottom of the box?*

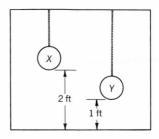

SITUATION 1. The box is at rest on the surface of the earth.

    A. Ball $X$ has more potential energy than ball $Y$ because, if the strings are cut and the balls allowed to fall, the force of gravity will act through a greater distance than it will on $Y$.

    B. Ball $X$ has more potential energy than ball $Y$ because, if the balls are allowed to fall, the force of gravity will act for a longer time on $X$ than on $Y$.

    C. Ball $X$ has less potential energy than ball $Y$ because the force of gravity on $X$ is less than on $Y$.

    D. The balls $X$ and $Y$ have very nearly equal potential energies because their distances from the center of the earth are very nearly equal.

    E. The data given are insufficient for a choice among A, B, C, and D.

SITUATION 2. The box is at rest 4000 miles above the surface of the earth. The *difference* in the potential energies of $X$ and $Y$ relative to the bottom of the box

    A. is now less than in situation 1 because the force of gravity is less.

    B. is now less than in situation 1 because the weights of the two balls are more nearly equal.

    C. is now less than in situation 1 because the ratio of the distances of $X$ and $Y$ from the center of the earth is more nearly equal to 1.

    D. is now greater than in situation 1 because the two balls are farther away from the center of the earth.

    E. is the same as in situation 1 because the difference in the heights of $X$ and $Y$ is the same as before.

The statements in exercises 2 and 3 below are followed by a list of conditions or assumptions. Choose those that are *necessary* for the statement to be true and put their numbers in the blank. If none of the conditions or assumptions is a necessary one, put 0 in the blank. Note: Some items require more than one answer.

1.21-2   If a circuit of 20 ohm resistance is connected across a 110 volt ac supply, the current will be 5.5 amperes, only if
   0. None of the conditions below is a necessary one.
   1. the circuit has no condensers.
   2. the circuit has no coils.
   3. the circuit has the power factor of 1.
   4. the circuit has no iron in it.

1.21-3   The efficiency of a heat engine operating between the temperatures $T_1$ (high) and $T_2$ (low) is equal to $(T_1 - T_2)/T_1$ only if
   0. None of the conditions below is a necessary one.
   1. the process is reversible.
   2. $T_2$ = absolute zero.
   3. the working substance is a perfect gas.
   4. heat generated by the friction of mechanical parts could be neglected.

In the problems below, each answer is considered a *single datum*, even though it may contain values of more than one quantity. You are to decide on the *smallest* number of data, that is, the smallest number of answers, which would be sufficient to make the required calculation. Write the letters of the answers in the blank.

   EXAMPLE: To calculate the net force acting on a body, it is sufficient to know
   A. the mass of the body.
   B. the acceleration of the body.
   C. the time during which the force has acted on the body and the change in the body's momentum.

The proper answer is C. Although A *and* B would give sufficient information, they involve two data. Note that "time" and "change of momentum" in answer C are counted as *one* datum.

1.21-4   To calculate the emf induced in coil 2 when a current is flowing through coil 1, it is sufficient to know
   A. the number of turns of coil 1.
   B. the number of turns of coil 2.
   C. the rate of change of current in coil 1.
   D. the coefficient of mutual inductance.
   E. the relative position of the two coils.
   F. the permeability of the medium inside the two coils.

1.21-5   To calculate the mechanical work done by a gas as it expands under constant pressure, it is sufficient to know
   A. the pressure of the gas.
   B. the increase in volume of the gas.
   C. the mass of gas involved.
   D. the temperature change of the gas.
   E. the rate of expansion of the gas.

1.21-6    In this exercise all symbols have their usual meanings. It may be helpful to consider the "dimensions" of the formulas. Neglecting friction and the mass of the pulley, the tension in the string is given by

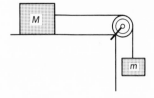

    A.  $mg/(M + m)$.
    B.  $mg$.
    C.  $Mg/(M + m)$.
    D.  $(M - m)g/(M + m)$.
    E.  $Mmg/(M + m)$.

1.21-7    It is required to determine $f$ from the expression $f = 4\pi^2 mn^2 R$. The quantities are measured with the following precision: $m$ with an error of $\pm 2\%$; $n$ with an error of $\pm\frac{1}{2}\%$; and $R$ with an error of $\pm 1\%$.

The maximum error in the value of $f$ introduced by the inaccurate measurements of the three quantities, $m$, $n$, and $R$, is nearest

    A.  $3\frac{1}{2}\%$.
    B.  $5\frac{1}{4}\%$.
    C.  $3\frac{1}{4}\%$.
    D.  $4\%$.
    E.  $3\frac{1}{2}\pi\%$.

1.21-8    A hoop of radius $r = 2$ feet and mass $m = 10$ pounds starts from rest and rolls, without slipping, down the incline shown. Using $g = 32$ ft/sec$^2$, find the speed, $v$, of the center of the hoop at the bottom of the incline; the time of descent, $t$; and the angular acceleration, $\alpha$, on the incline. The speed, $v$, equals (in ft/sec)

    A.  $4\sqrt{10}$.
    B.  $8\sqrt{5}$.
    C.  $8\sqrt{10}$.
    D.  $16\sqrt{\frac{5}{3}}$.
    E.  none of the above.

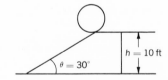

1.21-9    The following exercise involves interpretation of graphs. Complete the sentences below by writing in each blank the *number* of that *response* which completes the sentence correctly. If *none* of the responses listed completes the sentence correctly, write the correct response at the bottom of the column labeled Responses and write its number in the blank.

The diagram below gives the *B-H* curve and the hysteresis loop of a ferromagnetic substance.

If a permanent magnet is made of the substance, it will be a strong magnet if ———.
The magnet will keep its magnetism well if ———.
Permeability of the substance (at point $E$) is high if ———.
The substance is used to make the core of an ac electromagnet. The heat loss in the core will be high if ———.

*Responses*

(All responses must be in terms of geometrical properties of the graph.)

1. *OF* is large.
2. *OF* is small.
3. *EF* is large.
4. The area *GDECG* is large.
5. *OC/OA* is large.
6. _____
7. _____
8. _____
9. _____

1.21-10    In solving the following problem write down the necessary equations and formulas, using the notation given in the problem. (If you use your own notation, define each symbol.) One or more equations will embody the *fundamental principles* involved. Give the name of the principle in the space to the right of the equation.

EXAMPLES

| *Equation* | *Fundamental Principle* |
|---|---|
| $F = Vd$ | Archimedes' principle |
| $mgh = \frac{1}{2}mv^2$ | Conservation of energy |

Use the space provided for solving the problem. Only the purely arithmetical steps, such as long division, should be made on some other piece of paper.

A balloon at sea level, where temperature $t_1 = 20°C$, has a volume $V_1$ of 1000 cubic feet. What will its volume, $V_2$, be in the upper atmosphere where the pressure $P_2 = 5$ cm of mercury and the temperature $t_2 = 50°C$?

Give one important factor that is neglected in stating this problem.

_____

_____

_____

_____

_____

*Equations*                          *Fundamental Principles*

1. _____          _____
2. _____          _____
3. _____          _____
$V_2 = $ _____  _____
          answer    units

Meaning of symbols you are using other than $t_1$, $V_1$, $V_2$, $P_2$, and $t_2$

_____          _____

*Solution* (Use the space below for solving the problem.)

Comments on exercises 1.21

Exercise 1 tests for knowledge of the principle that differences in potential energy are determined by work done. Work involves two factors, force and distance, both of which the student is asked to assay. Because of this complexity the items belong under objective 1.2 rather than 1.1. It is assumed that gravitational potential energy has been adequately discussed. For students in a more elementary course, on the other hand, who have only worked a few stereotyped problems involving a formal definition of potential energy, the use of this definition in the situations shown would call for a deeper kind of understanding, which would be classified under objective 2.1. The stem common to the two items is properly directive. The exercise is slightly faulty because the correct response in each item is one of a formally identifiable group: in the first item the clue is the word *more*, which "pairs" responses A and B; and in the second item, the word *less*, which has the same effect. One correction for such formal attractiveness of the right response is to have wrong responses grouped or paired in other exercises.

Items 2 and 3 test for knowledge of conditions under which given generalizations are valid. The use of "zero" to number the "none" response is apt; it aids the student's memory and thus makes rereading the directions unnecessary. The items can be cast into true-or-false form without appreciably changing the competence measured.

Items 4 and 5 test for knowledge of a generalization that goes somewhat beyond the ability to use a formula in solving routine problems. In item 4, for example, the student has to know the physical content of the phrase *coefficient of mutual inductance*—that the coefficient embraces permeability and geometry. The form of the items is awkward in that the student has to understand a fairly complicated stem. Because it is uneconomical, it is not recommended for less than a series of five items. It is included here primarily to illustrate the variety of possible formulations.

Item 6 normally involves a two-step process, calculation of acceleration and then of tension. Identifying the formula for acceleration could be done, however, by rote memory and thus would belong under objective 1.1. It should be noted that students familiar with dimensional analysis could eliminate all but two responses; their average guess-score on the item would be 50 percent rather than 20 percent. Rewarding students with such knowledge is legitimate and desirable if the knowledge is considered an aspect of the principal ability needed to derive the correct expression. A student can finally decide between responses B and E if he realizes that the tension must be less than $mg$. A reasoning process of this sort lies closer to understanding phenomena than does the more formal process of a complete solution. The responses are formulas rather than numbers for the additional reason that, in testing for the ability to solve numerical problems, it is efficient, in some problems, to stop short of actual calculations.

Items 7 and 8 are the standard fare of many introductory physics tests. Their inclusion should clarify the meaning and scope of ability 1 and more specifically of objective 1.2. It is assumed that problems of rolling bodies, not necessarily of hoops but perhaps of solid cylinders or spheres, have been discussed in text or class. The step the student has to make to go from cylinders to hoops and from, say, 45° to 30° is a short one indeed. It is therefore better to say that the student *knows* than that he *understands* how to solve rolling-body problems, and to classify the ability to solve numerical problems of familiar types under knowledge. If, on the other hand, the student has had practice with problems about rolling on a horizontal plane only, his ability to combine this knowledge with the one concerned with bodies sliding down inclined planes may be classified under 2.2, understanding of interrelationships. It should be clear from this example, first, that the competence tested by an exercise is a function of the student's preparation and, second, that there is room for defensible difference of opinion on how properly to classify an exercise.

The form of exercise 9 is a combination of objective and essay forms. Insofar as it is an essay, it is a highly structured one, for it specifies even the form of the desired responses. The responses should therefore be easy to evaluate accurately. It is assumed that the students have had a thorough discussion of the kind of information obtainable from a hysteresis loop. If, on the other hand, only the means of obtaining the curve and the meaning of $B$ and $H$ are known to the students, the exercise requires a high level of understanding.

Item 10 is in the form of a highly structured essay. Such essays can be graded with considerable objectivity. In this example, the student who includes correct equations with properly identified symbols deserves a good deal of credit. If he writes down *only* the relevant equations and no others he can probably solve the problem and should be given nearly full credit. If, on the other hand, a student gives incorrect equations and an incorrect answer, his arithmetic is not worth deciphering unless it is clearly and methodically arranged. Assigning specific places for the equations and other entries makes for faster and more accurate scoring.

**Content 1.22, Knowledge of relations (explicitly treated in the course) between theories and phenomena**

1.22-1    Which of the following is the best evidence for the theory that light is a wave motion?
      A. Light travels through empty space.
      B. Two beams of light illuminate a spot more brightly than either would alone.
      C. Light is spread on passing through a small opening.
      D. White light can be separated into many colors.
      E. Light travels in straight lines.

1.22-2   A fundamental assumption of the theory of relativity is that for any two bodies, $X$ and $Y$, the effect on $X$ produced by $Y$ is the same
  A. as the effect on $Y$ produced by $X$.
  B. whatever the relative motion of $X$ and $Y$.
  C. whether $Y$ moves or is stationary.
  D. whether $X$ moves or is stationary.
  E. whether $X$ approaches $Y$ or $Y$ approaches $X$.

1.22-3   According to the modern theory, which of the following is the most acceptable description of the nature of a beam of electrons?
  A. Electrons are particles that possess some wave characteristics.
  B. Electron particles are arranged in the form of a wave.
  C. Each electron is a wave concentrated in a small space.
  D. Each electron is a wave composed of particles.
  E. Each electron has some particle characteristics and some wave characteristics.

1.22-4   Below is a list of observations followed by a list of statements of theory. Before each *statement* write the letter of the *one* observation that provides the best experimental support for the statement.

### Observations

A. Some alpha particles are deflected through large angles on going through thin metal foils.
B. The spectrum of neon is a line spectrum.
C. Compton Effect.
D. The mass of an element deposited in electrolysis is proportional to the atomic weight of the element.
E. The energy required to ionize an inert gas such as helium is relatively high.
F. The electrical resistance of metals increases with temperature.
G. The specific heat of some gases increases with temperature.

### Statements

Atoms of a molecule may vibrate with respect to each other.
A molecule may rotate about an axis through the molecule.
Electrical charges occur only as multiples of a certain charge.
Certain groupings of electrons are attached more firmly to the nucleus than are other groupings.
The nucleus of an atom occcupies a very small volume.
The electrons of an atom exist only in states of definite amounts of energy.

1.22-5   In deriving equations in physics certain simplifying assumptions are usually made. In the following exercise the derivation consists of a series of statements. Before each statement, write the numbers of the assumptions that must be made in order to justify the statement. An assumption entered in its proper place may be considered to apply to the succeeding statements; therefore, do not enter the same assumption twice. If a statement does not involve any new assumptions (that are listed), put 0 in the blank.

Derivation of the expression for the pressure exerted by molecules confined in a box 1 cm on the side

### Assumptions

0. None.
1. Molecules are of negligible size.
2. Intermolecular forces are negligibly small.
3. All molecules have the same speed.
4. Collisions are elastic.
5. The number of molecules is large.
6. All directions of motion are equally likely.
7. All molecules have the same mass.
8. The motion of the molecule is at right angles to a wall of the cube.

### Meaning of Symbols

$P$ = pressure exerted by the molecules.
$m$ = mass of a molecule.
$n$ = number of molecules per cc.
$f$ = force exerted on a wall of the cube.
$A$ = area of the wall.
$v$ = velocity of a molecule.

### Statements

Change in momentum of a single molecule during a collision with a wall of the vessel = $2mv$.
Number of collisions a molecule makes per second with a given wall = $v/2$.
Average number of molecules striking a given wall per second = $nv/6$.
Change in momentum per second effected by a given wall = $2mnv^2/6$.
Constant force on the wall $f = mnv^2/3$.
$P = f/A$, $A = 1$ cm$^2$.
$p = mnv^2/3$.

### Comments on exercises 1.22

Item 1 tests for knowledge of *evidence* for a theory. It is assumed that diffraction as evidence for wave theory has been discussed in the text or class. It is also assumed that the text does not specifically state that spreading of light on passing through an opening constitutes evidence for its wave nature. Otherwise the item would belong under 1.12. If, on the other hand, the word *spreading* has not been used to describe diffraction, the item belongs under understanding. Response E can be treated as an F response, a response whose choice by a student would indicate profound ignorance, for it is better evidence for a corpuscular theory. The responses are homogeneous in the ability tested, for each of them is a correct statement of fact about the phenomenon under discussion. They differ only in their cogency as evidence. The choice of the right response, therefore, depends primarily on the student's knowledge of relevant evidence, and the item is generally valid. The responses are also formally homogeneous. The right response is not the longest, or shortest, or richest in qualifications, or most technical in its terminology. Thus it does not contain obvious formal clues.

Item 2 tests for knowledge of the basic *assumptions* of a theory. The responses are of graded difficulty. A and B are plainly wrong. In responses C and D, the language is nonrelativistic.

Item 3 takes up an important point of the use of classical *language* to describe a nonclassical theory. It is assumed that the text furnishes an answer to the question of the item though not in the wording used here. Some teachers may consider response A "too good," too close in correctness to the best response, E. If so, they should omit A.

Exercise 4 contains six items and tests for knowledge of *evidence* for theories, in the master-list form. This form is easy to construct: one merely writes down a series of theoretical statements and thinks up one good piece of evidence for each. Since good evidence for one theoretical statement does not often sound plausible as evidence for another, the student is effectively asked not to compare evidence but merely to judge whether or not it is evidence. For most students the number of plausible wrong responses is small, and a good deal of time is spent reading unattractive wrong responses. The reliability of the exercise is not high. Thus for the first two statements of item 4, the only wrong responses that are likely to attract students with any knowledge of the subject matter are A and F. (Response F is wrong if the atoms of a solid metal are not considered to form molecules.) Other wrong responses may be considered F responses.

The master-list form of exercise 4 has no real justification. The responses are not easy to remember: they are not short, do not form a complete set, and have no overall principle of organization. Moreover, the relations between statements and observations are not the same. Thus observation G is not evidence for the first two statements of theory; rather, it is relevant because it has led to a refinement of the theory. The exercise would be improved by being cast into a multiple-choice form. For example, the item on the small nucleus could be written as follows. (For brevity only three responses are included.)

1.22-4a   The Rutherford atom has a small, highly charged nucleus. The Thomson atom has electrons embedded in a distribution of positive charge. Which of the following constitutes the best evidence in favor of the Rutherford model?

    A. Most alpha particles go through thin metal foils without observable deviation.

    B. A few alpha particles, on going through thin metal foils, are deviated through large angles.

    C. All of the above can be equally well explained on the basis of either model.

Exercise 5 tests for an aspect of understanding a *derivation* of an expression—the ability to identify the assumptions necessary for each step of the process. This aspect contains the physics of the derivation, and it therefore represents a more important ability than the one involved in the essentially mathematical process that the students are usually asked to perform. The master-list form is justified here because the list of assumptions is complete.

**Content 1.23, Knowledge of relations (explicitly treated in the course) between instruments or experiments and conclusions**

1.23-1    Before each item, put the number corresponding to the *one* apparatus commonly used for making the required measurement. If the proper apparatus is not on the list, put 0 before the item.

_____ To detect the presence of a certain element in a star.

_____ To measure the temperature of molten gold.

_____ To measure humidity of air.

_____ To measure atmospheric pressure.

_____ To measure electron velocity.

_____ To detect the presence of isotopes.

_____ To measure pressures of about .1 mm of Hg.

_____ To measure the pressure of steam in a boiler.

_____ To measure the velocity of sound in metal.

_____ To measure lengths with the accuracy of $10^{-5}$ cm.

0. None of the apparatus below.
1. Aneroid.
2. Bourdon spring gage.
3. Cavendish apparatus.
4. Diffraction grating.
5. Electrophorus.
6. Electrostatic voltmeter.
7. Hydrogen thermometer.
8. Hygrometer.
9. Interferometer.
10. Kundt's tube.
11. Mass spectrograph.
12. McLeod's gage.
13. Micrometer.
14. Nicol prism.
15. Pyrometer.
16. Simple pendulum.
17. Voltmeter (permanent magnet type).
18. Wheatstone bridge.

1.23-2    Light falls upon a photoelectric cell connected in series with a galvanometer and a 90 volt battery (see diagram). A steady current flows through the circuit, as shown by the deflection of the galvanometer. Before each statement put the letter corresponding to the best classification of the statement.

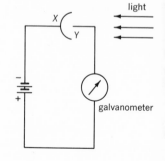

*Classifications*

A. It is one of the causes of the current flow.
B. It is a consequence of the current flow.
C. It is neither a cause nor a consequence of the current flow.
D. The information is not sufficient for a choice among A, B, and C.

*Statements*

Electrode $Y$ has a positive charge.
Part of the light is reflected.
The large electrode of the photoelectric cell is coated with an active metal.
The light is polarized.
A potential difference exists between the electrodes of the photoelectric cell.

1.23-3   Purpose: To determine whether the products of combustion weigh more than the material that was burned. Procedure: the material to be burned is magnesium. Magnesium and oxygen are sealed in a glass tube. The glass tube and its contents are weighed. The tube is heated until the magnesium ignites. After the magnesium stops burning, the tube is cooled to room temperature and weighed again. The tube and contents are found to weigh no more than before. Which of the following is the best comment on, or criticism of, the experiment?
   A. In some cases, the products of combustion weigh the same as the material that was burned.
   B. The tube should not have been cooled before being weighed the second time.
   C. The experiment should have been repeated several times and the results averaged.
   D. The tube should have been left open during the experiment.
   E. Some of the product escaped through the walls of the container.

1.23-4   The volume of a wooden cube, $L$ cm on the side, can be calculated from the buoyant force it experiences when submerged in water. The cube absorbs water in the process. The volume, calculated on the assumption that no water is absorbed, will be
   A. greater than $L^3$.
   B. less than $L^3$.
   C. equal to $L^3$.

1.23-4a  Defend your answer to the preceding question.

1.23-5   Refractive indices of five hundred compounds are known with an accuracy of .1 percent to be between 1.742 and 1.329. Their mean index of refraction is 1.536. Which of the following statements is a logical inference?
   A. A large number of the compounds have their refractive indices close to 1.536.
   B. There is at least one compound whose refractive index is 1.536.
   C. At least two compounds have the same refractive index.
   D. Approximately half the compounds have refractive indices below 1.536.

1.23-6   Increasing the number of times that a quantity is measured with the same measuring instrument
   A. decreases neither the random nor the systematic error.
   B. decreases the random error only.

C. decreases the systematic error only.

D. decreases both the random and the systematic error.

1.23-7   A measurement is said to be *precise* if its random error is small, and to be *accurate* if its overall error (combined random and systematic errors) is small. A student wants to check one of the weights commonly used with the equal-arm platform balance. He uses a good analytical balance and good technique, but a defective (chipped) set of weights. His results will be

A. precise and accurate.

B. precise but inaccurate.

C. imprecise but accurate.

D. imprecise and inaccurate.

1.23-8   A student measures a given voltage four times using a voltmeter that has a systematic error of $+3$ percent. His readings are (in volts): 1.36, 1.38, 1.36, and 1.37. If he wishes to increase the accuracy of his measurement, is it sensible for him to try and do this by taking more readings? Answer yes or no. Explain.

1.23-9   A student used a meter stick to measure the length of a straight thin wire five times and submitted the following data: 10.1 cm, 10.2 cm, 10.3 cm, 10.3 cm, and 11.6 cm. What is the most likely length of the wire?

A. 10.2 cm.

B. 10.3 cm.

C. 10.5 cm.

D. 10.9 cm.

E. No estimate can be made with such inconsistent data.

1.23-10   What is the name of the instrument shown? What is the reading of the instrument? [The figure may be a drawing or photograph of a vernier caliper, hydrometer, or some other instrument.]

### Comments on exercises 1.23

The subject matter of the exercises in content 1.23 is laboratory experiments. The competence tested by the exercises is defined or at least restricted by the requirement that the tests be of the paper-and-pencil variety. It is not restricted, however, to what may be learned in the lecture-discussion part of the course; in dealing with some of the exercises, students' laboratory experience should be helpful or even necessary. The validity of paper-and-pencil tests as measures of laboratory learning can be greatly increased by using certain test materials. Such test materials may be photographs of instruments or setups, either included in the test booklet or large enough to be seen by the whole class. It is not difficult to have a slide projected on a screen while keeping the room light enough for reading and writing. A short movie may be good test material; several written questions can be asked about its content. In fact all the audio-visual aids usable in teaching are usable in testing, and are often less objectionable when used in testing.

Exercise 1 has the master-list form. The responses are short. The list of responses is long, but reference to it is made fairly easy by organizing the responses. The principle of organization in this case is alphabetical.

The terms of analysis of the photoelectric effect in exercise 2 are not photons and electrons but observable phenomena. For this reason it belongs in content 1.23. A master list seems the best form for this exercise because the list is short and comprehensive. The exercise is at a very elementary level. Exercise 3, also at a very elementary level, tests for knowledge of the proper precautions in a well-known experiment. The item is made easier but more specific and therefore better if "metal" is substituted for "material." Exercise 4 tests for knowledge of the sign of error in a particular experiment. From the students who have neither performed a similar experiment nor had a discussion of buoyant force on air-containing objects, the exercise requires a synthesis of their knowledge of Archimedes' principle and of porosity; for such a class, the exercise belongs under objective 2.2. Exercise 4a requires a written response. Such supplementary exercises often show whether the objective exercise is valid. If the correlation between the essay and the objective exercises is high, the latter is probably valid, and in future tests the essay may be omitted. Presence of "clues" in the objective item diminishes correlation.

Exercises 5 to 10 deal with interpretation of data primarily in terms of experimental error. Exercise 5 tests for the student's knowledge that two quantities are to be treated as equal if their difference is smaller than the probable error. The right response C may be legitimately interpreted to go beyond this and is therefore not strictly correct. It is the best response, however, of those available, and item analysis has shown that the better students prefer it. The item has not worked as well with a more nearly correct response: "The data assign the same refractive index to more than one compound." The "justify your answer" technique has shown that such a response appeals to the student who merely observes that there are more compounds than indices of refraction without considering precision or significant figures. Because such a simple-minded attack will be successful even with the present version of response C, the exercise cannot reliably measure the specified competence if there are many students in the class who are likely to think in this fashion. The exercise therefore should not be used in a very elementary course. Exercise 6 tests for knowledge of the sources of random and systematic errors. Exercise 7 tests for knowledge of factors affecting precision and accuracy of measurement. If the terms are not systematically used in the course, they may be defined, as is done in this exercise. Exercise 8 is partly objective and partly essay. Essays are often much easier to read and evaluate if it is clear what position the student is defending. Exercise 9 emphasizes the fact that misreading an instrument may often be spotted, and the resulting data should be disregarded. Response B, which gives the mode instead of the mean, may be considered an F response. Exercise 10 tests for the ability to read an instrument and the knowledge of its name. For many instruments, such an exercise is likely to correlate very highly with the ability to read the actual instrument.

### Content 1.24, Knowledge of relations between broad concepts or classifications and specifics

Here the student is to be tested for knowledge of those concepts and classifications that were specifically taught in the course. A certain number of the items under 1.24 could probably be answered by some students who have not been taught the methodology of science in the above sense. Such a performance, however, would indicate not knowledge but the possession of mental skills of rather high order. This is an additional illustration that an item cannot be classified as to the competence it tests unless the preparation of the student is to some extent known. The examinations in which these items actually appeared were for courses in which the relations mentioned above were taught, but in contexts rather different from the contexts of the items. Such items then tested something more than memory; a translation between the contexts was required of the student. The decision to place these items under 1.24 rather than under 2.3, understanding the nature and structure of physics, was based on the judgment of the examiner that the translation presented so little difficulty that it was within the grasp of most of the students in the course.

1.24-1    Each statement below is to be marked at the left as factual (F), theoretical or hypothetical (H), or definitional (D); and as right (+) or wrong (0).

If the statement is *factual,* mark
F and + if the statement has been proved to be true by direct experiment or observation.
F and 0 if the statement has been proved to be false by direct experiment or observation.
If the statement is *not* factual (i.e., hypothetical or definitional) mark
H and + if the statement is a part of a presently accepted theory.
H and 0 if the statement is in contradiction to an accepted theory.
D and + if the statement is true simply by virtue of the definition of a word or words used.
D and 0 if the statement becomes self-contradictory when the words used are correctly defined.
Note that each item requires *two* answers. For the purposes of illustration, the correct answers and the reasons for these answers are given in the first six items.

F, +    Iron is denser than wood. (A *true factual* statement.)
F, 0    Gold floats on water. (A *false factual* statement.)

H, +    A molecule of hydrogen consists of two atoms. (A theoretical statement in accordance with an accepted theory.)

H, 0    A molecule of hydrogen consists of four atoms. (A theoretical statement in contradiction to accepted theory.)

D, +    One can see through a transparent medium. (True because of the definition of the word transparent.)

D, 0    Specific gravity of water is 1.5. (Wrong because specific gravity means the ratio of the density of the substance to the density of water. The statement can be reworded as follows: The ratio of density of water to density of water is 1.5, which is of course impossible.)

Molecules attract one another at certain distances and repel one another at smaller distances.

An ideal gas shows no deviation from Boyle's law.

Atoms of a metallic conductor, by vibrating more violently when the conductor is hot, facilitate the flow of an electric current through the conductor.

Radium emits penetrating rays.

Some substances rotate the plane of polarization of light passing through them.

The force exerted by a liquid on an area is proportional to the product of the area and the average pressure on the area.

If a body is acted upon by a single force, the acceleration produced by the force is directly proportional to the force.

The photoelectric effect is explainable by the photon theory of light.

### Comments on exercise 1.24

Exercise 1 tests the student's knowledge of the very commonly used classification scheme that divides assertions of science into factual, theoretical, and definitional. As is true of all scientific classifications, some assertions do not fit well in any one of the three categories. In this particular case, even the classes are not rigorously, and certainly not permanently, defined. Nevertheless a large number of assertions will have certain important differences that would commonly be classified on the above scheme. One difference involves the probable future of the assertion. Thus facts are essentially permanent; theories will be modified, perhaps radically, as new facts are accumulated; and definitions are subject to sudden, more or less arbitrary change. Such distinctions should be of help to the beginning student in his efforts to understand the structure of physics.

The examples that precede the exercise are usually necessary when a new form of exercise is first introduced and are often useful even with old forms. The classification of the exercise under knowledge presupposes that the terms *fact, theory,* and *definition* have been used consistently in class or text. The examples and the directions remind the student of their meaning; in fact, they are almost enough to define the terms. The occurrence of a theoretical term such as *atom* or *molecule* is often a purely formal clue to the theoretical nature of the whole statement. The items of this exercise involving the terms *plane of polarization* and *photon* should warn the student against following such clues blindly. It should be noted that it is only the ability to enter the proper letter, F, H, or D, in the first blank that corresponds to objective 1.2. The knowledge of the correctness of the assertion, shown by the entry in the second blank, corresponds to objective 1.1. The two exercises are combined because of the obvious saving in students' time. The master-list form is quite appropriate here because it is exhaustive.

# 17

## TESTS FOR UNDERSTANDING

**ABILITY 2, UNDERSTANDING**

*For a discussion of this ability see page* 21.

### Objective 2.1, Understanding the individual topics and principles taught in the course

Test situations must be new to the student; their complexity, however, should be about the same as that of the situations used in the course for illustrative purposes. Usually an understanding of a single law, theory, experiment, or concept—assumed to be familiar to most students—should be sufficient for the analysis of the situation.

### Content 2.11, Understanding of empirical generalizations

The understanding is tested by asking the student to relate laws of nature and specific phenomena. Although the student must be familiar with the generalization and may be familiar with the specific phenomenon, the particular relation between them used in the test question must be one that has not been taught in the course.

EXERCISES 1–4. *Application of Principles*

2.11-1  One can see objects more distinctly through plate glass than through ordinary window glass chiefly because plate glass (as compared with ordinary glass)
  A. is made of better material.
  B. has faces that are more nearly parallel.
  C. reflects less light.
  D. transmits a greater range of wavelengths.
  E. is thicker.

2.11-2  A hot-water tank is heated from the bottom rather than around the sides principally because
  A. the density of water decreases with a rise in temperature.
  B. there is less heat loss at the bottom.

  C. the flame counteracts the water pressure on the bottom.

  D. there is more pressure at the bottom than anywhere else.

  E. the sides of the tank are easier to insulate than the bottom.

2.11-3 Sound can be *heard* around a corner of a building when the source of sound cannot be *seen*. This is because

  A. sound has a lower velocity than light.

  B. the sound is reflected from neighboring buildings.

  C. long waves are more easily diffracted than short waves.

  D. sound is refracted on entering a different medium.

  E. the sound waves are carried around the corner by air currents.

2.11-4 A piece of shiny white china is heated until it gives out enough light to be barely visible in a dark room. If a piece of dull black china is heated to the same temperature, how will it appear in a dark room?

  A. It will probably be invisible.

  B. It will be visible but less bright than the white china.

  C. It will be as bright as the white china.

  D. It will be brighter than the white china.

EXERCISES 5–8. *Choice of Principle*

2.11-5 Before each statement of fact below, write the letter of the *one* explanatory principle, from the list preceding the statements, which is most directly useful in explaining the fact. If none of the principles listed is applicable, write 0 in the blank.

*Explanatory Principles*

0. None of the following.

A. Force is equal to mass times acceleration.

B. Friction exists between any two bodies in contact with each other.

C. Conservation of momentum.

D. Conservation of energy.

E. Conservation of angular momentum.

F. In equilibrium, the sum of components of forces in any direction equals zero.

G. In equilibrium, the sum of the torques about any point equals zero.

*Statements of Fact*

Shears used to cut sheet metal have long handles.

The extension of a spring varies directly with the load.

A brick can be pulled along a fairly smooth surface by means of a string; the string would break, however, if jerked sharply.

A glass test tube dropped from a height of 10 feet will break if it falls on a concrete sidewalk but will not break if it falls on soft ground.

2.11-6 The detailed structure of minute organisms can be seen more distinctly through a microscope by using violet light than by using red light for illumination. Which of the following principles is most directly useful in explaining this?

  A. The resolving power of a lens depends upon the wavelength of the light used.

B. Our eyes are more sensitive to light of shorter wavelength.

C. The speed of light in glass depends upon the wavelength.

D. The index of refraction of glass depends upon the wavelength.

E. A photon of violet light carries more energy than a photon of red light.

2.11-7   If a wire carrying alternating current runs close to a telephone wire, a humming sound may be heard in the telephone receiver. Which of the following principles is most directly useful in explaining this?

A. The strength of a magnetic field depends upon the number of lines of force per unit area.

B. When a conductor moves through a stationary magnetic field, a current is induced in the conductor.

C. A varying magnetic field induces an electromotive force in conductors located within the field.

D. The strength of a magnetic field depends upon the magnetic permeability of the medium through which the field extends.

E. An oscillating magnetic field produces a back electromotive force in the wire containing the current that produces the field.

2.11-8   Two charged metal spheres S and P mounted on insulating supports are connected by a wire as shown in the diagram. As a large uncharged metal sheet was 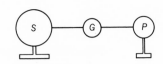 being brought near S, a momentary flow of current was observed through the galvanometer G. Which of the following principles is most directly useful in explaining the current?

A. The greater the curvature of the surface of a conductor, the greater the density of electric charge.

B. A moving electric charge produces a magnetic field.

C. The capacity of a sphere is proportional to its radius.

D. The resistance of a wire is proportional to its length.

E. The potential of a conductor depends on its distance from other conductors.

2.11-9   *Applicability of an equation*
Under certain conditions the distance, $s$, covered by a body in a time, $t$, is correctly given by the equation

$$s = v_0 t + \tfrac{1}{2} a t^2,$$

where $v_0$ is the initial velocity, and $a$ is the acceleration. Before each situation below, write the letter corresponding to the response that best describes the applicability of the equation.

*Responses*

A. The equation can be used to give a correct result.

B. The equation will give a good approximation.

C. The equation is not applicable to the situation.

D. The information is insufficient to choose among A, B, and C.

*Situations*

It is desired to calculate

the distance a feather falls in an evacuated tube.

the distance traveled by a body that is being pulled on a horizontal frictionless surface.

the time it takes a 2 pound stone to reach the ground from an altitude of 5000 feet.

the distance traveled by an electric charge under the force of attraction exerted by a stationary electric charge.

the distance covered by a body given an initial push and allowed to be slowed down by the constant friction of a horizontal plane.

the length of the arc described by the bob of a simple pendulum.

2.11-10    *Interpretation of data*

It is desired to know the electrical resistance of a sample of material at various voltages, $V$, and at various temperatures, $t$. The values of $V$, $t$, and $I$ (the direct current through the sample) are tabulated below.

| $V$ (*volts*) | $I$ (*amperes*) | $t$ (°C) |
|---|---|---|
| 1.00 | 2.00 | 0 |
| 1.10 | 2.20 | 0 |
| 10.0 | 22.0 | 0 |
| 1.00 | 2.05 | 100 |
| 1.05 | 2.20 | 100 |
| 11.0 | 26.0 | 100 |

In the items below the voltages 1.00, 1.05, and 1.10 are described as *low* voltages; voltages 10.0 and 11.0 as *high* voltages; $t = 0$°C as *low* temperature; and $t = 100$°C as *high* temperature. In the blank before each statement below, write the letter corresponding to the best response.

*Responses*

A. The data above lend *support* to the statement.
B. The data above *contradict* the statement.
C. The data above *neither contradict nor support* the statement.

*Statements*

Ohm's law is obeyed for
   low $V$, high $t$.
   low $V$, low $t$.
   high $V$, high $t$.
   high $V$, low $t$.
The temperature coefficient of resistivity is positive for
   low $V$.
   high $V$.

2.11-11   *Forming an hypothesis*
In the diagram the double pole, double throw switch can connect the circuit to a battery $B$ or to a source of ac current of 60 cycles/sec. The circuit contains ammeters $A_1$ and $A_2$, a voltmeter $V$, and an unknown circuit hidden in the box $X$. In the problems below describe the simplest circuit that would account for the readings. Give numerical answers whenever possible.

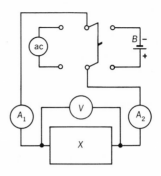

With the box $X$ as shown we have the following readings:

| Switch at Left | Switch at Right |
|---|---|
| $V = 100$ volts | $V = 100$ volts |
| $A_1 = $ 10 amperes | $A_1 = $ 10 amperes |
| $A_2 = $ 0 amperes | $A_2 = $ 10 amperes |

What does the box $X$ contain?

Next, a box $Y$ is substituted for the box $X$. The readings are:

| Switch at Left | Switch at Right |
|---|---|
| $V = 100$ volts | $V = 100$ volts |
| $A_1 = $ 5 amperes | $A_1 = $ 10 amperes |
| $A_2 = $ 0 amperes | $A_2 = $ 10 amperes |

What does the box $Y$ contain?

What conclusions can you draw about the two ammeters?

EXERCISES 12 AND 13.   *Numerical Problems*

2.11-12   The power of a lens in diopters is equal to the reciprocal of its focal length in meters. A person holds a lens close to his eye. He finds that the maximum distance at which he can see an object clearly is 17 cm from the lens and the minimum distance is 10 cm. By how many diopters can he change the power of his eye?

2.11-13   A uniform sphere of radius $r$ and mass $m$ is projected along a rough table; it has an initial velocity $v_0$ and a back spin of $\Omega$ radians per second (see diagram). Let $\mu = $ coefficient of

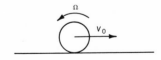

friction between the sphere and the table, and let $g = $ acceleration of gravity. Calculate the time $t$, after projection, which is required for the sphere to stop slipping on the table. (Express $t$ in terms of the quantities above.) Note: The moment of inertia of a sphere about an axis through its center is $\frac{2}{5}mr^2$.

## Comments on exercises 2.11

All the exercises under content 2.11 require a student to analyze a situation in terms of laws of physics. They are grouped under different headings, for example, Application of Principles, primarily to illustrate fairly systematically the variety of form in which the task of analysis can be presented to the student. No statistical data are available to support the assertion that the different groups of exercises test for different abilities. But it seems reasonable to suppose that various exercises call for different patterns of the student's skills and abilities: some students may find certain ones, and other students others, easiest to deal with. A variety of exercises, therefore, helps ensure a fairer sample of each student's ability; it also prevents the accidental neglect of an important aspect of the desired competence.

In using a law of physics to analyze a particular situation, one of the first steps, and often the most difficult one, is to choose the relevant law. Exercises 5 to 8 demand just that choice. Exercises 1 to 4 require the student to recall the right principle and then use it. Exercises 1 to 3 ask for an explanation, and they differ from exercises 5 to 8 only in that the responses are less formal and not as narrowly restricted in subject matter. Exercise 4 asks for prediction. In exercise 9, the relevant principle is stated mathematically, and the student is then asked to analyze various situations and decide how accurately the principle applies. Here both the situations and the principle are expected to be familiar to the student. The novel element, necessary for all exercises on understanding, lies in the relation between the principle and the situations, that is, the degree of applicability.

Exercise 10 asks the student to analyze and interpret a two-parameter set of data. It is assumed that the student will have a knowledge of Ohm's law and of the phrase *temperature coefficient of resistivity*. The principal ability measured by the exercise is a fairly complex one involving the interrelation of a generalization, Ohm's law, and a set of measurements. The purely mathematical analysis of a set of numbers, without relating it to physics proper, would belong under 3.22, for it would not measure either knowledge or understanding. It would not be an oversimplification to say that exercise 11 measures an *understanding* of Ohm's law.

The data of exercise 11 are rather complex, for they involve two types of ammeters, one of which does not visibly respond to alternating current. The exercise can be made much more difficult by omitting the last question, which is on the ammeters. Whether to call the mental processes involved in working the exercise forming a hypothesis or interpreting data is a matter of choice. The important consideration is that exercises 10 and 11 very likely evoke in the student different patterns of images and responses. Therefore the inclusion of both exercises contributes to variety.

Items 12 and 13 are fairly conventional numerical problems. They can be conveniently patterned after item 1.21-10. The problems qualify for inclusion in category 2 only for those students to whom they are novel in important respects. In item 12, for example, the concept of the diopter may be new to the student, and in item 13, the combination of rolling and slipping. These examples suggest that concepts and principles of physics that are beyond the course, perhaps those taught in the next course, are a ready source of ideas for items on undertanding. If the students have not been taught the second law of thermodynamics or conservation of angular momentum, for example, these principles can be briefly stated and questions based on them. The *form* of the items may be that used in content 3.11, ability to apply stated principles; the complexity of the situation, and the degree and kind of knowledge expected of the student, may place the item in categories 2.1, 2.2, or 2.3.

The stems of the multiple-choice exercises (exercises 1 to 4 and 6 to 8) are properly directive: the student can formulate an answer before reading the responses. The responses of exercise 1 are homogeneous: each response describes a property likely to be possessed by plate glass, and the student's attention can be safely directed to the cogency of the property. Some of the responses in items 2 and 3, on the other hand, are in terms of physical principles, while others are in terms of the characteristics of the situation. This heterogeneity is perhaps justified because it allows a greater number of attractive wrong responses without distracting the student from the problem at hand. Response C in item 2, however, carries the heterogeneity too far by being factually wrong and nonsensical, and it should be discarded. Its presence distracts the student's attention from his job, which is to evaluate the relevance of an assertion, by tempting him to try to decipher the meaning of the assertion. Heterogeneity of responses of this sort must contribute to the student's tension and fatigue. It should be noted here that the assertion in the best response in item 2 is not strictly true. Improving its correctness, however, by a reference to temperature range may make the item-writer happier but is almost certain to ruin the item. Items 1 and 4 are homogeneous in their responses, and are therefore probably better than item 2 or 3. The easily prepared master-list form of exercise 5 is justified because the set of responses is a nearly complete list of laws of mechanics and because the responses are short. The student is likely to remember the list after one or two readings, and he is not likely to want a law that is not listed.

**Content 2.12, Understanding of theories: ability to relate theories and facts**

The relation between the theory and the facts of the test question must be new to the student.

EXERCISES 1–4. *Theoretical Explanations*

2.12-1 Two electric lamps emit radiant energy at the same rate, 5 joules/sec. According to the photon theory of light, what must be true about the two lamps?
  A. The two lamps emit photons at the same rate.
  B. The two lamps emit light of the same frequency.
  C. The rate of photon emission and the frequency of light are the same for the two lamps.
  D. Either the rate of photon emission *or* the frequency of light is the same for the two lamps.
  E. None of the conclusions above is justified.

2.12-2 Which of the following observations can be explained on the basis of the theory that the molecules of a real gas have finite size?
  A. The pressure of a gas in a rigid container rises when it is heated.
  B. As the volume of a certain gas is decreased by one half at constant temperature, the pressure becomes 2.5 times as great.
  C. As the volume of another gas is decreased by one half at constant temperature, the pressure becomes twice as great.
  D. As the volume of a third gas is decreased by one half at constant temperature, the pressure becomes 1.5 times as great.

2.12-3 Both diamond and soot are pure carbon. Which of the following is the best explanation of the difference in their appearance?
  A. Individual carbon atoms are black.
  B. The two substances are made up of different kinds of carbon atoms.
  C. The arrangement of the carbon atoms is different.
  D. The diamond is more highly polished.
  E. In the diamond the carbon atoms are very far apart allowing light to go through.

2.12-4 The two components $X$ and $Y$ of a binary star are observed with a large telescope and the following facts noted.
  a. They are 0.1 sec of arc apart and are observed to revolve halfway around each other in 50 years.
  b. Star $X$ appears much fainter than star $Y$.
  c. The spectrum of star $X$ shows lines of ionized helium, while star $Y$ shows molecular bands in its spectrum.
  d. After correction for the earth's orbital motion, the Doppler shift of the spectrum lines of star $X$ changes periodically from $+6$ to $-6$ mi/sec, while the Doppler shift for star $Y$ changes from $-2$ to $+2$ mi/sec.

As compared to the temperature of star $Y$, the temperature of star $X$ is
  A. greater.
  B. less.

C. the same.

D. of unknown relative magnitude.

This conclusion is based on

A. fact a.

B. fact b.

C. fact c.

D. fact d.

E. absence of sufficient data.

With respect to the sun, the net or progressive motion of stars $X$ and $Y$ is that of

A. approach.

B. recession.

C. neither approach nor recession.

D. either approach or recession.

This conclusion is based on

A. fact a.

B. fact b.

C. fact c.

D. fact d.

E. absence of sufficient data.

2.12-5  Which of the following best indicates that radioactive disintegration is not due to collisions between atoms?

A. Many radioactive substances are solids.

B. The rate of disintegration is independent of the temperature.

C. Some disintegrations are very slow.

D. The energy involved is extremely large.

E. More than one kind of radiation may be emitted.

2.12-6  Each statement in the list labeled Theoretical Statements belongs to, that is, is a part of, one of the four theories that have been listed below. In the *first* blank at the left of each of the theoretical statements you are to write the letter of the *theory* to which the statement belongs. In the *second* blank at the left of each of the theoretical statements you are to write the number of the *one best observation* that is listed below the *theory* you have previously selected. The best observation is the one that furnishes the best experimental support for the theoretical statement. If no good experimental evidence is listed, write a zero sign in the blank.

EXAMPLE: If you decide that a given theoretical statement belongs in the theory of nuclear structure, you are to put $N$ in the blank at the left and to choose experimental support *only* from the list under Theory of the Structure of Nuclei. Correct answers are given for the first theoretical statement.

## M

### Theory of the Structure of Molecules

0. None of the observations below.
1. Two different substances may have the same proportion by weight of the elements composing the substances.
2. The chemical properties of $H_2SO_3$ and $H_2SO_4$ are quite different.
3. $CH_4$ is known; $CH_3$ does not exist.
4. Glucose, dextrose, and lactose have a sweet taste.

## K

### Kinetic Molecular Theory

0. None of the observations below.
1. Ice will evaporate if kept in a dry room at a temperature below its melting point.
2. Two gases interdiffuse rapidly.
3. A piece of camphor does not appreciably change its mass for years although it emits an easily noticeable odor.
4. Liquids are almost incompressible.

## A

### Theory of the Structure of Atoms

0. None of the observations below.
1. Alkali metals have many properties in common.
2. Iodine is chemically less active than chlorine.
3. Gas spectra consist of a series of sharp lines.
4. When an electric current passes through a solution of a salt, the metal of the salt goes to the negative plate, while the nonmetal goes to the positive plate.
5. The mass of an element deposited in electrolysis is proportional to the atomic weight of the element.
6. Beta-ray emission does not change the atomic weight of the radioactive element.

## N

### Theory of the Structure of Nuclei

0. None of the observations below.
1. Isotopes are usually very difficult to separate.
2. One of the most frequent products of radioactive disintegration is helium gas.
3. The atomic weights of pure isotopes are very nearly whole numbers.
4. Beta-ray emission does not change the atomic weight of the radioactive element.

### Theoretical Statements

K, 3    The number of molecules in one gram of a substance is extremely large.

The combination of two protons and two neutrons is extremely stable.

The presence of electron shells between an outer electron and the nucleus acts to diminish the attraction of that electron by the nucleus.

Nuclei contain no electrons.

Molecules exert attractive forces on one another.

Some molecules of a solid have considerable kinetic energies.

The presence of a given group (for example, OH, $NH_2$, etc.) in a molecule of a substance is responsible for certain chemical properties of the substance.

All electrons have the same charge.

The mass of an electron is very small in comparison to the mass of an atom.

The mass of a neutron is nearly the same as the mass of a proton.

The chemical properties of an element are nearly independent of the number of neutrons in the atom.

Distances between the molecules of a gas are great in comparison to the size of the molecules.

Chemical properties of an element are determined to a great extent by the number of electrons in the outer shell.

Electrons can occupy only certain orbits in an atom.

### 2.12-7   *Modification of a theory*

A crystalline solid may be thought of as a group of spheres in three dimensions, each sphere connected to its neighbors by a stiff spring. The spheres are vibrating in various directions. A number of facts about crystalline solids are given below. Before each fact write the letter of the response that best states the applicability of the model as an explanation of the fact. Note that only one response should be given for each fact.

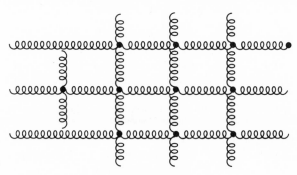

### *Responses*

A.  The fact is explained by the model given above.
B.  The fact can be explained by modifying the model as follows: the amplitude of vibration of the spheres depends upon the temperature.
C.  The fact can be explained by modifying the model as follows: there are irregularities in the arrangement of the spheres.
D.  The fact can be explained by modifying the model as follows: the elasticity of the springs is different for different solids.
E.  The fact *cannot* be explained on the basis of the model, even by changing it as above.

### *Facts*

Solids contract on cooling.
Solids may be compressed slightly.
Solids do not diffuse through one another.
Solids conduct heat.
Some solids are harder than others.
The speed of sound through steel is greater than its speed through lead.

### 2.12-8   *Rival theories*

Two theories are advanced to explain the burning of material in air. Both theories assume that no substance can have negative mass or weight.

Theory A. During combustion, the burning material unites with a certain component of the air.

Theory B. During combustion, a substance escapes from the burning material into the surrounding gas, for example, into air. The capacity of a gas to take up this escaping substance is limited.

Before each fact below write the letter of the response that best describes its relation to theories A and B. Note: A statement is said to lend greater support to theory X than to theory Y if it can be more readily (with fewer or more reasonable additional assumptions) explained by X, or if it contradicts Y but not X.

*Responses*

A. The fact lends more direct support to theory A than to theory B.
B. The fact lends more direct support to theory B than to theory A.
C. The fact supports the two theories about equally well.
D. The fact could not be used to support either theory.

*Facts*

Illuminating gas burns more brightly in chlorine than in air.

A candle in a closed jar stops burning before the candle is used up.

The product formed by burning magnesium in air is heavier than the magnesium used up.

When a candle is lighted in a closed jar containing air, the pressure in the jar is increased.

The weight of a piece of wood decreases as the wood burns.

The rusting of iron produces the same substance as the burning of iron.

A candle burns more brightly in a breeze than in still air.

2.12-9    *Forming an hypothesis*

Facts: Gases $X$ and $Y$ react readily when mixed in a glass flask. If, however, just before the gases are introduced, the flask is heated strongly and cooled, no reaction takes place. If a copper container is used, no reaction occurs. Consider each hypothesis in the light of the facts above and write the letter corresponding to the best response before the hypothesis. If the hypothesis is untenable or is not stated in a way that could be tested experimentally, choose response A. Otherwise choose the response describing the experiment that will best test the hypothesis.

Hypothesis: Water is a necessary participant in the reaction between $X$ and $Y$.

A. Hypothesis is not tenable or cannot be tested experimentally.
B. Dry the flask without heating it, before introducing the gases.
C. Leave the flask open after mixing the gases.
D. Moisten the walls of the copper container before introducing the gases.
E. Heat the glass flask strongly, allow it to cool, and leave it open for several days before introducing the gases.

Hypothesis: Copper forms a stable compound with the gas $X$ and prevents reaction with the other gas.

A. Hypothesis is not tenable or cannot be tested experimentally.
B. Inspect the interior surface of the copper container with a high-power microscope.
C. Increase the concentration of gas X but not of gas Y in the copper container and note whether the gases react.
D. Moisten the walls of the copper container before introducing the gases.
E. Coat the interior with paraffin.

Hypothesis: The reaction between X and Y takes place by a simple collision of X and Y molecules in the body of the gas.
A. Hypothesis is not tenable or cannot be tested experimentally.
B. Carry out the reaction in a glass container whose interior is lined with copper.
C. Carry out the reaction with gases X and Y dissolved in water.
D. Cover the interior of the flask with paraffin.
E. Increase the gas concentrations of gas X in a glass flask and note whether the rate finally reaches a constant limiting value.

Hypothesis: When glass is present, molecules are absorbed on the glass in such a way that their active portions project outward (away from the glass).
A. Hypothesis is not tenable or cannot be tested experimentally.
B. Fill the container with broken glass and note any change in the rate of reaction.
C. Dry the flask without heating it, before introducing the gases.
D. Cover the interior of the flask with paraffin.
E. Examine the inside walls of the container with a microscope during the reaction.

Hypothesis: Molecules of gas X are absorbed on the glass; molecules of the other gas react by striking this layer.
A. Hypothesis is not tenable or cannot be tested experimentally.
B. Fill the container with broken glass and note any change in the rate of reaction.
C. Cover the interior of the flask with paraffin.
D. Increase the concentration of one of the gases in a glass flask and note whether the rate finally reaches a constant limiting value.
E. Examine the inside walls of the container with a microscope during the reaction.

## Comments on exercises 2.12

The exercises in this section are separated into groups, for example, theoretical explanations, not because of evidence that radically different principal abilities are involved: all the exercises are intended to test for an understanding of the relation between theory and experiment. But the groupings, as in content 2.11, serve the cause of systematic variety: they provide for a better sample of auxiliary abilities and of the patterns in which these abilities occur, and thus test different aspects of the criterion competence, ability to deal with real-life situations involving physics or perhaps science in general. Convincing statistical evidence is lacking even for persistent differences in competence involved in contents 2.11, 2.12, 2.13, and 2.14. Therefore, even these larger subdivisions must be justified on grounds other than lack of intercorrelation. Besides their contribution to systematic variety, however, they are convenient because they refer to different subject matter. Furthermore, many students find it more difficult to relate a particular phenomenon to a generalization if the generalization is theoretical than if it is an empirical law of nature.

In exercises 1 to 6 the student is asked to relate a theory and a phenomenon. The theory is assumed to have been taught in the course. The phenomenon may or may not be familiar to the student, the familiar phenomenon being preferable because it can be described more briefly, but the particular relation must be new to the student. Thus, for example, item 1 belongs here only if sources of equal intensity have not been analyzed in terms of photons. It seems likely that exercises 1 to 4 and 5 to 6 test very similar abilities, even though the former ask for an explanation while the latter ask for evidence. The presence of both kinds does contribute to variety, nevertheless. The responses for item 3 are not homogeneous: response D is not a theoretical statement; and of the theoretical statements, only the right response is correct. A student may therefore reject other responses not because they do not offer an acceptable explanation, but because they are wrong in an absolute sense. In doing this he shows knowledge but not understanding. Exercise 4 asks the student to provide an explanation and to indicate its observational basis. This form is seldom effective, for it is difficult to write the basis-item without making its responses correspond in a one-to-one way to those of the explanation-item. Such correspondence may offer the student a formal clue to the basis-item response. Physical sciences other than physics, in this case astronomy, are excellent sources of simple situations that are likely to be unfamiliar to the majority of the students and yet involve little if any knowledge outside of physics. In item 5, many teachers may consider responses B and D equally right; only one of these should be used. Exercise 6 tests for two things: the ability to decide in what general theory a given theoretical statement belongs, and the ability to select evidence for it. It is possible to score the exercise for the first ability alone (by considering the student's marks in the first column of blanks only) or jointly for both of them. Since there are twenty-two responses to choose from, blind guessing is practically eliminated. At the same time, for students who have the modest ability to identify the relevant theory by name, the time spent looking over various responses is not great. To aid the student's memory, the letters to be put in the first blank are chosen to remind them of the theory. The theoretical statement beginning with "The mass of an electron" may be equally well classified under atomic or nuclear theory; with long master lists this is not always easy to avoid. The last item (and perhaps other items) tests for knowledge, for it is unlikely that a student can choose the proper evidence without having been told what it is.

Exercises 7 and 8 are different from exercises 1 to 6 because they present the student with a theory that is new to him. Such exercises have the advantage of almost certainly measuring the ability to relate theory and phenomena, rather than measuring knowledge or memory. They have the disadvantage that few accepted theories can be accurately described in a few lines; it is usually necessary to modify them radically or invent new ones. As a result, the test-maker cannot depend on existing opinion and argument but must think through the relevant relation of the theory to phenomena. With artificial theories or situations ambiguity is hard to avoid. The "artificial" type of item is very valuable, however, because of the purity of the ability it measures, for diagnosis and for tests designed to evaluate teaching method.

In exercise 7 the theory involved is artificial in that mechanical springs are substituted for the intermolecular forces of the usual model of a solid. As is well known, many features of the model are preserved under this substitution. Nevertheless, it is desirable to base several items on this situation. The "overhead" (the relative time spent on the long stem) is reduced, and one can be much more certain that the better student will work more items correctly than that the better student will mark a particular item correctly. In exercise 8 the artificial theory maintains its contact with physics by being a modified version of the old phlogiston theory. The exercise points up that isolated phenomena may support one theory more strongly than another, even though the latter theory may be overwhelmingly supported by the totality of known phenomena. In exercise 8 the master list seems the natural form. In exercise 7 it works well enough and certainly saves the test-maker's time, but much better items can be written by using the multiple-choice form. Whether or not the spring model or the phlogiston theory was explained in the course, those items whose content was not explicitly treated in the course in terms of these theories belong under understanding. Exercise 8 can be used to identify the students of greater than average over-cautiousness, for these students will prefer response D to the right responses A or B. Since "theory" A is now an established fact many students may find it difficult to bring themselves to "vote" for theory B. Exercise 8 therefore contains some items that may measure objective 3.3, disciplined thinking.

Exercise 9 requires the student to judge the aptness and propriety of an explanation of a moderately complex phenomenon. The subject matter is ostensibly chemistry, but the analysis of the phenomena does not involve specifically chemical knowledge. It is a matter of opinion whether the exercise belongs in content 2.12 or 2.13.

## Content 2.13, Understanding of experiments

The questions asked about the experiment must be new to the student.

EXERCISES 1–3.    *Criticism of an Experiment*

For each of the following three experiments, carefully read the purpose of the experiment and the procedure involved. Then choose the *one* best comment or criticism.

2.13-1    Purpose: To determine whether chemical reactions are speeded up by a rise in temperature. Procedure: When two solutions, both at 20°C, are mixed, a chemical reaction accompanied by release of hydrogen takes place. The weight of hydrogen released during five minutes is found to be 2 grams. The mixture of solutions is then quickly heated to 30°C. Hydrogen collected during the next five minutes weighs 1 gram. Which of the following statements is the best comment on or criticism of the experiment?

    A. Not all reactions are speeded up by a rise in temperature.
    B. Fresh solutions should have been used in the second experiment.
    C. Some of the hydrogen remained dissolved in the water.
    D. The experiment should have been repeated several times and the results averaged.
    E. A greater rise in temperature would have shown a gain in the rate of formation of hydrogen.

2.13-2    Purpose: To determine the solubility of potassium nitrate in water for a temperature of 60°C. Procedure: Potassium nitrate crystals are added to 100 grams of water at 60°C until no more will dissolve. The solution and the remaining solid are filtered through filter paper contained in a funnel. The clear filtrate (part which comes through the paper) is evaporated to dryness, and the residue of potassium nitrate is weighed. It is found that the solubility determined in this experiment is much lower than the correct value given in the handbook. Which of the following statements contains the best comment on or criticism of the experiment?

    A. Too much potassium nitrate was used; there should have been no solid remaining to filter off.
    B. Part of the water evaporated because of the slowness of the experiment.
    C. The funnel and paper should have been heated to 60°C during the filtration.
    D. Powdered potassium nitrate should have been used instead of crystals.
    E. The solubility should have been looked up in the handbook, and exactly the indicated weight of potassium nitrate should have been used.

2.13-3    A bell was continuously rung inside an airtight glass jar. The
sound could be clearly heard in
the room. As air was pumped
out of the jar, the sound of the
bell became less and less audible.
Finally no sound could be heard
at all. It was concluded that
sound cannot travel through a
vacuum. Mark each of the following criticisms of the conclusion + if the criticism is justified
and relevant; − if the criticism
is either not justified or is irrelevant.

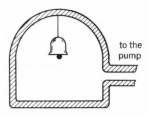

to the
pump

### Criticisms

We cannot be certain about the conclusion because some of the sound may have
traveled through the string supporting the bell.

We cannot be certain about the conclusion because some of the sound may have
traveled through the air remaining in the jar even at the end of the experiment.

EXERCISES 4–8.    *Identification of Important Experimental Factors*

2.13-4    A mercury-in-glass thermometer, reading 20°C, is plunged into boiling
water. The thermometer reading goes down to 19.5°C before climbing
up to 100°C. How would this momentary temperature dip be affected by
each of the following changes?

If the thermometer were made of thicker glass, the temperature dip
would be
  A. greater.
  B. smaller.
  C. the same.

If glass that better conducts heat were used, the temperature dip would
be
  A. greater.
  B. smaller.
  C. the same.

2.13-5    In the circuit shown, $V_1$, $V_2$, $V_3$,
and $V_4$ are accurate voltmeters;
$R$ is a resistance; and $B$ is a bat-
tery. Which pair of voltmeters
is *sure* to have the same reading?
  A. $V_1$ and $V_2$.
  B. $V_2$ and $V_4$.
  C. $V_1$ and $V_4$.
  D. $V_2$ and $V_3$.
  E. None of these.

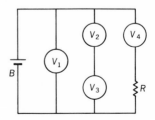

2.13-6   An experimenter notices that the mercury column height of barometer 1, kept in the basement, stands consistently higher than that of barometer 2, kept on the second floor. He discovers that the mercury of barometer 2 is contaminated with a little water. The best explanation of the difference in mercury heights is that

    A. the atmospheric pressure decreases with increasing altitude.

    B. the weight of a given mass of mercury increases as the mercury is brought nearer to the earth.

    C. water vapor exerts a pressure.

    D. mercury evaporates less easily in the presence of water vapor.

    E. the evaporation of water cools the mercury and causes it to contract.

2.13-7   Theory: A dissolved substance lowers the freezing point of a solvent because of the hindrance offered by solute molecules to the process of the assumption of regular lattice arrangement by the solvent molecules during crystal formation. This hindrance is purely mechanical: the molecules of the solvent are prevented from forming the lattice by chance collisions with the molecules of the solute. In those cases to which this theory is applicable the following generalization is true: the lowering of the freezing point is a linear function of the hindrance, that is, of the concentration of solute molecules only.

Below is a list of special cases. Each special case is described by giving one of the factors characterizing the special case. For each case choose the response that best specifies to what extent the presence of the factor would influence the applicability of the theory and therefore of the generalization.

### Responses

A. The factor described is *not* likely to interfere with accurate applicability of the generalization.

B. The factor is such that the generalization is applicable but only approximately.

C. The factor makes the generalization not applicable.

D. The information given is not sufficient to decide between A, B, and C.

### Special Cases

The dissolved substance contains charged particles.

The freezing point of the pure solvent is low, say, 50°C.

The dissolved substance readily reacts chemically with the solvent.

The solute and the solvent are both liquids at room temperature.

2.13-8   The following experiment is performed to determine the rate at which radiation is emitted through an opening of 25 square feet in a furnace whose inside is at about 1000°C. A thin flat sheet of metal 1 square foot in area is held for several minutes in the path of the radiation at a distance of about 5 feet from the opening. Its rise in temperature is measured by means of a thermocouple. For each factor below, choose the response that best describes the importance of the factor in this experiment.

*Responses*

A. The factor must be taken into account before even a rough estimate can be made.
B. The factor need be taken into account only if a fairly accurate determination is to be made.
C. The factor is not likely to affect the determination to any measurable degree.

*Factors*

The shape of the flat metal sheet (whether circular or square, and so forth).
The angle at which the sheet is held to the opening.
Whether the surface of the metal is blackened or shiny.
The radiation emitted from the outside of the furnace.
The heat conductivity of the metal sheet.
The temperature of the room.

2.13-9  *Choosing an appropriate method of investigation*
Explain briefly how you would measure the thermal conductivity of liquid mercury. You may limit your explanation to a drawing of the experimental setup, with each important part properly labeled, and a brief defense of the setup.

## Comments on exercises 2.13

In items 1 to 3 the student is asked to point out errors in the design or technique of an experiment. The first two items deal with content on the borderline between physics and chemistry, to make sure that the experiment is new to the student. The stems are made directive by stating the purpose and the procedure. A good student on reading these and noting the word *criticism* in the directions should anticipate the correct response. Students who choose response A in item 1 show rash judgment and may have a general tendency to jump to conclusions.

Items 4, 5, and 6 deal with the behavior of measuring instruments. Item 5 illustrates that instruments may be not mere "observers" but intimate parts of a setup, and that their structures—in this case their resistances—may therefore have to be taken into account. In item 6 the student is to decide whether an observed fact is caused by a faulty instrument.

In exercise 7, which may almost as well be in content 2.12, the student is to decide how well a theory applies in view of various experimental factors that cannot be controlled. The exercise can also be used to help identify the overcautious students, who often choose response D, and the rash students, who often choose response A. Exercise 8 presents the student with a similar problem, except that the various factors can be controlled. It therefore tests an aspect of the student's ability to design an experiment. The master-list form seems natural since essentially the same question is asked in each item. The form has the weakness, however, of using for different items the same imprecisely defined scale of applicability. In some items, as a result, two responses may be so nearly equal in correctness that credit (not necessarily equal) should be given for each. Thus, for example, response C to the item on charged particles of exercise 7 should be given some credit. The same is true of responses A and B, respectively, in the third and fourth items of exercise 8. With these precautions, and even without them, the better students are likely to choose a larger number of "right" responses in each exercise, even though such reliance cannot be put on an individual item.

The difference between the right and wrong responses in exercises like 7 and 8 can always be sharpened and made easier to read by using the multiple-choice form. The third item of exercise 8 can be rewritten as follows:

2.13-8a    If the surface of the metal is shiny rather than blackened,
        A. its temperature will be a few degrees lower.
        B. its temperature may be lower by as much as 300°C.
        C. its temperature will be lower by an unobservably small amount.
        D. its temperature will be exactly the same.

In exercise 9 the student is asked to choose the appropriate experimental procedure.

The three groups of items, 1 to 3, 4 to 8, and 9, have been placed in content 2.13, because, although the questions asked of the students in these three groups are different—what is wrong, what is important, and how to proceed—there is no evidence that the principal ability varies measurably from group to group. It is the importance of presenting the student with a variety of test situations that justifies the inclusion of all three groups. However, the essay item of exercise 9, if it deals with an experiment that is genuinely novel to the student, may require an ability that is different from that required in exercises 1 to 8. It can be called the ability to plan an experiment.

### Content 2.14, Understanding of broad concepts and classifications

The content of 2.14 is the same as that of 1.24. It is concepts and classes that cut across subject-matter areas: operational definition, mechanics, theory, fact, conservation laws, symmetry, probability, proof, evidence, explanation, significant figures, probable error, and others. Exercises appropriate to 2.14 must, however, have important novel elements.

2.14-1    Which of the following is the best *operational* definition of the North Celestial Pole (N.C.P.)?
        A. The N.C.P. is the point at which the axis of the earth, extended, would pierce the celestial sphere.
        B. The N.C.P. is the geometric center of the circular star paths in the Northern Hemisphere.
        C. The N.C.P. is located on the perpendicular erected in the center of the plane of the earth's revolution.
        D. The N.C.P. is the point directly overhead at the North Pole, and on the horizon at the equator.

E. The N.C.P. is the equivalent of the earth's North Pole but is located in space in order to serve as a reference point.

2.14-2    Assume that "the sun rises in the east" is a complete and accurate definition of east and that north-south lines are perpendicular to east-west lines. Which of the following comments is most justified?

A. It follows that Gary may be northeast or southeast of Chicago depending on the season of the year.

B. The definition is inconsistent with observations.

C. North-south lines are only perpendicular to the east-west line constituting the equator; the two statements are contradictory.

D. The definition is incorrect since the earth really moves around the sun.

E. Since the definition reiterates known facts it is an unnecessary appendage.

2.14-3    The *mass* of a body is defined in terms of, and measured by, the amount of force required to give the body a given acceleration, that is, the mass of the body is large if it takes a large force to give a given acceleration to the body. It has been found by experiment that when a body is moving at a high speed, a larger force is required to give the body a given acceleration than would be required if the body were moving slowly. Assuming that the above statements are true, mark each of the assertions below as right (R) or wrong (W).

The mass of a body increases as the body's speed increases.

It is possible that at higher speeds some other property of the body changes, but the mass remains constant.

The faster a body is moving, the greater is the force required to give the body a given acceleration even if the mass remains the same.

2.14-4    Which of the following is the best analysis of the statement, "All verticals pass through the center of the earth"?

A. It is an operational definition of vertical.

B. It is based on the geometric construction using perpendiculars to tangents of a circle.

C. It is a deduction from the definition of vertical.

D. It is a deduction from the definition of vertical and from observations on the angles verticals make with one another.

E. It is a law that sums up countless observations on plumb lines.

F. It is a theory, incapable of proof, since the center of the earth is inaccessible.

2.14-5    In the following two items assume that flipping a coin produces no physical changes in the coin. A completely symmetrical coin was flipped 20 times and came up "heads" 18 times and "tails" 2 times. In the 21st trial, the chances that the coin would come up "heads" rather than "tails" are

A. much smaller.

B. somewhat smaller.

C. the same.

    D. somewhat greater.

    E. much greater.

In an experiment, 100 identical coins were to be flipped simultaneously. In a second experiment, one of the 100 coins was to be flipped 100 times. How do the probabilities that the number of "heads" would equal the number of "tails" compare in the two experiments? In the second experiment the probability is

    A. much greater.

    B. somewhat greater.

    C. the same.

    D. somewhat smaller.

    E. much smaller.

2.14-6   An investigation is made of the relationship between the thickness of silver deposited in a photographic film and the time of exposure. The small circles in the graph represent the data obtained in several experiments. Three curves, X, Y, and Z, are drawn in an attempt to clarify the relationship. For each curve choose the response that best evaluates the curve.

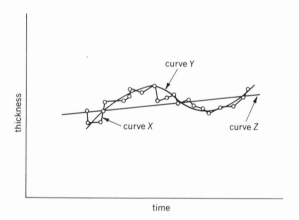

Curve X is

    A. satisfactory, because it passes through all of the points.

    B. satisfactory, because it shows that there is a value of thickness corresponding to each interval of time.

    C. unsatisfactory, because it does not extend far enough beyond the first and last points.

    D. unsatisfactory, because its deviations from a smooth curve are probably due to experimental error.

    E. unsatisfactory, because the relationship must be linear.

Curve Y is

    A. satisfactory, because it represents the general trend of the data points.

B. satisfactory, because there are as many points on one side of it as on the other.

C. unsatisfactory, because it misses so many of the points.

D. unsatisfactory, because it extends beyond the first and last data points.

E. unsatisfactory, because no relationship between thickness and time could involve such a complex curve.

Curve Z is

A. satisfactory, because it represents the simplest relationship between thickness and time.

B. satisfactory, because the slope of the curve (rate of deposit) can be determined quickly and easily.

C. unsatisfactory, because it does not properly follow the general trend of the data.

D. unsatisfactory, because it misses so many of the points.

E. unsatisfactory, because it extends beyond the first and last data points.

To get a truer correspondence between thickness and time, one should

A. average the three curves drawn above and plot the average.

B. draw larger dots for the data points so that the best curve above will touch them all.

C. use only those data points which fall on or very near the straight line.

D. extend the straight line as far as possible in both directions, and then place additional data points on the extensions.

E. None of the procedures above is appropriate.

## Comments on exercises 2.14

Items 1 to 3 deal with the concept of "definition." Item 1 belongs here only if an operational definition of the North Celestial Pole was not given in class. Item 2 illustrates the unchallengeable nature of an accepted definition. (Outside of Illinois, well-known landmarks at nearly the same latitude should be used instead of Gary and Chicago.) Exercise 3 tests for a similar but not identical objective because it involves the concepts of force, mass, and acceleration and thus has a somewhat richer physics context. This is a desirable characteristic; items involving no physics may be valuable for testing the student's intelligence but are out of place in a physics achievement test. On the other hand, items that require the understanding of one concept only—"definition" in item 2—are diagnostically convenient, since they pinpoint the student's weakness. Item 4 deals with an assertion that involves definitions and observations. It is a matter of opinion whether response D or F is better; only one should be included. Some teachers may consider the distinction between responses D and E too fine and may omit E. Exercises 5 and 6 have been included here because both the laws of probability and graphical representation of data cut across most subject-matter areas. Exercise 6 could almost as well be put in 2.13, understanding of experiment.

**Objective 2.2, Understanding the interrelationships of physics principles and their relationships to principles of other disciplines**

Exercises included under this objective are to be limited to situations that have not been taught in the course and that require more than one principle —or even more than one branch of science—for their analysis.

### Content 2.21, Situations involving more than one area of physics

2.21-1    Small spherical particles of various radii $r$, but of the same chemical composition and of density $d$, are suspended in a liquid whose density is less than $d$ and whose viscosity is $k$. As a particle falls under the force of gravity, it is retarded by the buoyant force and by the force of viscosity $6\pi krv$, where $v$ is the velocity of the particle. In the two situations that follow, assume that particles reach terminal velocities.

If the liquid is whirled in a centrifuge, the terminal velocity of larger particles, as compared with smaller particles, will be
A. greater.
B. smaller.
C. the same.
D. any of the above, depending on the viscosity, $k$.
E. any of the above, depending on the angular speed of the centrifuge.

If the particles start to dissolve somewhat in the liquid, the *difference* in the terminal velocities of a large and a small particle will
A. become greater.
B. become smaller.
C. remain the same.
D. be any of the above, depending on the rate of dissolving.
E. be any of the above, depending on the viscosity.

2.21-2    Two bodies of the same shape and size but of different weights are thrown upward with the same initial velocity in a liquid that is less dense than the lighter body. Assume that the average force of viscosity is much greater than the buoyant force. The heavier body will be found to rise
A. higher than the lighter body.
B. less high than the lighter body.
C. to the same height as the lighter body.
D. The data are insufficient to decide.

### Content 2.22, Situations involving more than one physical science

2.22-1    *Physics and chemistry*
A utility company changed its gas for domestic use from water gas (about 50 percent by volume hydrogen, $H_2$, and 50 percent carbon

monoxide, CO) to coke-oven gas (about 30 percent hydrogen and 70 percent methane, $CH_4$) without altering burners or pressure. A suit was filed against the utility by a man who claimed that he was made ill by carbon monoxide escaping unburned from a lighted cookstove. Under proper conditions, hydrogen is known to burn to $H_2O$, carbon monoxide to $CO_2$, and methane to $H_2O$ and $CO_2$.

$$2H_2 + O_2 \rightarrow 2H_2O$$
$$2CO + O_2 \rightarrow 2CO_2$$
$$CH_4 + 2O_2 \rightarrow CO_2 + 2H_2O$$

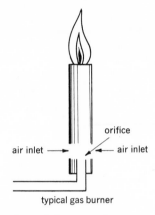

orifice

air inlet ──→        ←── air inlet

typical gas burner

If oxygen is limited, carbon monoxide may be formed from methane.

$$2CH_4 + 3O_2 \rightarrow 2CO + 4H_2O$$

Which of the following should be most useful in investigating the possibility of CO formation due to oxygen deficiency?
  A. The law that gases combine in fixed ratios by volume.
  B. The table of atomic weights.
  C. The laws relating pressure, volume, and temperature of gases.
  D. The laws of chemical equilibrium.
  E. The law of definite proportions by weight.

It was demonstrated that the rate of gas flow from a given orifice was the same for either gas. This evidence
  A. suggests that the changeover could not have resulted in incomplete combustion.
  B. suggests that incomplete combustion was due to lack of oxygen.
  C. indicates that the burner is of proper design.
  D. is irrelevant in this situation.

The complainant's attorney held that the utility should have increased the gas pressure in the mains. What would probably have been the result?
  A. It would have allowed a more complete combustion.
  B. The combustion would have been more complete, but a large waste of gas would have resulted.
  C. It would have rectified the condition but would have produced a flame of a lower temperature.
  D. It would have made the combustion even less complete.

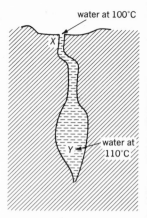

2.22-2  *Physics and geology*
A cross-section view of a geyser is shown in the diagram at the right. The fissure is filled with water. The temperature difference shown between the levels $X$ and $Y$ is best explained on the basis that

A. salts dissolved in the water settle toward the bottom.
B. the fissure is wider at the level of $Y$ and a greater area of contact with the hot rock is made.
C. the lower portion is deeper in the earth and therefore receives more heat.
D. the pressure of the overlying water raises the boiling point of the water at the lower levels.
E. the compression of the water is very great at the lower levels, and it heats the water.

Which of the following is the most plausible explanation of the fact that the geyser erupts at fairly regular intervals?

A. The high temperature decomposes water into hydrogen and oxygen, which force their way upward.
B. Water boils out at the top, thus lowering the pressure at the lower levels.
C. Water at 110°C meets water at 100°C; the shock produces large volumes of steam.
D. Rock movements compress the fissure and expel the water.
E. Molten rock reaches the water through cracks in the containing walls.

2.22-3  *Physics, chemistry, geology, and astronomy*
The statement is often made that "physics and chemistry are basic sciences; astronomy and geology are derived sciences." Which of the following is the best interpretation of the statement? (Obviously statements as short as those below cannot do full justice to the matter. Choose the least incorrect.)

A. Physics and chemistry rest on a sound foundation of proven laws; much of astronomy and geology is pure speculation.
B. The development of astronomy and geology requires the use of physics and chemistry; the converse is not true.
C. All findings of astronomy and geology have been explained by physics and chemistry.

D. Physics and chemistry are of more basic importance to human activity than astronomy and geology.
E. It is possible to carry out laboratory experiments in physics and chemistry but not in astronomy or geology.

## Content 2.23, Situations involving nonphysical sciences

2.23-1  *Physics and mathematics*
Lobachevsky based his geometry on the assumption that through a given external point more than one straight line can be drawn parallel to a given straight line. This assumption
A. has been found true under certain circumstances and is now considered a basic law of nature.
B. is obviously incorrect but is useful in checking the accuracy of other geometries.
C. can be shown to be incorrect by drawing lines through a point and demonstrating that all but one line intersect the given line.
D. cannot be established or disproved experimentally.

Which of the following statements best describes the comparative natures of geometry and physics as fields of knowledge? (Obviously statements as short as those below cannot give full justice to the subject. Choose the least incorrect.)
A. Deductive reasoning is dominant in geometry; inductive reasoning is dominant in physics.
B. Geometry is highly symbolic; physics uses no symbolism.
C. Geometry rests on a base of unprovable assumptions; physics is based on experiment.
D. The theorems and postulates of geometry are universal and exact truths; physical measurements approximate the same truths but only to the extent permitted by the instruments used.
E. Any set of assumptions can be built into a workable geometry; the assumptions of physics represent the way nature really works.

2.23-2  *Natural and social sciences*
A man finds that his rosebushes wither in a short time, although his lawn remains in perfect condition. He suspects that fumes from a nearby lead smelter are the cause. Which of the following is the most reasonable course of action?
A. He should collect some of the fumes and note their effect on a healthy rosebush.
B. He should analyze samples of the fumes taken at various times of the day and different seasons of the year.
C. He should secure permission to grow some rosebushes inside the fences surrounding the lead smelter.
D. He should move to the suburbs.
E. He should start legal proceedings to stop the smelter from operating.

A man is buying a diamond engagement ring. He wants to be sure that the diamond is genuine and not a crystal or glass imitation. The most reasonable course of action would be
- A. to buy a very expensive ring, to be sure of getting the best quality.
- B. to have the stone removed from its setting, and its index of refraction determined.
- C. to chip a small fragment from the stone and have it analyzed.
- D. to have the ring selected by friends, all of whom own diamond rings.
- E. to buy the ring from a long-established and respected jeweler.

2.23-3   *Science and philosophy*
(a) Before each question below, write S if it is a question that can be answered fully by using the methods of empirical science: either by using established theories and facts or by performing new experiments. Write N if it is *not* such a question. (b) In the space below each question, briefly defend your judgment.

Is the orderliness of nature real or is it in man's mind only?

Why is heat given off when a violent chemical reaction takes place?

Can we know the true nature of matter?

Why are there only two kinds of electric charge, positive and negative?

Can the standard of living in the South be raised by subsidizing industry in the South?

Can dogs distinguish between green and blue?

Has philosophy influenced the development of science?

**Comments on exercises 2.2**

Most teachers hope that their students will learn to use understanding of physics in dealing with real phenomena, both in and outside the physics classroom. Real phenomena are notably complex: they may involve several areas of physics, other physical sciences and mathematics, biological and social sciences, and even philosophy. If the physics course grade is to predict the student's ability to use physics in such complex situations, it seems desirable to include in achievement tests some exercises that measure the relevant competence. Exercises of this sort usually require a good deal of the student's time unless they are to some degree simplified and idealized. If the exercise is to belong in objective 2.2, however, the idealization should stop short of reducing to one the number of generalizations required for working the exercise.

**Exercises 2.21**

Exercises 1 and 2 involve physics concepts only: gravity, centrifugal force, buoyancy, viscosity, and rate of solution (in its dependence on the area exposed). This complexity is hardly greater than that of many laboratory experiments, and the exercise may therefore form a legitimate part even of an examination that is not slanted toward prognosis. It is not at all difficult to select situations on which similar exercises can be based; for instance, in treating falling bodies the student may be asked to take into account the nonuniformity of the earth's gravitational field and air friction. The time allowance for exercises in objective 2.2 should be generous. For example, the first item of exercise 1 may be allowed five minutes; the second and succeeding items, however, may not require more than the standard 90 to 120 seconds allowance for objective items that are not workable by recall. It is economical, therefore, to have several items for each exercise of considerable complexity.

### Exercises 2.22

Exercise 1 requires the ability to determine gas volumes from the equations of chemical reactions and to combine the information thus gained with the simple physics of gas flow. The required knowledge of chemistry is very small, but the analysis of the situation requires keeping in mind both chemical and physical principles. The exercise was based on a contemporary newspaper story; the situation was therefore a real one. Except for adding a little touch of drama, the court-suit idea is, of course, entirely irrelevant. There isn't much geology in exercise 2, but the situation the student is asked to analyze is quite different from academic ones. Therefore, although in the final analysis "academic" physics is entirely adequate, the path to this decision requires weighing the relevance of several factors. The exercise illustrates certain advantages of objective exercises over essays. An essay asking for an explanation of a geyser is much too difficult for a student unfamiliar with the subject. Objective items, on the other hand, though testing for a related understanding, can be made of any degree of difficulty by varying the attractiveness of the wrong responses. Exercise 3 deals with the distinction between the basic and derived sciences. The distinction may not be permanent, but today it is illuminating.

### Exercises 2.23

The saying, "He who hasn't been out of England does not know England," applies to knowledge of physics. The student of physics should know not only the main methodological and subject-matter differences between physics and other branches of physical science, but also the differences between physical science and other disciplines, especially mathematics. The first item of exercise 1 illustrates the essentially unchallengeable status of an axiom. The stem is not directive: after reading it, the student does not yet know what he is going to be asked about the assumption. This fault can be remedied to some extent by inserting after the first sentence of the stem the following question: "What may be said about the correctness of the assumption?" This remedy will be unnecessary if the students have learned to expect homogeneous responses and the problem is well defined by the stem and the first response. The second item deals with differences between mathematics and natural science. Exercise 1 (and exercise 2.22-3) differs from other exercises (in objective 2.2) in that it asks for formal statements rather than for application of principles to concrete examples. Testing for the understanding of a concept by asking a student to define it (or to select a good definition) is less direct than asking him to use the concept. An aspect of understanding exhibited in wording or verbalizing, however, is important both for reinforcement of learning and for communication. In such exercises it is particularly important to make the responses quite different from statements in the text. Note the parenthetical warning to the student included in the stem.

The main decision the student is asked to make in exercise 2 is whether performing an experiment is a sensible procedure. Such items can therefore be used to assess the student's attitude toward the methods of empirical science. Thus, for example, the student who frequently chooses responses similar to responses B and C of the second item probably overestimates the value of laboratory experimentation in the conduct of daily life.

Exercise 3 tries to establish some rough boundary between empirical science and philosophy. This seems desirable because quite frequently the teacher of introductory courses, in answering students' questions—or refusing to answer—feels obliged to classify them as philosophical. The boundary is at any rate not very sharp, and it is enough that students be able to classify extreme cases. The essentially true-or-false form of the exercise lends itself well to crude distinctions. To provide for defensible differences of opinion, space may be left below each question for a short essay comment. To bring home to students the danger of following formal clues, the last item, though it has the clue-word *philosophy* in it, can surely be answered through methods of empirical science. There are scientists who believe that questions that cannot be answered by science cannot be answered at all or—as the less polite positivists put it—that such questions are meaningless. Such belief is an article of faith that will not be disputed here; exercise 3 is in any case noncommittal as to the value of non-science questions.

### Objective 2.3, Understanding the nature and structure of physics

Under this objective are exercises that can show what image the student has of physics as a science. The temptation of asking very general and grand questions, however, has been resisted in order to avoid verbalizations *about* physics. Instead, the student is asked again to analyze quite specific situations in physics, even though the exercises are therefore rather like those under objective 2.1.

### Content 2.31, Understanding of physics as a body of knowledge: criteria for empirical generalization, theory, model, experiment, concept, and definition

2.31-1    If the length of the sidereal day is assumed constant, the solar day varies.
If the length of the solar day is assumed constant, the sidereal day varies.
Why was the second alternative not chosen?

A. Time rates of laboratory phenomena (for example, the period of a pendulum) would have been found to vary during the year.
B. The length of a sidereal day can be determined more accurately than that of a solar day.
C. Observations show that the solar day does vary with respect to the sidereal day.
D. Observations show that the sidereal day is of constant length.
E. The choice is purely arbitrary and could have been made either way with identical results.

2.31-2   Which of the following is the best comment on the definition of mass as "the amount of matter in a body"?
A. It fails to indicate a method for finding the mass of a given body.
B. It indicates how the mass of a given body can be determined.
C. It states what mass really is.
D. It is a self-evident axiom, necessary as a basis for Newtonian mechanics.

2.31-3   The apparatus shown at the right consists of a light pulley, a flexible string running over the pulley, and two bodies of masses $m_1$ and $m_2$ attached to the ends of the string.

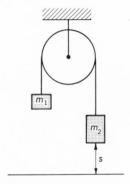

The apparatus was used in an experiment in which various bodies of known masses were allowed to move under the influence of gravity. In each case the distance $s$ through which the bodies moved from rest, and the time $t$ required for this motion, were measured. Assume that the experiment was conducted properly and that the usual relations were found among various quantities.

In answering the following questions use Newton's definition of $F$, $m$, and $a$.

What may be concluded *from this experiment* as to the validity of Newton's second law, $F = ma$?
A. The experiment constitutes an experimental proof of the law.
B. The law is proved to be true within experimental error.
C. The law is proved for vertical motion.
D. The law is proved for vertical motion within experimental error.
E. None of the above is true.

What may be concluded *from this experiment* as to the validity of the statement that "the total mass of the two bodies is $m_1 + m_2$"?

A. The experiment shows that the statement is consistent with $F = ma$.
B. This particular experiment throws no light on the validity of the statement.
C. The statement is true because the amount of material in the two weights is $m_1 + m_2$.
D. The statement can be deduced from $F = ma$ without experimentation.
E. The statement can be proved experimentally without the use of the law, $F = ma$, by weighing the two masses together.

What may be concluded *from this experiment* as to the validity of the statement that "the larger weight descends with a constant acceleration"?
A. The experiment can be used to test the validity of the statement without using the law, $F = ma$.
B. The statement is a logical consequence of the law, $F = ma$, and is thus essentially incapable of experimental verification.
C. To verify the statement it is necessary to use both the law, $F = ma$, and experimental observation.
D. We define constant acceleration as the acceleration that results when a constant force acts on a constant mass. Therefore the weight moves with constant acceleration by definition.

2.31-4   Our inability to form an accurate mental picture of the electron is best attributed to
A. a lack of knowledge about the electron.
B. the structure of our eyes, which makes it impossible for us to see the electron.
C. an essential difference between the electron and any object familiar to us.
D. the imperfect state of the theory.
E. our inability to experiment with a single electron.

2.31-5   Electrons have been found to have wavelike properties; light has been found to have properties of particles. What conclusion is justified by these discoveries?
A. Science has reached a region in which the experimental method fails.
B. Observation has gone too far ahead; it is time to stop and think.
C. All natural phenomena can be explained on a single basis.
D. Electrons and the particles of light are identical.
E. The distinction between radiation and particles is no longer clear cut.

2.31-6   An electron may be represented by a wave packet. The exact position of the packet cannot be described because, in theory, the packet spreads with the passage of time. This impossibility of exact description
A. constitutes a defect of the wave theory of the electron.
B. constitutes a defect that is removed by assigning particle properties to the packet.

C. is desirable because it corresponds to the experimental evidence about the electron.

D. is desirable because the electron does spread with the passage of time.

E. is an inherent fault of any theory of the electron.

2.31-7 The temperature in deep mines is known to rise about 1°C for every 100 feet of depth. Which of the following is the most reasonable and accurate hypothesis as to conditions at a depth of 1,900 miles?

A. The temperature is about 100,000°C.

B. The temperature is higher than at the surface, but the difference may be large or small.

C. The temperature is high enough to keep the interior molten.

D. The temperature is much higher than at the surface.

E. The temperature may be higher or lower than at the surface.

### Comments on exercises 2.31

Item 1 illustrates the point that the choice of a definition in physics is not really arbitrary but is governed by various criteria, one of which is the simplicity of the mathematical description of nature. Item 2 deals with a defect of a nonoperational definition. Exercise 3 tests the student's understanding of the relation between observations with which he is thoroughly familiar—the Atwood machine experiment—and an equally familiar assertion, $F = ma$. Newton's second law, sometimes called a law of nature but sometimes treated as a definition, is apparently an assertion that cannot with full justice be classified as factual, theoretical, or definitional. The relation seems to be subtler than the usual "Atwood machine experiment proves (or verifies) the truth of $F = ma$." The subtlety lies in the fact that the masses used in the experiment are measured or checked by weighing them and using the relation $W = mg$, which is of course a particular form of $F = ma$.

Items 4 and 5 deal with a realm of thought in which empirical science and philosophy, in particular, epistemology, are not separable without irreparable damage to both. Such overlapping realms exist in every area of physics, but they are particularly obvious in the so-called modern physics, so much so that physics teachers who have thus far successfully avoided getting into "philosophy" can no longer do so. The consequently different treatments of classical and modern physics undoubtedly contribute to the students' greater interest in the latter. Item 6 brings up a criterion for theory that is distinctly modern.

Item 7 tests for the understanding of extrapolation. It is undoubtedly rash to choose A as the right response, but a student who chooses E is overcautious. The refusal to formulate any hypothesis from limited data shows a misunderstanding of physics methodology that is perhaps just as bad as the rashness of extreme extrapolation. Wrong responses inviting the two types of misunderstanding must be roughly equal in number in the test as a whole. On a test that penalizes rashness only, a student who knows little physics but who rejects "rash" responses through conservatism or timidity may get a higher score than he deserves. However, teachers who consider rashness a greater failing than overcautiousness can convey their point of view to the student by marking response A but not response E as an F response and assigning a −1 value to it.

### Content 2.32, Understanding of physics as inquiry

The factors dealt with here determine our growth in understanding of nature: contributions made by an invention or discovery, interactions between these contributions, and scientists' attitudes toward inquiry. The subject is not the history of events or names (as in content 1.15) but the disciplinary history; not chronological but logical or causal relationships.

EXERCISES 1–7.   *Contributions to Progress Made by an Invention or Discovery*

Examples of invention are a new theory or a new concept; of discovery, a phenomenon or an empirical generalization.

2.32-1   Kepler's contribution to astronomy is best summarized as
    A. the discovery of causes of celestial motions.
    B. the derivation of facts concerning planetary motions from self-evident axioms.
    C. the classification of data obtained by precise observation.
    D. the discovery of an all-encompassing principle governing celestial phenomena.
    E. the establishment of mathematical relations based on quantitative data.

Of what value has Mendeleyev's periodic law been to science?
    A. It demonstrated that reasoning makes experimentation less important.
    B. It demonstrated that not all problems can be solved experimentally.
    C. It correlated a great many hitherto unrelated facts.
    D. It showed that even the most complex phenomena can be explained by science.
    E. It proved that certain groups of elements have similar properties.

2.32-2   Bode's law states that the relative distances of the planets from the sun are given approximately by the relation $(0 + 4)/10$, $(3 + 4)/10$, $(6 + 4)/10$, $(12 + 4)/10$, $(24 + 4)/10$, and so forth. Why is this law considered valuable by astronomers?
    A. It proves that the universe is governed by simple mathematical laws.
    B. It enables one to check the experimentally measured planetary distances.
    C. It permits more exact determination than is possible experimentally.
    D. It gives a simple mathematical relation between the planetary distances that may indicate a common causal basis.

E. It gives a mathematical relation and must therefore express a fundamental principle; a relation between numbers selected at random cannot be described mathematically.

What was the main value of Balmer's discovery of the formula relating frequency of the lines in the hydrogen spectrum to a set of integers?
A. It permitted the development of equations for predicting emission frequencies for the rest of the elements.
B. It accounted for the frequencies in terms of electron transitions in atoms.
C. It provided an empirical basis for a theory of electron transitions in atoms.
D. It demonstrated the essential correctness of the photon theory.
E. It established a way of predicting properties of the elements from the wavelengths of their emission lines.

2.32-3   If in his study of free fall, Galileo had chosen to define acceleration as the rate of change of velocity with distance, what objection might be raised against such a definition?
A. It would have complicated the experimental procedures.
B. It would not have been consistent with the definition of velocity.
C. It would have yielded incorrect results for free fall.
D. The description of free fall would have been more complicated.
E. There could be no objection since definitions are arbitrary.

2.32-4   A major difficulty of the elastic-ether theory of light was that it predicted
A. that the speed of light should be infinite.
B. that longitudinal light waves should exist.
C. that light should not be polarizable.
D. that light should not pass through a vacuum, for example, from the sun to the earth.
E. None of the above answers is correct.

2.32-5   Planck's invention of energy quanta was made in order to
A. secure agreement of his empirical equation with the law of conservation of energy.
B. devise a single equation agreeing with both the Stefan-Boltzmann and the Wien laws throughout their ranges.
C. provide a conceptual basis for his empirical equation.
D. combine classical mechanics and Maxwell's laws into a unified picture of black-body radiation.
E. account for the lines observed in the spectrum of hydrogen.

Why was the existence of the neutrino postulated long before its discovery?
A. To account for the high energies observed in nuclear reactions.
B. To account for the apparent loss in mass-energy during some nuclear disintegrations.
C. To account for the short-range forces holding protons and neutrons together in the nucleus.

D. To account for the Compton Effect, in which photons lose part of their energy in collision with electrons.

E. To preserve the law of conservation of mass, apparently violated in nuclear transformations (masses of products at rest seemed less than the mass of the disintegrating nucleus).

2.32-6 The physical behavior of many gases is found to be described quite well by the equation $PV/T = k$, where $P$, $V$, and $T$ are the pressure, volume, and absolute temperature, and $k$ is a constant. Another relation can be obtained by the use of the classical laws of physics applied to a "model" gas. Let this gas consist of $n$ molecules, each having a mass $m$ and a velocity $u$; these molecules are of negligible diameter, lose no energy by collision, and do not attract one another. The behavior of this "model" gas conforms to the relation $PV/u^2 = \frac{1}{3}nm$.

A good reason for deriving the equation $PV/u^2 = \frac{1}{3}nm$ would be to
A. enable suitable corrections to be made in the law $PV/T = k$.
B. extend the law $PV = kT$ to molecular phenomena.
C. avoid the errors inherent in laboratory experiments.
D. test the assumptions underlying the equation.
E. prove that the law $PV = kT$ is correct.

Some gases are *not* well described by the law $PV = kT$. In such cases it is likely that
A. the theoretical equation will give a more accurate description.
B. the theoretical equation will be in error to about the same degree.
C. the kinetic-molecular theory of matter does not apply.
D. the two equations taken together will be satisfactory.
E. such gases are exceptions and may be ignored.

The statement that $T$ and $u^2$ vary proportionally may be considered as
A. an assumption made merely in order to verify both equations.
B. a logical necessity because of the correspondence of all other terms.
C. an operational definition of temperature.
D. a theory that has been proved to be true by the law $PV = kT$.
E. a reasonable hypothesis to be tested further in other situations.

2.32-7 Mechanical models are becoming less useful in explaining phenomena on the frontiers of modern physics; mathematical equations are frequently the only mode of expression. What bearing may this have on the future development of science?
A. Future progress will be principally in further refinements of measurements.
B. The exact methods of mathematics will bring nature under complete control.
C. Future physicists must depend less on visualization as an aid in thinking.
D. Practically no one will be able to understand future discoveries, not even the physicists.
E. direct observation is likely to be replaced by rigorous theoretical deductions.

What is the value of a theory in science?

A. It tells us what things are really like.

B. It serves as a guide in further work.

C. It enables the scientist to change facts that are "out of line" with correct scientific opinion.

D. It makes laboratory work unnecessary.

E. It has no lasting value since theories always change.

### Comments on exercises 2.32 (1 to 7)

Exercise 1 deals with the immediate contribution of an empirical generalization. In the second item, response E may be considered an F response and assigned a score of $-1$. The wrong responses A and B are "paired" by the word "demonstrated." Since pairing of responses is hard to avoid, it should occur with equal frequency in correct and in wrong responses; otherwise it would afford a clue. Exercise 2 emphasizes the value of a mathematical summary of data as a step toward theory; exercise 3, the importance of a careful choice of concepts in an investigation. Exercise 4 deals with defects of a theory that may lead to its downfall. Exercise 5 illustrates the usefulness of heuristic invention (Planck had at first little faith in the reality of quantized states).

Exercise 6 tests for an understanding of the interrelationship of a theory, during a stage of its development, and experiment. The first item deals with a possible use of a theoretical relationship that involves quantities not directly measurable. The second item shows that a model, invented to explain a certain regularity in a range of phenomena, cannot be expected to apply accurately to phenomena outside the range. The third item stresses the initial tentativeness in identifying features of the model with aspects of reality. A good deal of the required information is supplied in order not to penalize students for forgetting details. But the information is supplied in so condensed a form that only students who have had training in the kinetic theory can be expected to do well on these items. A formal clue to the right response in the last item of the exercise is the word *reasonable;* it should be dropped. Students know well that teachers like to have the best response as nearly right as possible, and that a popular means for making it right is to include words such as *reasonable, probable,* and *approximate.* The best place for such qualifications is in the stem. Exercise 7 is more general than the preceding exercises, and it runs the danger of stressing verbalization—a formal, not very deep or useful, understanding.

EXERCISES 8–15.  *Scientists' Philosophies or Attitudes Toward Research*

2.32-8  *Galileo*

The following is one possible criterion or requirement for a good scientific definition: "The definition should relate the quantities entering into the definition in a simple way." Which of the following statements best represents Galileo's judgment of this criterion?

    A. The criterion is an essential one for a proper definition.
    B. The criterion is desirable but not essential.
    C. The criterion is neither desirable nor essential but, if met, would not necessarily lead to an improper definition.
    D. The criterion would, if met, lead to an improper definition.
    E. The criterion cannot be met.

Which of the following reasons is most relevant to the way Galileo arrived at his judgment of the criterion?
    A. Natural phenomena are simple to explain.
    B. A study of natural phenomena should begin with description and classification.
    C. The fundamental laws of nature are simple in form.
    D. The task of science is an understanding of natural phenomena.
    E. Scientific definitions are true only for ideal cases, cases not occurring in nature.

The following is a possible criterion or requirement for a scientific study of the motion of falling bodies: "The study should include an account of the forces producing the motion." Which of the following statements best represents Galileo's judgment of this criterion?
    A. The criterion is essential for a proper study.
    B. The criterion is desirable but not essential.
    C. The criterion is neither desirable nor essential but, if met, would not necessarily lead to an improper study.
    D. The criterion would, if met, lead to an improper study.
    E. The criterion cannot be met.

Which of the following generalizations is most relevant to Galileo's judgment of the criterion?
    A. Natural phenomena are simple to explain.
    B. A study of natural phenomena should begin with description and classification.
    C. The fundamental laws of nature are simple in form.
    D. The task of science is an understanding of natural phenomena.
    E. Scientific definitions are true only for ideal cases, cases not occurring in nature.

Which of these statements best expresses Galileo's attitude toward seeking ultimate causes of natural phenomena?
    A. It is premature to inquire into ultimate causes before facts relevant to the phenomena are determined.
    B. Knowing ultimate causes is indispensable for planning an investigation.
    C. Ultimate causes are of less significance than generalizations based on the facts.
    D. Ultimate causes belong in the realm of metaphysics, not in natural science.

E. Scientific investigations proceed equally well from knowledge of ultimate causes or from knowledge of facts.

2.32-9    *Pascal*

If bellows are expanded, air enters into the bellows. In explaining this and similar phenomena, Pascal argued that his theory (that the air moves under the pressure of surrounding atmosphere) is better than the abhorrence-of-vacuum theory. Which of the following does he use as an argument?

A. The vacuum does not exist in nature.
B. The total weight of the atmosphere is experimentally determinable.
C. Only his theory explains the action of the bellows.
D. His theory is applicable to liquids as well as gases.
E. His theory is simpler and therefore more likely to be correct.

2.32-10    *Newton*

In Newton's study of astronomy culminating in his law of gravitation, an important objective appears to be

A. to show that laws inferred from terrestrial phenomena are valid for celestial motions also.
B. to provide an explanation for the law of universal gravitation.
C. to show that Kepler's laws are consistent with the concept of a system of planets revolving about a common center.
D. to demonstrate that phenomena occurring beyond the range of measuring instruments can be analyzed by mathematical methods.
E. to secure evidence for the laws of motion from data on celestial motion.

With which of the following *kinds* of statement would Newton be most likely to agree?

A. If a part of the spectrum of a star corresponds to the laboratory spectrum of sodium, we may assume that sodium is present in the star.
B. There can be no single fixed frame of reference to which stellar motions may be referred.
C. A hypothesis should not be used until contrary hypotheses are proved incorrect.
D. A scientist should not base his work on the assumption that laws which are valid on earth are also valid in outer space.

2.32-11    *Lavoisier*

It is commonly recognized that measurement plays an essential role in modern science. Discuss the role of measurement in the following inquiry: Lavoisier's predecessors believed that mercury (as well as other metals) was a compound substance, and that the red powder obtained by heating mercury in air was one of its constituent parts; thus

mercury (heated in air) → red powder + noxious gas.

Lavoisier showed that the red powder is, in fact, a compound of mercury and a constituent of air.

**2.32-12** *Joule*

Joule demonstrates in his experiments that heat can be produced by the expenditure of work. He does this by causing mechanical work to be done and noting the temperature changes in materials such as water, mercury, and cast iron. (a) Why does Joule *measure* the values of the quantities involved and engage in certain calculations with the measured quantities? (b) Why does Joule employ substances different from water (that is, mercury and cast iron)?

**2.32-13** *Faraday*

More than one of the following answers may be right. Faraday would accept as *facts* about electrochemical decomposition that
  A. the electrodes have attracting or repelling powers.
  B. the extent of the decomposing matter is bounded by the surfaces at which the electricity enters or leaves the decomposing body.
  C. the decomposable substance is separated into its ultimate principles.
  D. the products of decomposition appear at the electrodes after having traveled to them.
  E. the products of decomposition that appear at the positive electrode, or anode, are electronegative.

**2.32-14** *Rutherford*

The general method used by Rutherford in his argument in favor of the nuclear model of the atom consists in
  A. showing that alpha particles are doubly charged helium nuclei.
  B. showing that an atom is a mechanical system obeying Newton's laws of motion.
  C. assuming the nuclear model and showing that the observed scattering of alpha particles would be a consequence of the model.
  D. showing that the observed scattering of alpha particles leads logically to the nuclear model.

**2.32-15** *General*

A theoretical physicist conceived a model of the gross crystalline structure of an alloy. He used the laws of physics known to work for large-scale phenomena. He described the workings of the model mathematically. His answers disagree with experimental facts. Which of the following should he do next?
  A. Develop a model for a different alloy.
  B. Use the same model but a different kind of mathematics: for example, $ab \neq ba$.
  C. Use the same model but different fundamental postulates of natural science: for example, different effects from identical causes.
  D. Use the same model but different laws of physics: for example, nonconservation of energy.
  E. Use a different model.

**Comments on exercises 2.32 (8 to 15)**

The attitudes toward inquiry into natural phenomena dealt with in exercises 8 to 15 are modern in the sense that they are held by many, perhaps most, living scientists. Exercise 8 brings out the desirability of simplicity in a definition and of establishing an empirical generalization as a prerequisite to theory. (Galileo's belief that nature is fundamentally simple is, of course, not universal.) Exercise 9 and the first item of exercise 10 deal with the desirability of laws of wide applicability. The second item of exercise 10 exemplifies heuristic or provisional use of a hypothesis. Newton's language was perhaps stronger than we would now use, but his attitude coincides with the prevalent one today. Item 13 points up that in every investigation the scientist accepts or assumes that certain things are true. It also makes it somewhat more obvious than other exercises that we are dealing here with understanding that is difficult if not impossible to get, except from original writings. Item 14 illustrates the common relation between a new theory and experiment. Item 15 points out the essential conservatism of the physicist who, in his initial attack on a new phenomenon, invariably and persistently uses well-established rules and laws. To test further the student's knowledge of the hierarchy of conservative values, he may be asked to choose the path the physicist would take only as a last resort (presumably response C).

Exercises 11 and 12 are in the essay form and deal with the decisive role measurement can play in scientific investigations. Exercise 12 also introduces an aspect of control. Exercise 11 and part b of exercise 12 elicited fairly unambiguous student essays. Part a of exercise 12 was apparently ambiguous and produced essays that were hard to grade consistently. (See a discussion of essays on this topic in Section 11.2 of Part I of this book.)

EXERCISES 16–22.  *Relations Between Scientists' Investigations*

2.32-16  The discovery of X-rays, radium, and cathode rays within a few years of one another was probably the result of
    A. a happy accident.
    B. a carefully planned international research program.
    C. the state of development of the atomic theory.
    D. invention of electrical apparatus and methods of chemical analysis.
    E. dissatisfaction with the notion that an atom is a single particle.

2.32-17  The Copernican theory was originally preferred to the geocentric theory because
    A. the geocentric theory could not explain many new facts discovered since Ptolemy's time.
    B. not all of the observed planetary motions could be explained by epicycles.
    C. the Copernican theory came later and, therefore, could be assumed to be an improvement.

D. no assumptions were necessary in the Copernican theory.

E. None of these accounts for the preference.

Newton's theory of universal gravitation involves a correction to Galileo's theory of freely falling bodies in that Newton's theory

A. predicts that the acceleration of a body due to gravity should vary with its distance from the earth.

B. abolishes the distinction between celestial and terrestrial motion.

C. takes account of air resistance and buoyancy.

D. involves the assumption that accelerated motion in a vacuum is natural rather than externally caused.

An advance made by Maxwell's theory of light over the elastic-ether theory was that it established a connection between the sciences of

A. optics and mechanics.

B. electricity and mechanics.

C. electricity and optics.

D. Responses A and C, but not B, are correct.

E. Responses A, B, and C are correct.

Which of the following statements best describes the relationship between Faraday's experimental work and Maxwell's equations?

A. Maxwell's equations described Faraday's findings in terms that were more general than Faraday's.

B. The agreement between Maxwell's equations and Faraday's findings emphasized that the universe is mathematical.

C. Faraday's experimental findings were shown to be true by Maxwell's equations.

D. Maxwell's equations merely summarized the facts as discovered by Faraday.

E. Faraday and Maxwell together discovered the true nature of electricity.

2.32-18   In Letter II of *New Experiments and Observations on Electricity,* Franklin refers to a theory that electric fluid is "created" by friction, but he does not state the details of this theory or of its application to phenomena. The following two items deal with a comparison between the "creation" theory and Franklin's own theory of electricity. In order to answer some of these questions, you will have to infer, partly on the basis of Franklin's remarks, how the creation theory could have explained certain phenomena.

The creation theory would account for the electrification of a body by friction by postulating that when the body is rubbed it

A. attracts light objects.

B. gains electric fluid.

C. gains or loses electric fluid.

D. retains the same quantity of electric fluid, but the distribution of the fluid changes.

E. gains a kind of electric fluid different from that which it normally contains.

Franklin's theory accounts for the electrification of a body by friction by postulating that when the body is rubbed it
   A. attracts light objects.
   B. gains electric fluid.
   C. gains or loses electric fluid.
   D. retains the same quantity of electric fluid, but the distribution of the fluid changes.
   E. gains a kind of electric fluid different from that which it normally contains.

Experiments once used to support the idea that caloric is indestructible can now be used as evidence that
   A. matter is conserved.
   B. energy is conserved.
   C. heat is energy, not a fluid.
   D. temperature measures motion of matter.
   E. in the conversion of mechanical energy into work, part of the energy is dissipated as heat.

2.32-19   Rutherford's method of argument for the nuclear model of the atom, compared with J. J. Thomson's method of argument for the existence of negatively electrified corpuscles or electrons,
   A. is much the same, for both set up theoretical models and then compare the consequences with experiment.
   B. is much the same, for both systematize a body of experimental data without introducing interpretive hypotheses.
   C. is much the same, for both show by strict deduction that the facts can lead only to the theory each proposes.
   D. is different, since electrons are visible in the cathode-ray tube, while nuclei can only be assumed to exist.

2.32-20   Newton's study of motion differed most from that of Galileo in
   A. avoiding the use of unproved assumptions in the development of theories.
   B. seeking causes for motion.
   C. making no use of intuitive arguments.
   D. recognizing the importance of arriving at conclusions by using mathematical reasoning.
   E. making use of quantitative statements of relationship to derive hypotheses.

2.32-21   What are the mathematical relations among Newton's laws of motion and gravitation and Kepler's laws of planetary motions?

The inverse-square law (the relation between the force exerted by the sun on any planet and their distance apart)
   A. is deducible from Newton's laws of motion.
   B. is deducible from Kepler's laws.
   C. is deducible only from both of the above.
   D. is not deducible even from both sets of laws.

Kepler's laws
   A. are deducible from Newton's laws of motion.
   B. are deducible from Newton's law of gravitation.
   C. are deducible only from both of the above.
   D. are not deducible even from both of the above.

Newton's laws of motion
   A. are deducible from Kepler's laws.
   B. are deducible from Newton's law of gravitation.
   C. are deducible only from both of the above.
   D. are not deducible even from both of the above.

2.32-22   The column on the left contains passages from the *Opticks* by Isaac Newton, a contemporary of Huygens. You are to judge each passage in the light of Huygens' theory of light contained in his *Treatise on Light*. In the first blank at the left of each passage, write

   \+ if Huygens would agree with all the statements in the passage.
   − if Huygens would disagree with one or more statements in the passage.
   0 if the Huygens paper does not contain sufficient information to mark the passage + or −.

In the second blank, write the letter of the *one* comment from the column at the right that best expresses Huygens' attitude toward the statements of the passage.

*Passages from Newton*

———  ——— Are not all Hypotheses erroneous, in which light is supposed to consist in Pression or Motion, propagated through a fluid Medium? . . . If light consisted only in Pression propagated without actual Motion, it would not be able to agitate and heat the Bodies which refract and reflect it.

*Comments*

A. Bodies reflecting and refracting light are *not* agitated or heated.
B. Pression alone is sufficient to produce the effects of agitation and heat.
C. Motion alone is sufficient to produce the effects.
D. Light consists of both pression and motion.
E. None of these comments is consistent with Huygens' point of view.

———  ——— If it consisted in Motion propagated to all distances in an instant, it would require an infinite force every moment, in every shining Particle, to generate that Motion.

A. The shining particles have no mass.
B. The force required would be large but not infinite.
C. The force causing light is infinite but of extremely short duration.
D. The statement is true about particles but not about wave motion.
E. None of these comments is consistent with Huygens' point of view.

*Passages from Newton*

*Comments*

_____ _____ And if it consisted in Pression or Motion, propagated either in an instant or in time, it would bend into the Shadow. For Pression or Motion cannot be propagated in a Fluid in right Lines, beyond an Obstacle which stops part of the Motion, but will bend and spread every way into the quiescent Medium which lies beyond the obstacle.

A. Ether is not a fluid.
B. Light is not a mechanical or material phenomenon.
C. Since light travels in straight lines, there is no quiescent medium in the shadow behind the obstacle.
D. The pression which spreads into the shadow is imperceptible.
E. None of these comments is consistent with Huygens' point of view.

_____ _____ Gravity tends downwards, but the Pressure of Water arising from Gravity tends every way with equal Force, and is propagated as readily, and with as much force sideways as downwards, and through crooked passages as through strait ones. The waves on the Surface of stagnating Water, passing by the sides of a broad Obstacle which stops part of them, bend afterwards and dilate themselves gradually into the quiet Water behind the Obstacle. The Waves, Pulses or Vibrations of the Air, wherein Sounds consist, bend manifestly, though not so much as the Waves of Water. For a Bell or a Cannon may be heard beyond a Hill which intercepts the sight of the sounding Body, and Sounds are propagated as readily through crooked pipes as through streight ones.

A. The analogy is not good because light does not require a material medium for its propagation.
B. Sound from a bell reaches beyond the hill by either going through the ground or being reflected (echo).
C. Sound does not consist of "Waves of the Air."
D. The experiment with water waves works only in shallow water where unevennesses of the bottom produce the effect.
E. None of these comments is consistent with Huygens' point of view.

_____ _____ But Light is never known to follow crooked Passages nor to bend into the Shadow. For the fix'd Stars by the Interposition of any of the Planets cease to be seen. And so do the Parts of the Sun by the Interposition of the Moon, Mercury or Venus.

A. Light is not a mechanical or material phenomenon.
B. The bending of light exists but is too small to have been observed.
C. Light can be made to follow a crooked passage by means of mirrors and prisms.
D. The effect is not observed because of the tremendous size of the planets.
E. None of these comments is consistent with Huygens' point of view.

*Passages from Newton*

—— —— And against filling the Heavens with fluid Mediums, unless they be exceeding rare, a great Objection arises from the regular and very lasting Motions of the Planets and Comets in all manner of Courses through the Heavens. For thence it is manifest that the Heavens are void of all sensible Resistance, and by consequence of all sensible Matter.

*Comments*

A. Ether is almost infinitely rare.
B. Bodies moving through ether do not communicate their motion to the ether.
C. Ether is not sensible matter.
D. As bodies move through ether, ether flows *around* the bodies without producing friction.
E. None of these comments is consistent with Huygens' point of view.

## Comments on exercises 2.32 (16 to 22)

Item 16 emphasizes a certain kind of coherence and cumulativeness of physics: its theories affect all of its areas and make these closely articulated. As a result, a discovery is made possible or even likely by previous discoveries and the general state of knowledge. Since the causal chain of events leading to a discovery is usually not known, the student can only be asked to make crude distinctions. The wrong responses should therefore be quite wrong.

Exercise 17 illustrates various reasons for preferring one theory to another. Copernican theory seems originally to have been preferred for very complex reasons that lay in the general intellectual atmosphere of the time. The reason illustrated by the second item is better correspondence with facts; by the third item, a merging of previously distinct areas; and by the fourth item, mathematical elegance and generality.

Exercise 18 points up the possibility of explaining a phenomenon on two mutually exclusive theories. The existence of similarities—at a very general level—between two quite different investigations is illustrated by item 19. Item 20 is an example of a difference in the goals that scientists set for themselves. Exercise 21 deals with relations among empirical generalizations (Kepler's laws), a mechanics, and a grand theory. The stems alone of each item are not directive, that is, they do not tell the student what the problem is, but the stems plus the first responses do, because the responses are homogeneous.

To work exercise 22 the student must have considerable background information. If the course is so conducted, however, that this information has to be obtained primarily through reading, the exercise may measure principally reading ability. It is nevertheless desirable that the background information should not be based on memory of details, as it is not in the present exercise. The exercise has two desirable features. First, there are few formal clues to the right response; second, and more important, the student is asked to compare in some detail the views of two eminent scientists—a very good way to test whether he understands both views. Incidentally, the form of the exercise is well suited for testing an understanding of a book, in this case Huygens' *Treatise on Light*.

### ABILITY I2, INTUITIVE UNDERSTANDING

Test exercises on intuitive understanding must be problems that are, to the student, sufficiently new and complex so that he cannot solve them from memory or analytically. Nor should they require high imaginativeness, at least not the imaginative use of words or other symbols. The elements of whatever imagery or analysis the student uses should be mainly physical objects, either idealized (frictionless planes, nonextensible ropes) or real (in the case of LI2, intuitive thinking in the laboratory). Thinking, if that is a proper term, should be in terms of objects and processes and not words or mathematics. The content within which this ability can be exhibited may be any listed under 2.1, 2.2, and 2.3. The examples include content from 2.1 only.

I2.1-1   Three identical blocks are connected by metal rods of negligible mass and propelled along a horizontal plane by two equal forces $F$, one pushing and one pulling.

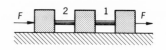

Is rod 1 under tension or compression?
   A. Tension.
   B. Compression.
   C. Neither.
   D. Any of the above, depending on the value of $F$.
   E. Any of the above (A, B, or C), depending on the value of $F$ and the coefficient of friction.

Is rod 2 under tension or compression?
   A. Tension.
   B. Compression.
   C. Neither.
   D. Any of the above, depending on the value of $F$.
   E. Any of the above (A, B, or C), depending on the value of $F$ and the coefficient of friction.

I2.1-2   A man is playing darts in an elevator moving at a constant speed. Should he aim higher or lower than he would in a stationary elevator?
   A. Higher.
   B. Lower.

C. Higher if elevator is moving up, lower if down.
D. Lower if elevator is moving up, higher if down.
E. None of the above.

I2.1-3   A uniform bar, lying on a frictionless horizontal surface, is
acted upon by two equal and
oppositely directed forces as
shown.

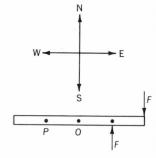

What is the direction of motion of the center $O$ of the bar?
A. Northward.
B. Southward.
C. Clockwise along a circle.
D. Counterclockwise along a circle.
E. Point $O$ will not move.

What third force applied at point $P$ would keep the bar motionless?
A. A force equal to $F$, directed north.
B. A force equal to $F$, directed south.
C. A force greater than $F$ and less than $2F$, directed north.
D. A force greater than $F$ and less than $2F$, directed south.
E. None of the above.

I2.1-4   Two balls, of masses 4 grams
and 8 grams, are suspended at
equal distances from the top of
a shaft. When the shaft rotates
about its vertical axis, the balls
move outward until their cords
make angles $X$ and $Y$, respectively, with the shaft. How do
these angles compare?

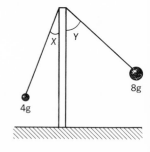

A. They are equal.
B. Angle $X$ is twice angle $Y$.
C. Angle $X$ is greater than angle $Y$, but not twice as great.
D. Angle $Y$ is twice angle $X$.
E. Angle $Y$ is greater than angle $X$, but not twice as great.

I2.1-5   Three straight copper wires of
uniform cross section and of indicated lengths are connected as
shown. The three free ends are
kept at indicated potentials, 6
volts, 5 volts, and 1 volt.

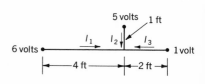

Which currents flow in the direction indicated? (More than one answer may be right.)
  A. $I_1$.
  B. $I_2$.
  C. $I_3$.
  D. None of the above.

Which current is the largest? (Disregard the direction.)
  A. $I_1$.
  B. $I_2$.
  C. $I_3$.
  D. The two largest currents are equal.
  E. The currents are equal.

Which current is the smallest? (Disregard the direction.)
  A. $I_1$.
  B. $I_2$.
  C. $I_3$.
  D. The two smallest currents are equal.
  E. The currents are equal.

I2.1-6   A uniform bar carrying a load $L$ is suspended from three equally spaced strings. What can be said about the tensions $T_1$, $T_2$, and $T_3$ in the strings? (More than one of the following answers may be right.)

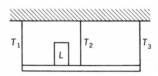

If the weight of the bar and the weight and position of load $L$ is known, one can calculate the value of
  A. $T_1$.
  B. $T_1 + T_2$.
  C. $T_1 - T_2$.
  D. $T_1/T_2$.
  E. None of the above.

With the position of the load as shown, which of the following inequalities are true? (More than one answer may be right.)
  A. $T_1 > T_3$.
  B. $T_1 > T_2$.
  C. $T_2 > T_3$.
  D. $T_1 < T_3$.
  E. $T_1 < T_2$.
  F. $T_2 < T_3$.
  G. Any one of the above inequalities may be wrong.

Which of the following inequalities are true?
  A. $T_1 > 0$.
  B. $T_2 > 0$.

C. $T_3 > 0$.

D. Any one of the above inequalities may be wrong.

E. All the inequalities are true.

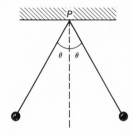

12.1-7    Two small electrically charged balls are suspended by threads of equal length from a point $P$. The fact that the angles $\theta$ are equal indicates that

A. the masses of the balls are equal.

B. the charges on the balls are equal.

C. both the masses and the charges are equal.

D. the ratio of charge to mass is the same for the two balls.

E. None of the above is a reasonable conclusion.

12.1-8    Given: A body $P$ and a perfectly elastic spring. The spring can just support the body if compressed 1 cm, as shown at $X$. At $Y$ the body is 1 cm above the spring and is allowed to fall. At its lowest point the body compresses the spring $h$ cm, as shown at $Z$. What is the approximate value of $h$?

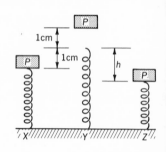

A. Between 1 and 2 cm.

B. 2 cm.

C. Between 2 and 3 cm.

D. More than 3 cm.

E. A, B, C, or D may be right depending on the mass of the body and the stiffness of the spring.

12.1-9    Given: Two wires $X$ and $Y$ connected in parallel across a battery, as shown. If their temperatures are equal, they lose heat to the surroundings at the same rate. With the switch open, their resistances are equal. However, the temperature coefficient of resistivity, which determines the rate of increase of resistance with temperature, is greater for wire $X$.

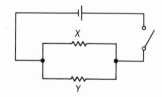

If the switch is closed, which of the wires will eventually be the hotter?

A. Wire $X$.

B. Wire $Y$.

C. They will be equally hot.

D. The data are insufficient to decide.

If the two wires were connected in *series* and the switch then closed, which wire would eventually get hotter?

A. Wire $X$.

B. Wire $Y$.

C. They would be equally hot.

D. The data are insufficient to decide.

I2.1-10   A very large number of hoops made of the same gage wire but of radii $r$, $r/2$, $r/4$, and so forth are arranged as shown. Neglect the thickness of the wires, that is, assume that all hoops pass through point $P$. If the distance between the center of mass of the system and the center of the largest circle is designated by $X$, approximately what is the ratio $r/X$?

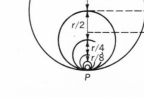

A. 5.

B. 4.

C. 3.

D. 2.

E. 1.

I2.1-11   A pendulum, consisting of a bar rigidly attached to a disk, is pivoted at $P$. An identical pendulum is pivoted at $O$, the center of the disk of the first pendulum. You may treat each disk as a point mass and neglect the masses of the rods. You may assume any initial values of $\theta_1$ and $\theta_2$. Plot as a function of time any *one* of the following: $\theta_1$, $\theta_2$, $\theta_1 + \theta_2$, $\theta_1 - \theta_2$, $\theta_1/\theta_2$.

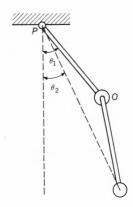

## Comments on exercises 12.1

Exercise 1 can be solved analytically by a student who is sophisticated and knowledgeable enough to assign mass $m$ to each block and a coefficient of friction $\mu$ to the surfaces. He will find that their numerical values are not necessary to choose the right response. (In fact, all the I2.1 exercises above can be solved analytically.) An equally or perhaps even more sophisticated approach is this: Each mass has the same acceleration (possibly zero); therefore each has the same force acting on it. Frictional force is the same for each. The outside forces must be divided evenly, $\frac{2}{3}F$ for each block. This can happen only if rod 1 pulls backwards on the first block. Hence it is under tension. The less analytically sophisticated student must operate with fragments of the preceding argument and with his feeling for symmetry. The student who is successful with this sort of attack should be credited with intuitive understanding of Newton's laws of motion. As has been said before, what an exercise measures depends on the students' caliber and preparation. The average freshman who is not a physics or math major will probably draw on his intuitive understanding to solve this exercise.

If intuitive understanding exists, intuitive misunderstanding is even more frequent. The large number of erroneous answers to exercises 2, 3, and 4 and subsequent discussion in class have demonstrated this.

To discourage analytical solutions of exercises 1 to 4, numerical values have not been assigned to some of the quantities. To the same end, closed circuits were not provided for exercise 5, and inequalities were used in exercise 6. Exercise 8 is rather difficult mathematically, and mathematical formulation can be made even more difficult by not giving the numerical values indicated in the diagram. None of the students in the author's physics-for-biology-majors course attempted to solve exercise 9 mathematically, and even those who had confidence in their answers were unable to outline a completely logical path to the solution. A rigorous solution of exercise 10 would require summing up of infinite series. Exercise 11 would require analytical mechanics.

# 18

## TESTS FOR ABILITY TO LEARN

**ABILITY 3, ABILITY TO LEARN**
*For a discussion of this ability see page* 24.

### Objective 3.1, Ability to understand prose (as distinct from both poetry and nonverbal symbolism)

Here the ability to interpret is used in its widest possible sense; it ranges from understanding the literal meaning of individual sentences to inferring the conceptual framework within which an author works. Appropriate reading material can be found in the usual textbooks, semipopular articles, and original papers, or it can be specially prepared. Since not the general reading ability but the ability to read in science is to be measured, the student should find his understanding of science always useful, and usually even necessary, in interpreting the reading material. On the other hand, since his ability to *read* is to be estimated, auxiliary abilities required for the exercise, of which the most important one is usually knowledge of science, should be kept down to the level of the great majority of students taking the test. Nor should the auxiliary abilities, without understanding the reading material, be *sufficient* to work the exercise. These precautions are especially necessary if diagnostic or prognostic use of test results is envisaged.

### Content 3.11, Ability to understand brief statements

In the first three exercises that follow, a statement of a physical principle is followed by one or more problems or questions. You are to consider the principle as true and to use it in answering the questions.

3.11-1    Principle: When a liquid flows through a constriction (narrower passage), its velocity increases and the pressure it exerts decreases. Boats $W$, $X$, $Y$, and $Z$ were anchored in a river, originally in the positions shown in the figure. They are free to move sideways. How will the river current affect the distance between $W$ and $X$ and between $Y$ and $Z$?

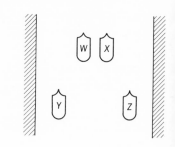

The two boats, $W$ and $X$, will
A. be drawn together.
B. be pushed apart.
C. remain as they were.
D. be pushed apart or drawn together depending on the direction of flow of the river.

The two boats, $Y$ and $Z$, will
A. be drawn together.
B. be pushed apart.
C. remain as they were.
D. be pushed apart or drawn together depending on the direction of flow of the river.

3.11-2    Principle: Skating is possible because the pressure of the skate blade melts the ice and forms a film of water under the skate. Pressure converts ice into water because water occupies a smaller volume than ice.

Another substance can be substituted for ice if
A. it freezes near zero degrees centigrade.
B. it expands on freezing.
C. it presents an extremely smooth surface.
D. its liquid form has a high surface tension.
E. its liquid form has the same density as water.

The ease of skating, as compared with sliding on the soles of shoes, is primarily due to the fact that
A. the force exerted by the skates acts on a smaller area.
B. the skates exert a greater force.
C. the skate blades are smoother.
D. the skate blade conducts heat away from the ice more rapidly.
E. the skate blades are at a lower temperature.

3.11-3    Principle: The better a surface absorbs radiation, the better it radiates it. The better a surface reflects radiation, the less well it absorbs it. An iron stove used for heating by radiation is most efficient if

    A. its surface is highly polished.
    B. it is covered with a thin layer of soot.
    C. its surface is smooth.
    D. its inner surface is covered with aluminum paint.
    E. its outer surface is covered with aluminum paint.

A piece of white china with a dull black decoration is heated in a furnace until it gives out enough light to be seen in the dark. In a dark room
    A. the entire piece will appear uniformly bright.
    B. the decoration will appear brighter than the rest.
    C. the entire piece will appear uniformly dark.
    D. the entire piece will appear gray.
    E. the decoration will appear a darker shade of red than the rest.

3.11-4  Consider the following criteria for definitions:
    A. The definition of a given term should contain only terms that are less complex or less obscure than the given term.
    B. The definition of a given term should not contain the term itself, nor any term defined by means of the given term.
    C. The definition of a given term should describe the term in sufficient detail to distinguish its species from other species of the same genus.
    D. The definition of a given term should describe the term in no more detail than is necessary.
Before each of the following definitions, write the letter of that criterion which is most seriously *violated* by the definition. If none is violated, write E.

    A rectangle is a parallelogram all of whose angles are right angles. (Here "parallelogram" is the "genus.")

    Hydrogen peroxide is a substance composed of hydrogen and oxygen.

    The sun is a heavenly body that shines only during the day.

    A circle is a geometric figure consisting of all points at a given distance from some fixed point.

## Comments on exercises 3.11

Exercises 1, 2, and 3, because they require little subject-matter knowledge, can be used not only to test the ability to learn, but also some aspects of understanding of physics of a group of students whose preparation is heterogeneous or unknown. For example, this type of exercise can be used in admission or placement tests without penalizing students who studied primarily applied physics or some other area or kind of physics. (The author is convinced by the measurements made in his own classes that competence 3.11 is indeed teachable.) The exercises are far from abstract, however, in the strict sense of the word. Thus, in working exercise 1, the student must be able to surmise what constitutes the constriction in the given situation and what is the effect of a difference in pressure. In fact, the physics of the situation is so complex that the exercise, especially its second item, is difficult, except for students who have studied Bernoulli's principle. For these students the exercise tests understanding—the ability to apply the principle, which they are reminded of in the stem, in a novel situation. If Bernoulli's principle were applied in class or text to objects floating on a liquid, especially a moving liquid, the exercise would test knowledge. A student who has not studied the principle must be able to understand a written statement rapidly and well enough to apply it to a problem. Such a student is likely to have high ability to learn from books, a very important ability to know about in prognosticating the student's success.

The remarks of the preceding paragraph apply to the other three exercises as well. Some of the knowledge required for working the exercises is as follows: in exercise 2, a knowledge of the word *pressure;* in exercise 3, of the appearance of a good reflector or good absorber; and in exercise 4, of geometrical terms and some chemistry. The use of the master-list form in exercise 4 is proper and economical because the number of possible homogeneous responses to the questions is strictly limited. The exercise can be made much easier by omitting the reference to response E and thus assuring the students that each definition *is* faulty.

### Content 3.12, Ability to understand a passage

The passage to be read and the questions asked should be such that the student cannot answer them without understanding a substantial part of the passage. To meet this requirement, the passage should be on a topic that has been discussed in the course either not at all or in considerably less detail or from a different point of view. In addition, each question should be so formulated that an answer to it is not to be found in just one or two sentences of the passage. The ability to understand a short passage is classified under content 3.11.

3.12-1 *Understanding of a descriptive passage, with emphasis on the content*

#### Determination of the Electronic Charge

The measurement of the elementary electric charge can be accomplished by means of the apparatus shown in the diagram. A cloud of fine drops of oil is introduced into the chamber $C$ from the nozzle $A$. Here they acquire charges by collision with molecules of oxygen and nitrogen that have been ionized by X-rays. In the lower part of the chamber are two metal plates, the upper of which has a small hole $H$. A drop passing through this hole continues to fall with uniform speed, its "terminal velocity," just as a raindrop falls. The terminal velocity is determined by observation with the aid of a microscope. It is known that the terminal velocity of a sphere is proportional to the square of its diameter; knowing the terminal velocity of the drop, its diameter may be calculated. From this value and the previously measured density of the oil, it is a matter of simple arithmetic to find the mass $m$ of the drop. The force urging the drop downward is equal to $mg$, where $g$ is the acceleration due to gravity.

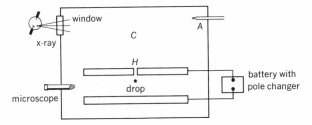

The plates are now given opposite charges by means of a battery. The drop undergoes a change in its velocity. The charge on the plates is adjusted both in sign and quantity until the drop comes to rest. At this time the downward force of gravitation is just balanced by the upward force of the electric field. The force on a charged particle in an electric field is proportional to the charge $Q$ on the particle and the strength $E$ of the electric field, where $E$ is equal to the voltage applied to the plates divided by the distance between them. At equilibrium, therefore, $mg = kQE$, where $k$ is a constant of proportionality whose value depends on the units used. The charge on the drop is found from the relation $Q = mg/kE$, all quantities other than $Q$ being known.

The results of hundreds of experiments show that although the value of $Q$ differs from drop to drop, no value smaller than $4.80 \times 10^{-10}$ electrostatic units has been found and all values of $Q$ are integral multiples of this charge. This finding is explained on the basis that charged oil drops always carry an integral number of electric charges of $4.80 \times 10^{-10}$ electrostatic units each. This basic electric charge is the smallest possible quantity of electricity.

Which of the following values for the charge on an oil drop would not be possible?
A. $12.0 \times 10^{-10}$ electrostatic units.
B. $48.0 \times 10^{-10}$ electrostatic units.
C. $9.60 \times 10^{-10}$ electrostatic units.
D. $52.8 \times 10^{-10}$ electrostatic units.
E. All of these values are possible.

Which of the following conditions must be maintained during the determination of the *mass* of the drop?
A. The plates must not be charged.
B. The charge on the drop must remain constant.
C. The charge on the plates must be just enough to suspend the drop.
D. Air must be removed from the chamber.
E. The downward acceleration must remain at a constant value.

Under which of the following conditions would the experiment give the poorest results?
A. If glycerin were substituted for oil.
B. If air were removed from the apparatus.
C. If a drop acquired a positive charge.
D. If a drop acquired more than a single charge.
E. If the drop came to rest closer to one plate than the other.

Which of the following is an assumption *specific to this experiment* that was made in the determination of the charge?
  A. The force of gravity is the same whether the drops are charged or not.
  B. Opposite charges attract each other.
  C. Only a single charge is present on a drop.
  D. The mass of a drop is equal to its density multiplied by its volume.
  E. Electric charges are multiples of the electronic charge.

Why are small drops preferable to large drops in this experiment?
  A. Their terminal velocities are less and therefore more easily measured.
  B. Their size is more nearly that of an electron.
  C. Small drops carry fewer charges.
  D. Evaporation of small drops is slower.
  E. The value of *g* for small drops is more conveniently determined.

Extremely small drops move erratically under the conditions of this experiment. Which of the following affords the best explanation?
  A. They are affected considerably by small fluctuations in the electric field.
  B. They cannot retain charges.
  C. The force of gravitation on them is too weak to balance the electrical force.
  D. They lack uniform motion.
  E. They are affected by collisions with molecules of air.

3.12-2   *Understanding of a point of view, with emphasis on inferences to be drawn*
Read the following passage on scientific theories carefully; pay particular attention to the author's attitude or point of view.

### Scientific Theories

The scientific value of a theory is purely practical: (1) it summarizes numerous experiments; (2) it suggests new experiments; and (3) it predicts experimental results. But theory has also a philosophic value in giving us a deeper and truer insight into what the world is like. Yes, we mean *truer*. But how can we reconcile such an assertion with our previously stated view that theoretical statements are not claimed to be true but are merely temporarily accepted as the best available notions? Let us illustrate our position by an example. The statement that gases are made up of tiny particles that are in constant motion is not a statement of a known truth. But the statement that, in all the experiments so far tried and within the accuracy at our disposal, gases behave *like* a swarm of tiny particles in constant motion is a true statement. Our knowledge that gases behave like a swarm of tiny particles gives us a much better understanding of gases than do the experiments alone from which the notion of tiny particles was derived. We acquired some knowledge of the nature of gases by observing that gases interdiffuse, exert pressure, and so forth. But when someone got the brilliant idea that a swarm of tiny particles in constant motion would behave just like that, our knowledge of the nature of gases became greater than before.

As new experiments are tried and greater accuracy is achieved, our present picture of the gases will probably prove to be inadequate at least in some respects. The scientists will try to change the presently accepted theory in such a way as to account for the new facts. But our present theory will naturally continue to be completely adequate for those experiments (and that accuracy) which it has explained so far. Thus, the statement that under certain conditions gases behave like a swarm of tiny particles in constant motion will always be true. This of course is a requirement for every true statement; there is no sense in calling something true that is true today but will be false tomorrow.*

> Read the following statements and decide whether or not they are in agreement with the author's point of view. Then choose the appropriate response. You may reread the passage any number of times.

### Responses

A. The statement is in agreement with the author's point of view.
B. The statement is in disagreement with the author's point of view.
C. The information given in the passage is not sufficient to indicate the author's point of view on the statement.

### Statements

The kinetic-molecular theory is the best theory of gases available at present.

Under certain experimental conditions, a gas is a swarm of tiny particles in constant motion.

A part of any future theory of gases will be the idea that gases are made up of tiny particles in constant motion.

A theory, being a summary of certain experiments, cannot give us more knowledge than did the experiments.

It is true at present that gases are made up of tiny particles.

The molecular theory of gases is going to be modified in the near future.

No statement in which the word *molecule* occurs can be true.

Since the presently accepted theory will not be able to explain all the future experiments, it cannot be used for prediction.

Since theories are made by scientists, they alone can judge the worth of a theory.

Theories are more valuable than experiments.

Some theoretical statements are true.

Science helps philosophy more than philosophy helps science.

### 3.12-3   Understanding of a conceptual scheme

#### Concept of Inertia and Definition of Mass

Everyone recognizes one distinction among bodies, which we call the difference in weight. Of two small spheres of the same size we can say that one is heavier than the other, but the idea of weight is not very precise and cannot be made so until we investigate an even more fundamental property of bodies, namely

---

* Adapted from Leo Nedelsky, *The Physical Sciences* (New York, 1945), pp. 151–52. Reprinted by permission of McGraw-Hill Book Company.

their *inertia,* the quantitative measure of which is the *mass* of the body. Consider the two spheres just mentioned. When the two are set in motion by the same force, their accelerations will not in general be the same. The one that has the larger acceleration under such conditions is said to possess the smaller inertia or mass.

It is difficult to obtain a logically rigorous physical definition of mass, for it is obviously hard to be sure that in accelerating two material particles the same influence acts on them both. However, this is ideally possible in the following way. Let there be two particles $X$ and $Y$ that are completely isolated from all others in the universe. Under their mutual action they will exhibit accelerations that, with reference to their original positions, we may denote by $a_{XY}$ and $a_{YX}$, respectively. Now all experiments that have ever been performed on real bodies lead us to conclude, in our hypothetical case, that these accelerations are opposite in direction and that their ratio is a *constant,* independent of all factors other than those mentioned. The presence of other particles will indeed produce accelerations in $X$ and $Y$, but our assumption is that the ratio of the acceleration of $X$ *due* to $Y$ to that of $Y$ due to $X$ is not influenced by these. We thus have, regardless of the magnitudes of the individual accelerations,

$$\frac{a_{XY}}{-a_{YX}} = K_{YX}. \tag{1}$$

Let us take any other particle $Z$. For the mutual actions of $Z$ and $X$, and $Z$ and $Y$, respectively, we shall then have analogously to equation 1:

$$\frac{a_{XZ}}{-a_{YZ}} = K_{ZX} \quad \text{and} \quad \frac{a_{YZ}}{-a_{ZY}} = K_{ZY}. \tag{2}$$

Now, experiment indicates that one of the $K$'s equals the ratio of the other two $K$'s. Our notation is such that the relation is

$$K_{ZY} = \frac{K_{ZX}}{K_{YX}}. \tag{3}$$

By substituting equation 3 in the second of the relations (2), we get

$$K_{YX} \, a_{YZ} = -K_{ZX} \, a_{ZY}. \tag{4}$$

The relation in equation 4 indicates that we are able, by choosing $X$ as a "unit" particle, to associate with every other particle a *constant that does not depend at all on the particle with which the one in question interacts.* We shall name the constant $K_{YX}$ "the mass of $Y$ relative to $X$," or more simply "the mass of $Y$," it being understood that $X$ is our "unit" particle. Thus we write $K_{YX} = m_Y$, $K_{ZX} = m_Z$, so that equation 4 becomes

$$m_Y a_{YZ} = -m_Z a_{ZY}. \tag{5}$$

It is essential to avoid such statements as "Mass is the amount of matter in a body." It is becoming increasingly clear that the expression "amount of matter" is physically meaningless. The only logical definition of mass is that which enables us to establish a method of comparing masses.

Choose the *one best answer.*

In the preceding excerpt, mass is defined in terms of
  A. weight and volume.
  B. change in momentum and force.
  C. force and acceleration.
  D. inertia and acceleration.
  E. quantity of matter.

The criterion by which the author of the excerpt distinguishes between appropriate and inappropriate definitions of physical quantities is
  A. the actual existence of the things referred to by the terms in the definition.
  B. the ease with which the concepts used in the definition can be understood.
  C. the usefulness of the definition for measuring the quantity.
  D. the inclusion of the causes of the physical quantity in its definition.

In answering this question use the excerpt's conceptions of theory and practice. The point at which the author's logical and theoretical construction most takes account of reality is in the statement that
  A. ". . . we investigate an even more fundamental property of bodies, namely their *inertia*."
  B. ". . . the two are set in motion by the same force."
  C. ". . . under their mutual action they will exhibit accelerations."
  D. ". . . the one that has the larger acceleration . . . is said to possess the smaller inertia or mass."

Assume that the definition of mass developed in the excerpt is the only definition of mass utilized by the author. In order then to have his theory of mechanics cover the common experience of the varying *weights* of bodies, he must establish a relationship between
  A. weight and force.
  B. weight and inertia.
  C. weight and acceleration.

The use of the particle $X$ as a unit particle in calling $K_{YX}$ the mass of $Y$ implies that
  A. the mass of $X$ is 1.
  B. the mass of $Y$ might be different if the particle $X$ were not present.
  C. the mass of $Y$ would be different if the gravitational attraction between two particles were to vary.
  D. particle $Y$ is composed of several particles each identical to $X$.

In the excerpt, the use of the acceleration of a particle—due solely to the mutual action of it and one other particle—in determining masses is justifiable
  A. only if no other particles affect the two particles considered.
  B. only if the initial acceleration of each particle is used, since the acceleration of each particle will depend on the distance between the particles.

    C. only if the total acceleration of a particle is analyzable into component accelerations, each of which can be considered as affecting the particle independently.

    D. since acceleration is itself a directly measurable quantity.

If the relationship $a_{XY}/-a_{YX} = K_{YX}$ alone is interpreted as indicating a mass $K_{YX}$ for particle $Y$, with reference to particle $X$, one must assume that

    A. the force of $X$ on $Y$ is exactly equal to the force of $Y$ on $X$.

    B. $a_{XY}$ remains constant, regardless of the separation of $X$ and $Y$.

    C. $K_{YX}$ is equal to $K_{XY}$.

    D. $a_{XY}$ is greater than $-a_{YX}$.

3.12-4   *Understanding of the nature and structure of the argument*
Read the following passage carefully.

JONES: The constant activity that you people display in your famous arsenal suggests to the studious mind a large field for investigation, especially that part of the work which involves mechanics; for in this department all types of instruments and machines are constantly being constructed by many artisans, among whom there must be some who, partly by inherited experience and partly by their own observations, have become highly expert and clever in explanation.

SMITH: You are quite right. Indeed, I myself, being curious by nature, frequently visit this place for the mere pleasure of observing the work of those who, on account of their superiority over other artisans, we call "first-rank men." Conference with them has often helped me in the investigation of certain effects, including not only those that are striking but also those that are recondite and almost incredible. At times, also, I have been put to confusion and driven to despair of ever explaining something for which I could not account, but which my senses told me to be true. And notwithstanding the fact that what the old man told us a little while ago is proverbial and commonly accepted, yet it seemed to me altogether false, like many another saying which is current among the ignorant; for I think they introduce these expressions in order to give the appearance of knowing something about matters which they do not understand.

JONES: You refer, perhaps, to that last remark of his when we asked the reason why they employed stocks, scaffolding, and bracing of larger dimensions for launching a big vessel than they do for a small one; and he answered that they did this in order to avoid the danger of the ship parting under its own heavy weight, a danger to which small boats are not subject?

SMITH: Yes, that is what I mean; and I refer especially to his last assertion, which I have always regarded as a false opinion, though it is current; namely, that in speaking of these and other similar machines one cannot argue from the small to the large, because many devices that succeed on a small scale do not work on a large scale.

(A) Now, since mechanics has its foundation in geometry, where mere size is unimportant, I do not see that the properties of circles, triangles, cylinders, cones, and other solid figures will change with their size. If, therefore, a large machine be constructed in such a way that its parts bear to one another the same ratio as in a smaller one, and if the smaller is sufficiently strong for the purpose for which it was designed, I do not see why the large also should not be able to withstand any severe and destructive tests to which it may be subjected.

JONES: (B) The common opinion is here absolutely wrong. Indeed, it is so far wrong that precisely the opposite is true, namely, that many machines can be constructed even more perfectly on a large scale than on a small; thus, for instance, a clock that indicates and strikes the hour can be made more accurate on a large scale than on a small.

(C) There are some intelligent people who maintain this same opinion, but on more reasonable grounds, when they cut loose from geometry and argue that the better performance of the large machine is owing to the imperfections and variations of the material.

(D) Here I trust you will not charge me with arrogance if I say that imperfections in the material, even those that are great enough to invalidate the clearest mathematical proof, are not sufficient to explain the deviations observed between machines in the concrete and in the abstract. Yet I shall say it and will affirm that, even if the imperfections did not exist and matter were absolutely perfect, unalterable, and free from all accidental variations, still the mere fact that it is matter makes the larger machine, built of the same material and in the same proportion as the smaller, correspond with exactness to the smaller in every respect except that it will not be so strong or so resistant against violent treatment. The larger the machine, the greater its weakness.

(E) Since I assume matter to be unchangeable and always the same, it is clear that we are no less able to treat this constant and invariable property in a rigid manner than if it belonged to simple and pure mathematics.

(F) Therefore, Smith, you would do well to change the opinion that you, and perhaps also many other students of mechanics, have entertained concerning the ability of machines and structures to resist external disturbances, thinking that when they are built of the same material and maintain the same ratio between parts, they are able equally, or rather proportionally, to resist or yield to such external disturbances and blows. For we can demonstrate rigorously that the large machine is not proportionately stronger than the small.

(G) Finally, we may say that for every machine and structure, whether artificial or natural, there is set a necessary limit beyond which neither art nor nature can pass; it is here understood, of course, that the material is the same and the proportion preserved.*

> The passage above includes several paragraphs marked by letters A to G. Each of the following five items is intended as an *illustration* of a *general* proposition in those paragraphs. Find the paragraph in which the relevant general proposition occurs and write its letter before the item. Note: Write only *one* letter before each item.

A rectangular wooden frame is reinforced by a wire running diagonally between the opposite corners of the frame. A similar frame, but with sides twice as long as the first one, will require a wire twice as long.

* Reprinted, with adaptations, from *Dialogues Concerning Two New Sciences,* by Galileo Galilei, trans. by Henry Crew and Alphonse de Salvio, by permission of Northwestern University Press. Copyright 1946 by Northwestern University Press.

A house requires 400 square feet of lumber for its floor. A house of the same shape as the first one but twice as long, twice as wide, and twice as tall would require 1,600 square feet of lumber for its floor.

A lathe is capable of turning shafts of proper diameter within $\frac{1}{100}$ inch. If the shaft is 1 inch in diameter, the error introduced by the lathe will be about 1 percent; the error in a shaft 10 inches in diameter will be .1 percent.

A wooden board 10 inches wide and containing knot holes 1 inch in diameter was safely used for scaffolding. It was cut longitudinally into eight strips 1¼ inch wide. Some of the strips were found to be so weak (because of knot holes) as not to be usable even for the lightest construction.

Although the same drawing—with a change in the indicated scale—may be used for building two similar iron bridges of different size, the *actual* bridges would not be equally stable. This difference in stability cannot be greatly reduced by using better iron for both bridges.

> The next five items are statements taken from a discussion of the relation between how long fishes live and the depth at which they live. Although the subject matter of this discussion is obviously different from that of the discussion carried on by Jones and Smith, there is a parallel between the *kinds* of assertion or argument used in the two discussions. For each statement below find the part of the passage that contains an argument or assertion most analogous to the statement. Note: Write only *one* letter for each statement.

Since water is the same at any depth and the fish are completely surrounded by it, a given type of fish should live as long at any depth.

Unless special precautions are taken, fish shifted to lower depths will live less long.

A certain type of fish cannot exist below a certain depth.

The physiology of a fish is such that depth will have an influence on the length of its life.

Chances of survival for sick fish are less at lower depths.

> It is impossible to predict the strength of a large bridge with absolute precision. Which of the following would Jones consider the most important reason?
>
> A. The drawing of the bridge is necessarily much smaller than the bridge.
> B. It is impossible to make a perfectly accurate drawing.
> C. Statements about matter—because it is matter—can never be as precise as statements in geometry.
> D. The particular pieces of steel used cannot be accurately described.
> E. None of the above would be considered a valid reason by Jones.

What is the most important criticism Jones makes of Smith's argument in paragraph D of the passage?

A. Matter is never perfect.
B. Human accuracy is limited.
C. The geometry of large and small structures is not the same.
D. Properties of matter should be taken into account.

E. None of the above; Jones disagrees with common opinion but agrees with Smith.

## Comments on exercises 3.12

The principal ability that exercise 1 is designed to measure is the ability to understand the plain sense of a passage. Therefore, though the exercise is in content 3.12 (ability to understand a passage), understanding of a small part of the passage is usually enough for working an item. These two contentions are well illustrated by the first three items. The fourth and fifth items call for some interpretation. The last item asks the student to apply his knowledge of physics, specifically of Brownian movement, to the given subject matter. The abilities called forth by these six items are treated as part of the ability to understand the content of a passage.

In passage 2, the author of the passage states his opinion of the truth value of a theory and its relation to experiment. The items test the student's understanding of this opinion. There is usually a sentence or two in the passage that suggest the right response to an item. It seems likely, though, that most students would find it more economical to try to understand the author's general point of view than to search for the relevant sentence for each item, because the wordings of the sentence and the item are different. It is of course possible to make general understanding necessary by not allowing students to consult the passage. They may be asked to read the passage before coming to the examination or given five to ten minutes for reading it during the examination. For the present exercise, however, such arrangements are probably not necessary.

The attitude of overcautiousness *vs.* that of rashness or going beyond data is conveniently measured by this exercise. These attitudes are exhibited respectively by students who choose response C too frequently and those who choose either A or B instead of C.

Exercise 3 presents the student with a passage in which a concept is operationally defined. The passage is difficult; at least one point in it is rather subtle, and there is some complexity of mathematical notation. The items based on the passage, however, are not overly difficult. As is done here, it is always possible to make easy an objective item that poses a difficult question by making the wrong responses unattractive. It is much harder to base an *essay* test on a problem that is important but the full understanding of which is too difficult for students. The point is illustrated by the last item of the exercise, which is based on the subtle reason for introducing a third particle, Z, into the passage. As it happens, however, the very unattractive wrong responses are unattractive for reasons having nothing to do with particle Z. Since many students work items by rejecting wrong responses, this particular item is faulty and will not reliably measure the relevant kind of understanding.

The first item requires understanding of content; the second, the author's criteria for definition; the third, the relation of the conceptual scheme to experiment; the fourth, a possible extension of the conceptual scheme; the fifth, content; the sixth, an assumption made; and the seventh, if its defects are disregarded, the overall design of the conceptual scheme. Most of the items require an understanding of at least several sentences of the passage.

If the reader works out exercises 3.12-1, 2, and 3 for himself, he will find that a single sentence in the passage often provides a clue to the correct response for an item. Since the aim is to measure the student's ability to understand not individual sentences but at least a paragraph, certain precautions must be made. Two possibilities have been mentioned: not allowing the student to consult the exercise or giving him too short a time for hunting out individual sentences. The device actually used in the above exercises was to make the wording of the item different from that of the clue sentence. In exercise 3.12-4, on the other hand, to test the student's understanding of the argument of the passage, not just the wording was made different, but the subject matter itself. Thus immediately recognizable similarities between an item and any individual sentence were eliminated.

In the first five items of exercise 4 the student is asked to *illustrate* assertions in the passage. Actually, he is asked to locate the generalization in the passage to fit the given illustrations, but the two abilities should not be too dissimilar. It is certain that they both involve a fairly deep understanding of the passage. The second group of five items tests the student's ability to discern the type of argument used. Thus, for example, paragraph A and the first item of the group are analogous in that both imply that *some* similarities in two phenomena justify our expectation that they will be similar in *any other* specified respect. The last group of two exercises asks questions about the passage in the direct way similar to that of the preceding exercises.

Exercise 3.12-4 is unambiguous in the sense that various instructors had no difficulty agreeing on the key. It is not particularly difficult but requires considerable time, say thirty minutes. Since this allows 150 seconds per item, more items than given here should be based on the passage—thus reducing the "overhead." It took the author some time to prepare the exercise, but the time was well spent because the exercise discriminated sharply between students of three simultaneously taught courses in similar subject matter. The main difference in the three courses was that in two of them the students were trained to ask, while reading a book, questions of the following kind: What is the author trying to prove? What is his argument? What does he take for granted? What evidence does he present? And, is his conclusion justified? The students of these two courses did considerably better on this exercise than the students who were not specifically trained in analytical reading.

### Content 3.13, Ability to understand a chapter, article, or book

The material may have been read and discussed in the course or it may be assigned to be read as preparation for the test. The particular questions that appear in the test, however, should not have been discussed in the course. For economy of space a long article on which questions can be based is not included here; appropriate *types* of item may be as follows. The student may be asked about the author's intent, his main conclusions, the argument leading to the conclusions, and the assumptions made, explicit and implicit. He may also be asked to estimate the degrees of validity of the conclusions, argument, and assumptions or to compare them with analogous elements in the works of another author. Both essay and objective tests can be used to measure this sort of understanding. Below are a few illustrative items.

3.13-1  *Faraday's "Experimental Researches in Electricity"*
Faraday's paper consists of several well-defined parts, the first part being concluded in paragraph 476. What is the major stated purpose of the first part?
  A. To treat in detail the electrolysis of water so that extensions can be made by analogy to other substances.
  B. To demonstrate the validity of his law on theoretical grounds.
  C. To demonstrate the proportionality of intensity of current to quantity of matter decomposed.
  D. To find what size, shape, and material of the electrodes must be used to obtain results in accord with his law.
  E. To demonstrate that the decomposition of water provides a reliable measure of quantity of electricity.

In the second part of his paper (paragraphs 493–502), Faraday discusses the electrolysis of solutions whose behavior is more complex than that of solutions of sulfuric acid. What feature of the decomposition of muriatic acid did Faraday take advantage of in establishing the general law of constant electrochemical action for the case of muriatic acid?
  A. The solubility of chlorine was known; therefore Faraday could make a precise allowance for the amount not evolved.
  B. The amount of chlorine plus the amount of oxygen was found experimentally to be constant.
  C. The amount of hydrogen evolved at the cathode was definite, no matter what mixture of gases prevailed at the anode.
  D. The amount of oxygen evolved at the anode was constant, no matter how much hydrogen or chlorine was given off.
  E. The amounts of hydrogen and chlorine were always proportional.

Judging from the reading, if a single phenomenon is known that appears to constitute a contradiction to an otherwise well-supported theory, Faraday would be most likely to

A. modify the theory to include the phenomenon.
B. refuse to apply or further develop the theory until an explanation were found for the exception.
C. search for an alternative theory that includes the phenomenon.
D. leave the explanation for a more convenient time and continue developing the theory.
E. modify the phenomenon until it becomes rigorously true and in agreement with the theory.

In investigating the effect of electric current on substances, there are a number of variables to be considered that might conceivably have an effect on the electrochemical action of the current. Which of the following possible variables did Faraday *not* investigate in this paper?
A. The intensity of the electric current.
B. The shape of the electrodes.
C. The decomposition of two substances simultaneously in the same solution.
D. The size of the bubbles rising from the electrodes.
E. The electrode materials in the batteries generating the current.

3.13-2 *Galileo's "Two New Sciences"*
Galileo introduces and defends the plausibility of the proposition that the *final velocity* of a body sliding from rest down an inclined plane depends only on the height of the plane and not on its inclination (friction and effects of the medium being negligible). Why is the proposition stated above important for Galileo's argument that the motion of a body falling in a vacuum is uniformly accelerated?

**Comments on exercises 3.13**

The first item of exercise 1 asks for the purpose or thesis of a part of a paper; the second item, for the nature of the argument; the third, for the author's general methodology or attitude toward his inquiry; and the fourth, for assumptions—on variables that may be considered irrelevant. All but the first item require an understanding of a considerable portion of the paper. Exercise 2 asks for an essay on the function of a part of a book.

The best and often the only way of obtaining a usable and lasting understanding of science as a process of inquiry is to read scientists' own accounts of their investigations. If the students' understanding tested by the exercises included under 2.32 has been obtained primarily from reading original accounts, the exercises can just as well be classified under 3.13. Similarly, knowledge or understanding, acquired by students from a chapter in the text that was assigned but not discussed, is a measure of their ability to understand the chapter. We are thus reminded again that the competence or ability measured by an exercise depends on the student's previous experience.

**Objective 3.2, Ability to interpret nonverbal symbolism**

Content 3.21, Ability to carry out symbolically indicated operations

The exercises below test for the ability to grasp the meaning of a new symbolism, to surmise its main properties, and to apply it.

3.21-1  In the next four problems the following symbolic abbreviations will be used:

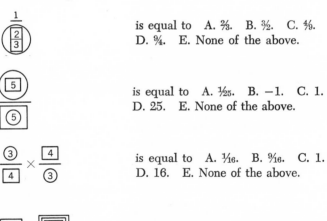

Work out the following problems and choose the correct answer. If no correct answer is given choose answer E. All mathematical symbols have their usual meaning.

is equal to   A. ⅔.   B. ³⁄₂.   C. ⁴⁄₉.
D. ¾.   E. None of the above.

is equal to   A. ¹⁄₂₅.   B. −1.   C. 1.
D. 25.   E. None of the above.

is equal to   A. ¹⁄₁₆.   B. ⁹⁄₁₆.   C. 1.
D. 16.   E. None of the above.

is equal to   A. ⅙.   B. −1.   C. −⅙
D. 1.   E. None of the above.

3.21-2  In the following problem the symbol Я will have the following meaning: Я $(a, b, c, d) = ac - bd$. *All mathematical symbols have their usual meanings.*

**EXAMPLES:** The symbol ⅂ $(a) = a + 2$. ⅂ $(4)$ is equal to $4 + 2 = 6$. The symbol И $(a, b) = a^2 + b$. И $(4, 3)$ is equal to $4^2 + 3 = 16 + 3 = 19$.
Я $(1, 2, 1, 1)$ is equal to
A. 1.
B. −1.
C. 3.
D. −3.

3.21-3   Symbols $\bigcirc$, $\square$ stand for operations to be performed on the enclosed algebraic expression.

Thus, if   (x) $= 2x + 3$   and   $\boxed{x}$ $= x^2$,

we have   $\textcircled{x}$ $= (2x+3) = 2(2x+3) + 3 = 4x + 9$

and   $\boxed{\textcircled{x}}$ $= \boxed{2x+3} = (2x+3)^2$.

Similarly,   $\boxed{x}$ $= (x^2) = 2x^2 + 3$.

For each of the following exercises, write the answer in the blank provided. Note: Your answer should apply to *any* value of $x$. Any answer that satisfies this condition is acceptable.

If $\textcircled{x} = x + 1$, $\textcircled{x} = $ _____

If $\textcircled{x} = x/2$, $\textcircled{x} = $ _____

If $\textcircled{x} = 2$, $\textcircled{x} = $ _____

If $\boxed{x} = 3x + 4$

and $\boxed{\textcircled{x}} = 1$, $\textcircled{x} = $ _____

### Comments on exercises 3.21

A student can solve the problems of exercise 1 by straightforward substitution. This method requires the ability to keep track of successive operations, which is a valuable enough ability but takes a lot of time. A more discerning student will use some general *property* of the symbolic operations: in the second item, that the two operations commute, and in the last item, that an even number of inversions leaves the quantity unchanged. Exercise 2 uses a functional form of operators. This form is more flexible and cheaper typographically than the geometric-figure form of exercise 1, but it has the disadvantage of more strongly suggesting the process of direct substitution. Exercise 3 is very difficult for most beginning students because it requires a decision on the form of the answer before working the problem. All the problems of exercise 3 can be solved by interpreting the "circle" operation as a linear transformation of $x$ into $ax + b$. In the third problem, for example, a direct substitution of this form gives $a = 0$ and $b = 2$. Most students, however, seem to use a more or less inspired trial-and-error method. It is to test the ability to pursue such a method that the exercise is designed. A knowledge of elementary algebra is presupposed.

Results of entrance tests at the University of Chicago seem to indicate that the ability to carry out symbolically indicated operations is important for success in most college courses, especially those in the physical sciences. It is therefore justifiable to include 3.21 under ability to learn. However, the exercises may test either for something that can readily be improved in a single course or mostly for a more general aptitude. If the latter is the case, the exercises are more suitable for an entrance than an achievement test.

**Content 3.22, Ability to interpret graphs, drawings, photographs, tables, and the like.**

Tables, graphs, and questions should be so chosen that the student would not be able to arrive at correct answers merely from his previous knowledge of the physical principles involved.

3.22-1  *Ability to interpret a table of values*
The table below gives the electrical resistances of five coils of wire at two temperatures. The resistance of each coil changes uniformly (linearly) between 0°C and 300°C. The coils are to be used within this temperature range. In each of the items below the table, choose the coil that answers the specifications most closely and write the letter of the coil (A, B, C, D, or E) before the item. (The dependence of resistance on temperature is measured by the percentage of change in resistance over a given temperature range.)

|        | Resistance at 10°C (ohms) | Resistance at 300°C (ohms) |
|--------|---------------------------|----------------------------|
| Coil *A* | 100.0                     | 100.3                      |
| Coil *B* | 2.500                     | 2.650                      |
| Coil *C* | 1.100                     | .999                       |
| Coil *D* | .250                      | .300                       |
| Coil *E* | .021                      | .015                       |

The coil whose resistance remains most nearly constant as the coil gets hot.
The coil whose resistance in the temperature range from 10°C to 300°C is to be not greater than 2.5 ohms nor smaller than .25 ohm and to show as little variation in resistance as possible.
The coil whose resistance is most influenced by temperature.
The coil whose resistance is to be as low as possible and is not to decrease with temperature.

3.22-2  A series of values of S for various measured values of *x*, *y*, and *z*, are given below. S is affected by *all three* of the factors *x*, *y*, and *z*; that is, the value of S cannot be obtained unless $x$, $y$, and $z$ are known. On the other hand, the factors $x$, $y$, and $z$ can be varied independently of one another.

| $S$ | $x$ | $y$ | $z$ |
|---|---|---|---|
| 6 | 1 | 2 | 2 |
| 8 | 4 | 2 | 6 |
| 8 | 2 | 2 | 3 |
| 12 | 4 | 2 | 4 |
| 16 | 4 | 2 | 3 |
| 20 | 5 | 2 | 3 |
| 24 | 4 | 2 | 2 |
| 24 | 1 | 4 | 2 |

What is the relationship between S and factor $x$? ($k$ and $c$ are constants whose values depend on $y$ and $z$ but not on $x$.)

A. $S = kx^2$.
B. $S = k/x$.
C. $S = kx$.
D. $S = kx - c$.
E. $S = k/x + c$.

3.22-3    Four properties I, II, III, and IV, of several substances were measured and are tabulated below:

| Substance | I | II | III | IV |
|---|---|---|---|---|
| 1 | 0 | 1.40 | 60 | 0.020 |
| 2 | 10 | 1.30 | 80 | 0.015 |
| 3 | 20 | 1.20 | 100 | 0.012 |
| 4 | 30 | 1.30 | 50 | 0.024 |
| 5 | 40 | 1.30 | 120 | 0.010 |

Property IV has a simple mathematical relationship to

A. property I.
B. property II.
C. property III.
D. All of the above.
E. None of the above.

An equation that describes this relationship has the form

A. $XY$ = constant.
B. $X + Y$ = constant.
C. $X - Y$ = constant.
D. $X/Y$ = constant.
E. None of the above.

3.22-4   *Ability to interpret graphical data*
Before each voltage write the letter corresponding to the *best* response.

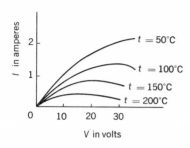
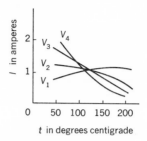

Fig. 1                              Fig. 2

The curves in the graph of Figure 1 show how the current, $I$, through an electrical device varies with the voltage, $V$, across the device for various values of the temperature, $t$, of the device. Figure 2 shows how the current through the same device varies with the temperature of the device for various values of the voltage.

In Figure 2 what are the values of the voltages?

| *Voltages* | *Responses* |
|---|---|
| $V_1$. | A.  About 10 volts. |
| $V_2$. | B.  About 20 volts. |
| $V_3$. | C.  About 30 volts. |
| $V_4$. | D.  Not in the range shown in Figure 1. |

Within the ranges shown in Figure 1, as temperature is increased, $V_{max}$, that is, the voltage required to produce maximum current,
   A.  becomes greater.      B.  becomes smaller.
   C.  may be greater or smaller, depending on the temperature.

In the range $t = 100°C$ to $t = 200°C$, which of the following equations best represents the relation between $V_{max}$ and $t$?
   A.  $V_{max}/t = $ constant.      C.  $V_{max} = t^2 + $ constant.
   B.  $V_{max}t = $ constant.       D.  $V_{max} = t + $ constant.

Before each value of $V$ in Figure 2, write the letter that best describes the dependence of $I$ on $t$. (Note that $c$ and $a$ are positive constants.)

| *Voltages* | *Responses* |
|---|---|
| $V_1$. | A.  $I = c - at.$ |
| $V_2$. | B.  $I = c - a\sqrt{t}.$ |
| $V_3$. | C.  $I = c - at^2.$ |
| $V_4$. | D.  $I = c - a/t.$ |

3.22-5   If a mixture of cadmium and zinc, hot enough to be a liquid throughout, is cooled, the resulting mixture will contain some of the following: crystalline Zn, crystalline Cd, liquid Zn, liquid Cd, and mixed crystals of Cd and Zn (single crystals containing both Cd and Zn). The composition of the resulting mixture is indicated in the graph as a function of the temperature and composition of the mixture. Before each statement below write the letter corresponding to the best response.

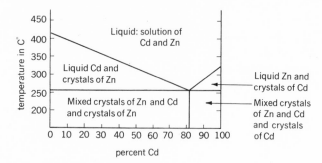

*Responses*

A. The statement is supported by the graph.
B. The statement is contradicted by the graph.
C. The statement is neither supported nor contradicted by the graph.

*Statements*

Pure zinc melts at about 430°C.

All mixtures of zinc and cadmium become liquid at lower temperatures than does either metal alone.

If a solution of 80 percent Cd and 20 percent Zn is cooled slowly to 200°C, solid Cd separates.

There is a composition of Zn-Cd solution that, upon cooling, will deposit mixed crystals of exactly the same composition.

Cadmium is easier to vaporize than zinc.

If a solution of 50 percent Cd and 50 percent Zn is cooled to 275°C, the part that remains liquid will be richer in cadmium.

At 300°C, zinc and cadmium are completely soluble in each other.

3.22-6   In the figure at the right, $W$ represents the weight of an organism and $t$ represents time. Choose the curve that best describes the behavior of each organism given below and write its letter before the description of the organism.

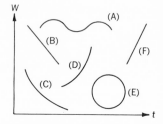

An organism that loses 10 grams per day.

An organism whose weight on each succeeding day is half as great as its weight on the preceding day.

An organism that gains weight during the day and loses weight during the night.

An organism that gains 10 grams per day.

An organism that doubles its weight each day.

3.22-7  Figure (a) represents a bicycle wheel rotating about a horizontal axis that is perpendicular to the plane of the paper. A point X on the rim is marked with chalk. On the graph of Figure (b) the vertical distance h of the point X from the horizontal axis is plotted against time. The following five questions refer to Figure (b).

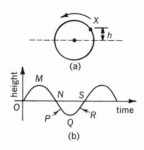
(a)

(b)

The vertical velocity of the point X is equal to zero
A. at N.
B. at P.
C. at Q.
D. at R.
E. None of the above.

Doubling the amplitude (height of the curve) without otherwise changing the conditions indicates that
A. the wheel is turning twice as fast.
B. the wheel is turning half as fast.
C. the radius of the wheel is twice as large.
D. the radius of the wheel is half as large.
E. None of the above.

The length of the graph required to represent a complete revolution of the wheel is
A. OM.
B. ON.
C. OQ.
D. OS.
E. None of the above.

A similar curve that starts at O and first crosses the t axis at S represents a wheel
A. that turns twice as fast.
B. that turns half as fast.
C. whose radius is twice as great.
D. whose radius is half as great.
E. None of the above.

A similar curve that crossed the t axis at N and S, but had a positive slope at N, would represent a wheel which, as compared to the original wheel,
A. rotated in the opposite direction.
B. was half a revolution ahead.
C. had its axis of rotation in a different plane.
D. was slowing down.
E. None of the above.

### Comments on exercises 3.22

Exercise 1 tests for the ability to use a table of numbers, an ability somewhat similar to that of using a handbook to locate a material of specified properties. Given enough time (ten minutes), almost all the students who are able to understand the specifications should find the right responses. If the time is cut to five minutes, only a few students are likely to get perfect scores, presumably those who at a glance can tell a rough percentage difference between two numbers. This shows that varying time allowance may vary the objective measured. Exercises 2 and 3 require the student to discern a mathematical relationship between two quantities described by a table of numbers. In exercise 2, he must understand that various parameters must be kept constant. The ability measured by exercises 2 and 3 is probably related to the ability to interpret data (see exercise 2.21-14). The exercises are placed in this section because they are entirely mathematical and thus abstract. Exercise 4 is a rather difficult one; it tests the student's understanding of the information conveyed by a one-parameter family of curves, a very common group of curves in physics. In the items requiring a translation between graphs and algebra no subtle points are involved. Thus, in the last four items the choice of the right response depends on the recognition of the sign of the first and second derivatives. Exercise 5 is based on a phase diagram that is somewhat more complicated than a triple-point diagram. Exercise 6 is an elementary and conventional one on the meaning of curves. Exercise 7 is different from the preceding three in that the physical object, whose behavior the curve represents, is described.

### Content 3.23, Ability to understand spatial relationships

3.23-1   An open field is defended against military tanks by the erection of steel posts 1 foot in diameter, placed systematically to form squares 12 feet between the centers of the posts. A military tank can safely pass through if it has 6 inches of clearance on each side. The maximum width (in feet) that a tank can have in order to pass through is

  A. 12.
  B. 11½.
  C. 11.
  D. 10½.
  E. 10.

3.23-2   Three equal spheres are in contact with one another. A plane passes through the center of two of the spheres and cuts the third without passing through its center. The intersections are

  A. three equal circles touching one another.
  B. two equal circles touching each other and a third smaller circle touching the other two.
  C. two equal circles touching each other and a third smaller circle not touching the other two.

D. two equal circles and a third smaller circle, with no points of contact.

E. two equal circles and an ellipse, all touching one another.

3.23-3  A triangular board of uniform thickness is to be suspended by means of a string attached to a point along the edge of the board. In order that the board may hang in the position shown, the string should be attached at

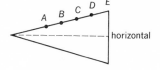

A. point *A*.
B. point *B*.
C. point *C*.
D. point *D*.
E. point *E*.

3.23-4  The area of the triangle *PQR* is 1 square foot. The area (in square feet) of the shaded portion is nearest (in square feet)

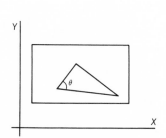

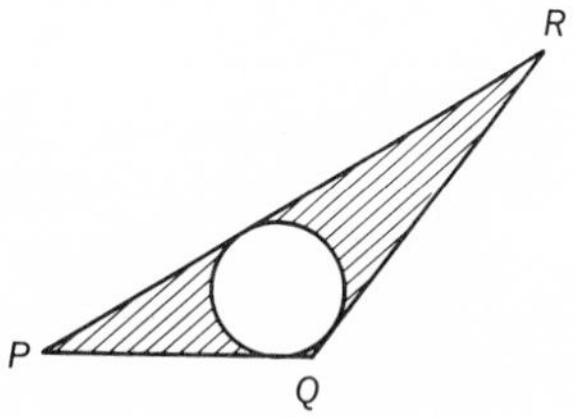

A. ⅜.
B. ½.
C. ⅔.
D. ⅞.

3.23-5  In the figure at the right what is the ratio of length *OP* to length *OR*?

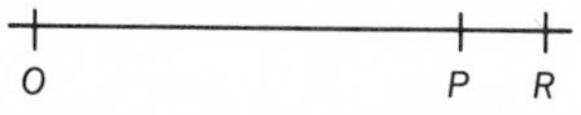

A. ⅔.
B. ¾.
C. ⅘.
D. ⅚.
E. ⁶/₇.

3.23-6  A triangle is drawn on a rubber sheet. The sheet is next stretched to twice its length parallel to the *X*-axis and to twice its width parallel to the *Y*-axis. If the stretching is the same for every part of the sheet, what happens to the triangle?

The perimeter of the triangle will be multiplied by a factor
A. between 1 and 2.
B. of 2.

C. between 2 and 4.

D. of 4.

E. greater than 4.

The area of the triangle will be multiplied by a factor of

A. 2.

B. 4.

C. 6.

D. 8.

E. None of the above.

Angle $\theta$ will be multiplied by a factor

A. of 1.

B. between 1 and 2.

C. of 2.

D. such that $\sin \theta$ is doubled.

E. None of the above.

## Comments on exercises 3.23

The ability to visualize, especially in three dimensions, seems to vary considerably from student to student. The author's informal studies indicate that the correlation between this ability and other abilities described in this book is low. Therefore, if it is considered important, it must be tested specifically. On theoretical grounds, the ability should be valuable to an experimental scientist; on the other hand, there is no evidence that success in college science courses depends on the possession of the ability—as measured by the type of exercise used in 3.23.

Items 1, 2, 3, and 6 deal with visualization fairly directly, although some students could get the right response to item 3 from theory alone. In items 4 and 5 the student is asked to estimate area and length respectively. The ability to estimate lengths ought to be of value to the student in reading scales of instruments.

## Objective 3.3, Disciplined thinking

**Content 3.31, Possession of, or at least an ability to conform to or to imitate, scientists' modes and habits of thought and action and their attitudes toward inquiry**

The types of exercises given below are hardly suitable for assigning grades, but they may be useful in guidance and for further experimentation.

### EXERCISES 1–5.    *Ability to Use Syllogistic Reasoning*

In these exercises there are some *statements*, a *conclusion*, and five *comments* about the conclusion. You are to assume that the statements are true and then select the comment that best agrees with your judgment as to the soundness of the conclusion, that is, whether it has been logically derived from the statements.

3.31-1   Statements: In nuclear reactions, loss of mass can only take place by emission of particles. Particles most commonly detected are alpha and beta particles, which can always be identified by cloud chamber experiments. In a certain nuclear reaction, an atom lost mass. Only a part of this loss was accounted for as due to an emission of an alpha particle. Cloud chamber experiments showed that there were no beta particles. Conclusion: A particle different from alpha and beta particles must have been emitted along with the alpha particle.

   A. The conclusion is sound.
   B. "A particle different from alpha and beta particles" needs definition, particularly as to whether the proposed particle is charged or neutral.
   C. The conclusion is false because we do not know whether the new particle could leave a trace in the cloud chamber.
   D. The conclusion is false because we do not know whether there was more than one new particle emitted.
   E. No conclusion can be reached without considerably more experimental evidence.

3.31-2   Statements: Electric charges move freely in a conductor. Like charges repel each other. The leaves of an electroscope are seen to be spread apart. Conclusion: The electroscope is charged.

   A. The conclusion is logically sound.
   B. If we knew the material of the electroscope leaves we could judge the soundness of the conclusion.
   C. The conclusion is satisfactory if moving charges do not leave the conductor.
   D. We must know whether the electroscope is well insulated before the conclusion can be judged.
   E. The conclusion does not necessarily follow.

3.31-3   Statements: Some scientists believe in the supernatural. Some believers in the supernatural are intelligent. Conclusion: Some scientists are intelligent.

   A. The conclusion is invalid since words such as "some" are too indefinite.
   B. The fact that some intelligent scientists are known proves that the conclusion is logically derived.
   C. The conclusion is valid since the supernatural can only be understood by intelligent persons.
   D. The conclusion is not derived logically.
   E. The conclusion is true because the statements are true.

3.31-4   If the statement "some $x$ are not $y$" is true, then the statement "some $x$ are $y$"

   A. must be true.

B. must be false.

C. can be either true or false.

If the statement "all $x$ are $y$" is *false*, then the statement "no $x$ are $y$"

A. must be true.

B. must be false.

C. can be either true or false.

3.31-5    Read the following description of "alcotes."

All of the chemical compounds known as "alcotes" (a fictitious name) have the following chemical properties: (a) they are alkaline; (b) they dissolve in water; and (c) they have a bitter taste. There are no other *chemical* properties common to all alcotes.

Each item below has statements and a conclusion. You are to find the strictly logical relation between the statements and the conclusion, using the following definitions: The statements constitute a *sufficient* condition (for the truth of the conclusion) if the truth of all the statements makes certain the truth of the conclusion. The statements constitute a *necessary* condition (for the truth of the conclusion) if *each* statement must be true for the conclusion to be true. Before each item, write

NS  if the statements constitute a *necessary and a sufficient* condition.

N    if the statements constitute a *necessary* but not a sufficient condition.

S    if the statements constitute a *sufficient* but not a necessary condition.

O    if the statements constitute *neither* a necessary nor a sufficient condition.

Statements: A powder is alkaline. It dissolves in water. Conclusion: The powder is an alcote.

Statements: A liquid is alkaline. It dissolves in water. It has a bitter taste. Conclusion: The liquid is an alcote.

Statements: No substance except an alcote is alkaline. A substance $X$ is alkaline. Conclusion: Substance $X$ is an alcote.

### Comments on exercises 3.31 (1 to 5)

The exercises under content 3.31 are abstract; no knowledge of content is presupposed. They test for the ability to pursue strictly logical reasoning from precisely stated premises. This is the kind of reasoning on which physics texts mainly depend. Yet large numbers of entering students possess very little of this ability, and many get through a physics course without improving it. It is not difficult to explain to students what constitutes a proof in physics and the meaning of necessary and sufficient conditions, and the students are invariably grateful. One of the main difficulties in teaching strictly logical reasoning is that the students are likely to want to check the conclusions against their preconceived ideas of what assertions are reasonable. In testing, this difficulty is indicated by the fact that many students find items 1 and 2 fairly easy; the completely abstract exercise 4, in which conclusions do not *sound* either reasonable or absurd, much more difficult; and item 3, which asks for a judgment contrary to the students' beliefs, most difficult of all. Exercise 5 is difficult for most students.

Questions calling for a judgment on the soundness of a conclusion lend themselves well to identifying students who are overcautious, for example, those who choose response B or E in item 1. Responses B and E in item 3 should appeal to students who do not have much faith in logical reasoning.

## Attitudes and habits

It is possible to learn something about the student's attitudes and habits of thought by analyzing the kind of *wrong* answers that he seems to prefer. All of the examples below illustrate the possibility of estimating only the *deviation* of a student's attitude from the norm established by the group taking the examination.

Overcautiousness

*vs.*

jumping to conclusions or going beyond data

| "Overcautious" | | "Beyond data" | |
|---|---|---|---|
| EXERCISE | STUDENT'S ANSWER | EXERCISE | STUDENT'S ANSWER |
| 1.23-6 | | 1.21-2 | O |
| Item 1 | A | 1.21-3 | A |
| Item 2 | D | 1.22-5 | O (when it is a wrong answer) |
| Item 3 | E | | |
| 1.24-1 | H (when F is right) | 1.23-6 | |
| 2.12-8 | D (when A or B is right) | Item 3 | A or B |
| 2.13-3 | + | 1.24-1 | F (when H is right) |
| 2.13-8 | D (when A, B, or C is right) | 2.13-8 | A (when B, C, or D is right) |
| 2.14-4 | F | 2.14-2 | E |
| 2.31-5 | B | 2.31-1 | E |
| 2.31-7 | B or E | 2.31-5 | C or D |
| 3.12-2 | C (when A or B is right) | 2.31-7 | A |
| 3.31-1 | B or E | 2.32-2 | |
| 3.31-2 | B | Item 1 | A or E |
| 3.5-1 | C or E (when A, B, or D is right) | 3.12-2 | A or B (when C is right) |
| | | 3.31-2 | A |

Underestimating *vs.* overestimating the power and value of science

| "Underestimating science" | | "Overestimating science" | |
| --- | --- | --- | --- |
| EXERCISE | STUDENT'S ANSWER | EXERCISE | STUDENT'S ANSWER |
| 2.23-3 | B or C (when A is right) | 2.23-1 | |
| 2.32-1 | B | Item 2 | E |
| 2.32-7 | | 2.23-2 | |
| Item 1 | D | Item 2 | B or C |
| 2.32-14 | A | 2.23-3 | A (when B or C is right) |
| | | 2.32-7 | |
| | | Item 1 | B |
| | | Item 2 | A |
| | | 2.32-15 | |
| | | Item 4 | B or E |

Underestimating the value of experiment or observation as tools of science

*vs.*

underestimating the importance of reason or theory

| "Underestimating experiment" | | "Underestimating reason" | |
| --- | --- | --- | --- |
| EXERCISE | STUDENT'S ANSWER | EXERCISE | STUDENT'S ANSWER |
| 2.31-3 | | 2.31-3 | |
| Item 2 | B or D | Item 1 | A, B, C, or D |
| Item 3 | B, D, or E | Item 2 | E |
| 2.31-5 | A or B | 2.32-7 | |
| 2.32-1 | | Item 1 | A |
| Item 2 | A | Item 2 | E |
| 2.32-6 | | 2.32-15 | |
| Item 1 | A, C, or E | Item 4 | D |
| 2.32-7 | | 3.31-3 | B |
| Item 1 | E | | |
| Item 2 | C or D | | |
| 2.32-15 | | | |
| Item 4 | C | | |

| "Possession of strong prejudices or preconceptions" | |
| --- | --- |
| EXERCISE | STUDENT'S ANSWER |
| 2.14-2 | B |
| 2.14-3 | Any wrong answer |
| 3.31-3 | E |

Learning things well or not at all
*vs.*
learning something of everything

In most of the test questions in this book there is a correct answer, and there are the nearly correct or relevant answers and the completely incorrect or irrelevant answers (F responses). A student with a smattering of knowledge will choose the nearly correct answers in preference to the completely incorrect ones. A student who learns things well or not at all will not show this preference; he either gets the right answers or marks the questions almost at random. Here again only those items should be analyzed to which the student has given a wrong answer.

3.31-6   *Miscellaneous attitudes and habits*

Some of the statements below may be considered right by some people and wrong by others; therefore you are not asked to mark the statements true or false, but to give us your own point of view by writing A before the statement if you are inclined to agree with the main idea of the item, and B if you are inclined to disagree.

Guessing of any kind or acting on a hunch should never be indulged in by a true scientist.

A true scientist should not be concerned with increasing the accuracy of laboratory measurements from 1 percent to .1 percent, and so forth; he should devote his time to seeking after the larger truths of nature.

The events in the lives of individuals can be predicted, in a general way, by the configuration of the planets and the moon at the time of birth.

With further development of scientific thinking, we may discover certain *facts* about nature, which we shall not be able to test by observation or experiment.

A real scientific genius can, without using any experimental data about matter, find out (by thinking) more about what atoms are really like than can an ordinary physicist by performing experiments.

A clear scientific thinker could have become convinced without experimentation that a feather falls more slowly than a stone only because of the interference of air. He could have predicted with certainty that in a vacuum all bodies would fall with the same acceleration, that is, gain the same amount of speed in one second.

Whatever scientists say about the inside of a star is really theorizing or speculation; they can never be sure about it.

The action of a radio tube has been explained completely satisfactorily in terms of the motion of electrons. No one has been able to explain it in any other way. Therefore, electrons exist.

If a scientist does his research into the nature of physical phenomena without being concerned how such knowledge can be applied practically, the chances that his discoveries will ever be useful in a practical sense are small.

In science, as is true in all endeavors, certain statements have to be accepted as true because of the judgment of an authority, even though he cannot definitely prove them.

Some of the scientific discoveries of recent years have led to misery and suffering. Humanity would in the long run be happier if such discoveries were never made.

> A photoelectric cell has been constructed on the theory that electrons exist. The theory explains the action of the cell very well, and the cell operates satisfactorily. What would be the proper course of action if in the future the scientists should decide that electrons do not exist? (Mark *each* statement A or B.)

We should stop using the photoelectric cell.
We would have to reconstruct the cell.
We could continue using the cell without changing it.
We could continue using electronic theory in explaining the action of the cell.

### Comments on exercises testing attitudes and habits

It should be emphasized that these exercises will not justify an absolute judgment of the student's attitudes or habits but only a comparison with the group taking the test. One of the main reasons is the great difficulty of estimating the relative attractiveness of the wrong answers. Thus, for example, the "beyond the data" answers may be only mildly so, while the "overcautious" answers may be quite extreme, with the result that a "normal" student would show preference for the former type of answer. To get an interpretable result, each student may be assigned a raw score of $X$ by subtracting the number of overcautious answers from the number of beyond-data answers and calculating the mean $M$ of the raw scores for the class and their standard deviation $S$. Then the standard score $z$, given by $z = (X - M)/S$, can be interpreted with some confidence. These computations are simplified if we first add to the students' raw scores $X$ a number—the same number for all students—such that none of the raw scores is negative.

### Content 3.32, Ability to organize and formulate ideas

The ability to organize should be tested either by an oral examination or by an essay. Only one exercise is given here.

3.32-1 Write an essay on Galileo's study of falling bodies. You are to use the material from the list of assertions given. You may, however, add other material and label it J, K, and so forth. As you write the essay, number each paragraph by writing 1, 2, and so forth, on the margin near the beginning of the paragraph. On the sheet labeled *Description of the Essay*, describe in one brief sentence the content of each paragraph, and in the blank at the left write the letters of the assertions specifically stated in the paragraph.

### List of Assertions
A. $a = dv/dt$  ($a$ = acceleration).
B. $V_t$ in vacuum is the same for all bodies ($V_t$ = terminal velocity).

C. $V_t$ in air is nearly the same for heavy bodies.
D. $V_t$ in water is not the same even for heavy bodies.
E. $V_t$ is proportional to weight (Aristotle's opinion).
F. $S = \frac{1}{2}at^2$, if acceleration is constant.
G. $s \propto t^2$ on an inclined plane.
H. $a$ is the same for all bodies falling in a vacuum.
I. Free fall is a special case (90°) of inclined plane.

### Description of the Essay

| Paragraph number | Assertions used in the paragraph | Content of paragraph numbered as indicated |
|---|---|---|
| EXAMPLE | C, E | Refutation of Aristotle by describing observations. |
| 1. | | |
| 2. | | |

## Comments on exercise 3.32

It is sometimes possible to judge the organization of an essay from just the "description of the essay." (For a discussion of this form of exercise see page 140.) It is, at any rate, much easier to grade an essay that is accompanied by the student's own description of it. In the exercise just above, almost all of the relevant material is included, to make possible an evaluation of the student's organizing ability alone, without considering the ability to recall. (The student must of course be familiar with Galileo's treatment of falling bodies.)

It is probably best to distribute the sheet for the description of the essay after the students have finished the essay, and then to give them a fairly short time to fill the blanks, say, fifteen minutes if the essay proper has been allowed two hours. The time limit will discourage the students from rewriting the essay.

Another method is to give the student an already completed essay, consisting of a good number of short paragraphs randomly arranged and labeled by letters A, B, C, and so forth, and to ask him to indicate the proper order of paragraphs. This sort of test is indirect and probably less valid than an essay test because it asks for *reorganization* only; it has the advantage that it can be objectively scored.

In most science courses the only essays the students write are laboratory reports. At the examination time, the students may be given back their reports and asked to number the paragraphs and to describe the content and function of each. Pedagogically, it is a good idea to tell the students in advance that one (unspecified) of their reports will be treated in this way.

This procedure may reduce the validity of the test, but the reports are likely to be better organized, easier to read, and perhaps more authentic.

### Objective 3.4, Imaginative thinking; ingenuity

There is no difficulty in devising exercises that require creativity or high-level imagination; after all, there are many unsolved problems in physics. At a lower level of preparation almost any problem that is very difficult, not because of the knowledge required but because of its unusual character or complexity, requires imagination. Problems, for instance, that are routine for an algebra student, may require extreme ingenuity to be solved arithmetically. Similarly, many exercises given here, which are designed to test the knowledge or understanding of a student with a year's training in physics, would test high imaginativeness if given to a student of a one-semester survey course in physical science. What is difficult is to invent exercises on imaginative thinking that are within the reach of a sizable fraction of the students of a class—not merely the top 1 percent.

Below are a few exercises given more or less in increasing order of difficulty. They have been used in discussion sections to make clear the nature and function of theory, especially its relation to facts. More than half of the students with whom they were used were able to contribute to the resolution of the questions. Similar exercises have been given as optional essay exercises in tests, with about the same degree of success. Various actual or possible students' responses follow each exercise, in parentheses.

3.4-1    Design an experiment to provide evidence for the theory that the motion of gas molecules is *chaotic*. (Equal pressure on the walls of a container of any shape. Equal rates of escape from equal size holes independent of location.)

3.4-2    Design a theory to explain the fact that gas pressure increases with temperature. Do not assume that molecular kinetic energy increases. (Molecules dissociate at high temperatures. Gas is a spring whose elasticity increases with temperature.)

3.4-3    Design an experiment to show that static and current electricity are different states of the same substance. (Electrolysis by a spark. Magnetic field near a static discharge. Magnetic field near a rapidly moving charged object.)

3.4-4    Explain bending of light around an obstacle on the theory that light consists of material particles. (Gravitational or other attraction between light and the obstacle.)

3.4-5    A small but visible star revolves about a much more massive, essentially stationary star. The line between the earth and the stationary star lies in the plane of the revolution. What observations would indicate that the speed of light is independent of the motion of its source? (The observed time interval between the initial positions of recession and of approach of the moving star is half that between two successive recessions.)

3.4-6   Use the theory that light is wave motion in ether—a fluid of very small and elastic material particles—to explain opacity. (Opacity is due to dampening effect of inelastic molecules.)

3.4-7   Two thin beams of light combine to produce a dark spot on a screen. One of the beams comes directly from the source, the other is reflected at a glancing angle from a mirror. Explain, on the theory that light consists of material particles. (Light particles are positively charged but acquire negative charges on hitting the mirror.)

3.4-8   Devise a theory to account for the law of definite proportions without assuming that a substance consists of identical molecules. (Molecules of any substance are rods or threads or ribbons of different lengths; they combine with equal lengths of other molecules.) Comment: This exercise is too difficult for most, sometimes all, beginning students of a class. An alternative exercise is to state the theory and ask the students to extend it to include the law of multiple proportions, say, for CO and $CO_2$. (Oxygen "ribbons" can adhere to one or two sides of the carbon "ribbon.")

3.4-9   The most probable value of a quantity is taken to be the mean $M$ of all the measured values. The result of all the measurements is often written as $M \pm d$, where $d$ is the average or standard deviation and is a measure of the dispersion of the measured values. The question often arises: "How many measurements should one make?" Invent a method for giving a reasonable answer to that question.

## Objective 3.5, Knowledge of sources of information

3.5-1   Answers to the specific questions below are desired. You have at hand only the sources of information listed below. For each question choose the source that will give the desired information most efficiently and quickly.

### Sources of Information

A. An unabridged dictionary.
B. A handbook of chemical and physical data.
C. A file of abstracts of papers from scientific journals.
D. High school physics and chemistry texts.
E. The answer to the question is best found by carrying out an experiment.

### Questions

Is there a liquid in which sand will sink but salt will float?
Are sun lamps harmful to the skin?
Which will remove a grease spot more quickly, carbona or gasoline?
How can a small amount of hydrogen chloride be prepared?
What length of No. 20 chromel wire is needed to make a 100 ohm resistor?
What elements make up the mineral chalcedony?

## Comments on exercise 3.5-1

A competence of rather permanent value, which students can develop in introductory science courses, is an acquaintance with common reference materials and library catalogues. This particular exercise deals with the first step in locating the desired information: identification of the *class* of proper reference material. The form of the exercise, master list, seems natural and appropriate.

# 19

# LABORATORY OR PERFORMANCE TESTS

Performance tests are those requiring apparatus and other laboratory materials, whether for manipulation or inspection.

## ABILITY L1, LABORATORY KNOWLEDGE

In measuring laboratory knowledge, only the materials and experiments with which the student has had a chance to become familiar in the course should be used. For diagnostic purposes and probably for assigning grades, skills should be measured separately.

## Objective L1.1, Knowledge of apparatus and materials

L1.1-1  You are given a circuit containing a multiple-scale voltmeter and ammeter. Write down the names of the instruments; close the switch and record the readings and their precision; and draw a diagram showing the connections and relative magnitudes of the internal resistances of the meters that correspond to different scales.

(Other suitable instruments are: a mercury barometer, a thermometer, a post-office-box resistor, vernier or micrometer calipers, a ballistic galvanometer, and various kinds of balances.)

L1.1-2  Estimate, without the use of any instruments, the length of a string and give the probable error of the estimate, for example, 30 ± 5 cm.

(Other exercises may be to estimate any of the following: the area of an irregular piece of paper; the volume of an irregular solid object and its weight [by lifting it]; the temperature of a liquid [by touch]; the brightness of a source of light or the intensity of illumination of a surface; and the frequency of the sound emitted by a tuning fork. The mass of a small loaded cart may be estimated by pushing it, but the student should not be allowed to lift the cart or to see its contents, for we want an estimate of the mass and not of the weight. The moment of inertia of a suspended object [by causing it to spin]; the time interval between two flashes of light; and the angle between two rigidly connected rods are other possible exercises.)

## Objective L1.2, Knowledge of laboratory procedures

L1.2-1    An ammeter-voltmeter circuit for measuring a resistance is set up, not completely correctly. Inspect the setup and write down a complete criticism of it: polarities, ranges of meters, size of resistors, connections, and the circuit as a whole.

L1.2-2    Measure the emf of a single dry cell. Make a list of the needed apparatus, set up the circuit, make the measurements, and then submit your result in the usual form, for example, $E = 1.53 \pm .04$ volts.

## Objective L1.3, Knowledge of relations between data and generalizations

L1.3-1    You may inspect, if you wish, an Atwood machine. Then list the sources of error *in their order of importance;* state the probable sign of each error; describe precautions that should be taken to obtain good data; indicate the results of your experiment, perhaps in the form of a graph of acceleration against the driving weight for various values of the total load; and explain the meaning of the slopes and the intercepts of the curves.

## COMMENTS ON EXERCISES L1

Exercises L1.1-1, L1.1-2, and L1.2-1 take a very short time. Various apparatus can be set up at numbered locations, and each student can be given a sheet for recording his results. With a proper ordering of the sequences of locations that various students should follow, it is possible to test a large number of students at a time. Presumably students have had a chance to demonstrate the knowledge tested by exercises L1.1-1 and L1.2-1 in their laboratory reports. The exercises then serve to test retention and the authorship of the reports. Exercise L1.1-2 tests for acquaintance with the physical aspects of phenomena. Students can collect data and write an acceptable report with only a hazy memory of the objects they have handled and about which they have written. Their hypnagogic state is maintained or supported by many laboratory manuals that specify what to push, what to pull, and what to record. Faced with the possibility of a test containing exercises similar to those of L1.1-2, most students should remain wide awake in the laboratory and preoccupy themselves with phenomena.

Exercises L1.2-2 and L1.3-1 do require considerable time and are perhaps best administered to a few students at a time, under examination conditions, during the regular laboratory periods.

**ABILITY L2, LABORATORY UNDERSTANDING**

Tests must be based on situations that have important elements new to the student.

## Objective L2.1, Understanding of processes of measurement

### Content L2.11, Understanding of apparatus

The student is asked to inspect, describe, and explain the functioning of apparatus or a setup that is new to him; to determine the reason for misfunctioning of familiar apparatus; or to set up apparatus to specifications (verbal or symbolic).

L2.11-1   Inspect the torsion balance and explain its mechanism and functioning with the aid of a diagram.

(Other possibilities are: a Van de Graaff generator; a setup for measuring thermal expansion of a metal rod; and a setup for producing a real image without a screen. Either the apparatus or the setup has to be new to the student.)

L2.11-2   Determine the cause of misfunctioning of a doorbell.

(An aneroid barometer, a voltmeter, or a simple—but new to the student—electronic circuit might also be used.)

L2.11-3   Using the given diagram, set up a circuit.

(The circuit should be sufficiently complicated to make it necessary for the student to understand the interrelationship of its parts. Other possibilities are: a setup for measuring thermal expansion of a metal rod, a setup for producing a visible real image without a screen, and a potentiometer circuit. All these must be new to the student.)

L2.11-4   Without disassembling a voltmeter (or an ammeter) increase its range by a factor of 2.

(Other possibilities are: to convert a single-scale meter into a multiple-scale one—the student must decide for himself that outside resistors are necessary; to make a specified change in the range of a hydrometer; and to increase the damping of a wall galvanometer.)

### Content L2.12, Understanding of measurement

Usually the required measurement should not be entirely new to the student but rather a modification of a measurement with which he is familiar  Otherwise the exercise may belong under L2.2.

L2.12-1   The student is asked to measure a very high or very low resistance. He should specify the apparatus and the setup, defend his method, and submit the result and the probable error.

(Other possibilities are: the weight of an object beyond the capacity of the balance, the focal length of a negative lens, the magnifying power of a combination of two coaxial lenses at some distance from each other, the length of a closed loop of wire, the resistance of an ammeter, and the refractive index of a plano-convex lens.)

## Comments on exercises L2.1

Since exercises L2.11 are intended to measure understanding and not highly imaginative thinking, the apparatus, though new to the student as an assembly, must consist of parts whose behavior is known to him. Thus, although the student should not have studied the Van de Graaff generator (L2.11-1), he is expected to be familiar with frictional electricity, discharge from sharp points, and capacity. A good source for exercises L2.11-1 and 3 is the apparatus the teacher uses in his lecture demonstrations. Another source for L2.11-3 is an unassembled apparatus and the directions for its assembly or operation that are furnished by the manufacturer. In assembling such apparatus or performing the diagnosis or repair asked for in exercise L2.11-2, the student not only takes a test but may perform a useful function. To some degree this is true of exercise L2.11-4. Since some of these exercises take considerable time, the student may be allowed to use his regular laboratory period for the job. He may learn a good deal from it, for his motivation and concentration will usually be very high.

It was stressed in Part I that improving teaching and facilitating learning are the most important function of tests. Tests must also, however, be used for certification. Moreover, unless grades are accurate and just, learning will suffer. Therefore exercises that are the same or very similar for all students are needed. Some of the exercises described in the preceding paragraph do not meet this criterion. Thus, for example, assembly or repair jobs can hardly be the same for all students, for they may require intuitive understanding, imagination, and skill—talents that are not universal.

## Objective L2.2, Understanding of experiment: understanding the relation between theoretical or "book" physics and phenomena

Theoretical physics means statements or assertions, both verbal and mathematical, about nature and about processes of inquiry. It is a creation of the human mind. Its relation or desired relation to phenomena—objects and processes of nature—is subtle and changing. The laboratory, however, is better suited to exploring those aspects of the relation that have remained essentially unchanged during the past few centuries; the subtlety and flux should be investigated in other parts of the course.

Understanding of the relation between real phenomena and their conceptualized counterparts—laws, theories, definitions; error, control, proof—should probably be the central objective of the laboratory. There is, however, no short test that can measure its attainment. Fortunately, a valid test can be easily incorporated into regular laboratory sessions by a redesign of one or more experiments performed in the course. The test can cover all three contents: L2.21, understanding of experimental design; L2.22, understanding of the experimental process; and L2.23, understanding of interpretation of experimental data.

Below are examples, in the form of the instruction sheets, of four experiments performed by the students of a one-year non-calculus course in physics.

### EXPERIMENT-PREDICT-VERIFY PATTERN
### OF LABORATORY EXERCISES

Your laboratory work will generally be done in two stages, as follows. First, one or more laboratory periods will be spent experimenting in various ways with given apparatus. The object of this *preliminary experimentation* (usually done by groups of students) is to enable you to predict the outcome of a *test experiment* that you will perform later. The general nature of the test experiment will be explained to you before you start your preliminary experimentation.

When it is time for you to perform the test experiment (the apparatus for it will be set up for you at the beginning of a specified laboratory period), you should inspect the setup and, on the basis of what you have learned from your preliminary experimentation, calculate the most probable outcome of the test experiment. Inspecting the test-experiment setup, which may require some measurements, and calculating the predicted outcome must be done by each student independently. Your next step will be to give the results of your calculation, which constitute a prediction of the results of the test experiment, to your instructor. Then, under his supervision, you will perform the test experiment in order to verify or test your prediction. You will be asked, finally, to submit a report covering various aspects of what you have done.

### Preliminary Experimentation

Your main concern here is to collect enough data to make it possible to predict the results of the test experiment. To make all possible measurements is, of course, out of the question. You will, therefore, have to make a tentative design of your preliminary experiment: make a list of instruments and materials you will probably need, and decide what measurements you need to make and how to make them. These decisions will naturally be influenced by the nature of the test experiment and the available apparatus. You may want to change your experimental design after you have made a few measurements. If you need additional apparatus, make another list.

### Prediction

It is almost never possible to predict the results of an experiment exactly, but it should be possible to set with some confidence their upper and lower limits. Thus, the prediction of a distance will normally be in the following form: $d_p = 105 \pm 3$ cm ($p$ stands for prediction). Your prediction will be judged primarily by whether it is true and secondarily by the narrowness of the claimed margin of error. If, for example, the result of the test experiment is $d_E = 107$ cm, your prediction is correct. But $d_p = 109 \pm 2$ cm would have been a better prediction. A result of $d_p = 106 \pm 0.5$ cm, on the other hand, would not even be true and thus would be by far the worst prediction of the three.

You will be given a fairly short time for making your prediction. Therefore when you come to the laboratory to perform the test experiment, the results of your preparatory experimentation should already be in a form that allows rather rapid calculation. A graph is an example of a convenient form for summarizing most experimental results. A mathematical formula is another one.

### Report

1. The preliminary design of the experiment and later modifications.
2. The data collected during preparatory experimentation, usually accompanied by graphs.
3. A complete explanation of how you arrived at the prediction.
4. The test-experiment result and the predicted value. These should be so arranged that a comparison between them can be easily made.
5. If your prediction was not true, a probable explanation of the discrepancy.
6. Other specified items.

L2.2-1   *Inclined plane (two hours)*

TEST EXPERIMENT: In the test experiment you will let a ball roll five times down a grooved inclined plane and onto a carpet. The mean of the five rolls is your test-experiment value. The angle between the inclined plane and the horizontal will be set at approximately 15°. The vertical height from which the ball will roll will be between 10 cm and 15 cm. *Before* performing the test experiment you will predict, using the height assigned to you by the instructor, how far the ball will roll on the carpet. Your prediction should indicate the margin of expected error; for example, you may calculate the distance rolled as $85 \pm 5$ cm. Give this result to the instructor before experimenting.

PRELIMINARY EXPERIMENTATION: Experiment with rolling a ball down an inclined plane (at least ten rolls for each vertical height) until you have enough data to make your prediction with fair certainty and reasonable precision. Use average or standard deviation for your estimated error. (The inclined plane is already set at the proper angle. Check the angle but leave it unchanged throughout the experiment.) Make a graph by plotting the distance rolled $d$ and the estimated error $\Delta d$ against the vertical height $h$. (A good way to determine the initial vertical height $h$ of the ball is to let the top of the ball touch a horizontal surface of known elevation.)

REPORT: How did you measure $d$ and $h$? Defend your method. Does your $d$-$h$ graph go through the origin of the coordinates? Explain.

L2.2-2   *Physical pendulum (two hours)*

TEST EXPERIMENT: Apparatus: a timer and a meter stick with holes drilled at various locations along its length. The pendulum (meter stick) can be made to oscillate if hung on a horizontal nail through any one of the holes. You will be asked to predict the period of oscillation for the hole assigned to you by the instructor (it may be *any* hole) and, after submitting your prediction to the instructor, to measure the period.

PRELIMINARY EXPERIMENTATION: The meter stick has many holes. Since you will want to make several measurements of the period $t$ (it is convenient to designate by $t_{17}$, for example, the period corresponding to the hole drilled near the 17 cm mark) for any one hole, it is impractical to try every hole. *You are to record data for five holes only;* they should be chosen judiciously. You can be guided in your choice of points of suspension by plotting roughly measured values of $t$, for as many holes as you like, against the distance from the hole to some fixed point on the meter stick. Some parts of the curve need more closely spaced points than do others. This suggests that you should bring graph paper to the laboratory.

REPORT: Defend your choice of the five holes.

L2.2-3    *Calorimetry (six hours)*

TEST EXPERIMENT: Put some water into an uninsulated calorimeter can, weigh the can, and add enough ice to cool the water about 10°C. Your problem is to predict the weight of the calorimeter after the ice is added. This prediction will be verified by weighing the calorimeter in the presence of your instructor. The instructor will specify the initial temperature of the water; it will be within 20°C of room temperature.

PRELIMINARY EXPERIMENTATION AND THEORY: If $m$ grams of ice at 0°C are added to $M$ grams of water whose temperature is $t_i$, and the final temperature after the ice has melted is $t_f$, then, approximately,

$$mS + mt_f = M(t_i - t_f),$$

where $S = 80$ cal/gm.

A number of factors have been neglected in writing the equation above. You will have to decide what the effect of these will be on your results. Some will have negligible effect. Some can be taken account of by *calculation*, some by *measurement* of the size of the effect; some, so-called *residual* errors, are not negligible but cannot be easily calculated or directly measured. Among the factors are the following.

Factor 1: The calorimeter can, the stirrer, and the thermometer gain and lose heat. This factor can be taken into account by *calculation*.

Factor 2: Heat is lost to and gained from the surroundings (air, table, your hand, and so forth). (One way of finding out how fast a given calorimeter loses [or gains] temperature is to fill it with water above [or below] room temperature. A graph of temperature against time, the cooling curve, will then tell you, for any temperature, how fast the calorimeter is losing [or gaining] temperature.) The effects of this factor can be taken into account by *measurement*.

Factor 3: The ice is invariably wet, even if you dry it with a paper towel. This may be considered a *residual* error. There is no way of easily calculating or measuring it. It can be estimated by blaming on it all discrepancies between theory and experiment. (For example, if the calorimeter weighs 50 grams more after the wet ice has been added to it, but the measured cooling corresponds to only 45 grams of ice [plus 5 grams of ice water], you may assume that the "ice" under your experimental conditions [size of ice pieces, method of drying, and so forth] is really 10 percent water.)

Some other factors: Ice may not be at 0°C. Room temperature may change during the experiment. The thermometer may be inaccurate. Stirring, which is necessary if the thermometer is to measure the average temperature of the mixture of ice and water, produces heat. It is difficult to determine the time at which all the ice has melted.

REPORT: Your report of this experiment should be a complete and formal one. Twenty percent of the grade will be based on organization of the report. All graphs should be carefully drawn and fully labeled; data well arranged; your experimental design carefully though briefly described; all calculations, in particular the *wetness of the ice*, neat and understandable—from the given data to the final prediction; reasons given for neglecting, calculating, or measuring the effects of various factors; and the comparison between predicted and test-experiment results made prominent.

L2.2-4    *Compound lenses* (*six hours*)

TEST EXPERIMENT: You will be given three lenses of known focal lengths and asked to predict the focal length, $f_p \pm \Delta f_p$, of a compound lens made up of the three lenses. Next, under the instructor's supervision, determine its focal length, $f_e$, experimentally.

PRELIMINARY EXPERIMENTATION: Measure the focal lengths of several positive and negative lenses. Next, make a positive compound lens of three lenses in contact with one another—the lenses may be held together by a strip of mending tape. Calculate the "formula focal length," $f_f$, of the compound lens from the equation

$$\frac{1}{f_f} = \frac{1}{f_1} + \frac{1}{f_2} + \frac{1}{f_3}.$$

Next, locate experimentally the positions of the foci of the compound lens and calculate its experimental focal length, $f_e \pm \Delta f_e$, from the equation

$$f_e^2 = xx',$$

where $x$ and $x'$ are the distances from the nearest focal point to the object and its image, respectively. Repeat for other compound lenses and prepare a graph showing the relation between $f_e$ and $f_f$. This graph should enable you to make your test-experiment prediction.

REPORT: Include a discussion of factors affecting $f_e$.

## Comments on exercises L2.2

The time allowance indicated for the four experiments or exercises does not include preliminary explanations, which may be necessary if the laboratory is out of step with textbook assignments or if there is a discussion (highly recommended) of the laboratory reports. Thus the total time required for each experiment is probably about twice that for an analogous conventional experiment. In the author's course, almost all the laboratory experiments are of the experiment-predict-verify type. But teachers who want greater coverage may assign only one or two experiment-predict-verify experiments per quarter or semester. During preliminary experimentation, students should have less supervision than in the conventional laboratory, but prediction and verification should be made under examination conditions and require appropriate supervision. If the apparatus is fresh in the students' minds, they can make their calculations for prediction in a classroom other than the laboratory. As they finish these—usually one at a time—they may be sent to the laboratory to set up the apparatus for their test experiment. Here, supervision is ordinarily necessary only for the actual measurement, which seldom takes more than two minutes.

Exercise 1 is designed to show that the mean is the most dependable measure for prediction and that the standard or average deviation is a reasonable index of the agreement between prediction and experiment. To bring out these generalizations, the experiment is made as simple as possible. Nevertheless it is not devoid of subtleties. Thus the length $d$ of the ball's roll can be measured with a string that follows the path of the ball, or it can be taken as the displacement (straight line from the bottom of the incline to the final position of the ball) or the component of the displacement parallel to the length of the carpet. The first of these measures (though theoretically the best) is impractical and unnecessarily refined, and the last is wrong. The empirical proof of these propositions is that the deviation $\Delta d$ is large enough to make following the curve unnecessary and has the largest value for the component. The best measure of $h$ is of course the vertical displacement of the ball—it may sink measurably into the carpet. Finally, the drawing of the $d$-$h$ curve is tremendously facilitated if the students can make the curve go through the origin (by choosing $h$ and $d$ so that for $h = o$, $d = o$).

Exercise 2 illustrates the use of a hypothesis in the design of an experiment. In this case, rough measurements of the period furnish a hypothesis as to the probable shape of the curve and lead the student to the most fruitful measurements. The better students may decide to use not the period but its reciprocal, in order to be entitled to an extra point on the graph— infinite period for the 50 cm point of suspension.

Exercise 3 is designed to measure the student's ability to estimate, control, and track down error. (Instructions in parentheses can be omitted in more advanced classes.) In the author's course the students were asked to write a complete, well-organized report of the experiment. This was the only such report of the quarter; other reports were usually only one page long (in addition to data and graphs). The extensive report can be used to measure the student's ability to organize his ideas (content 3.32).

Exercise 4 illustrates the uses and limitations of approximate formulas. It also rather forcibly illustrates the abstractness or ideality of the commonly used phrase *distance from a lens:* the quite thick and unsymmetrical compound lens simply does not have an obvious, unique point or plane from which measurements can be made. Similarly, the exercise shows the ambiguity of specifying a compound lens by its components, without giving their relative positions.

The student's understanding of experimental design (L2.21) is estimated directly from the lists of apparatus that he submits; his understanding of the experimental process (L2.22), from his test experiment (in which he sets up the apparatus and makes measurements); and his ability to interpret data (L2.23), from his report. In addition, all these aspects of understanding of experiment are indicated by the success of his prediction. The subscores or grades for successful prediction may be assigned as explained in Section 10.3.

With experiment-predict-verify experiments, the students' motivation seems high, and their actual participation *is* higher. Perhaps because they are faced with the necessity of setting up apparatus and making measurements in the test experiment, students vie for the chance to manipulate apparatus. The laboratory no longer has students who limit their activities to observing or to writing down numbers dictated by the partner. The instructor can leave the laboratory for a half-hour without visibly affecting students' activities. The drama of verification is high, and the verdict rendered by nature itself is usually accepted without demur.

Empirical evidence for the validity of the exercises as measures of understanding of experiment is meager. It consists primarily in finding students—many more than in the conventional laboratory—who do well in the laboratory but not on written tests of other kinds of understanding, and vice versa. Such evidence only shows of course that laboratory exercises measure something that written tests and conventional laboratory exercises do not. It is the *inspection* of the exercises that has suggested, though tenuously, that that "something" is understanding of experiment.

### ABILITY IL2, INTUITIVE UNDERSTANDING OF PHENOMENA

The simplest way to test this ability is to ask the student to base his prediction of a phenomenon on the inspection and handling of the relevant objects and not on their verbal or mathematical description.

IL2-1    Predict the period of a physical pendulum—a rectangular or triangular board—about a specified point of suspension from an inspection of the board and the observed period about another point of suspension.

IL2-2    Predict the period of a loaded spring. You are allowed to stretch the spring to estimate its stiffness, to heft the load to estimate its weight, but not to attach the load to the spring.

IL2-3    Predict the height to which a compressed spring will toss up a given body. (Same manipulation permitted as in the preceding exercise.)

IL2-4    Predict the angle at which a board must be set to allow a block of wood to start sliding down. You may try sliding the block on the horizontal board.

IL2-5    Predict the sag of a rod supported at both ends and loaded at a point.

IL2-6    Estimate the focal length of a glass lens from its shape. (The lens should be considerably smaller or larger than, or of a different shape from, those whose focal lengths the student may know.)

IL2-7    Estimate the temperature at a point of a T-shaped metal rod whose three free ends are kept at constant temperatures. You are allowed to touch the ends to estimate their temperatures.

IL2-8    Estimate the time a piece of ice placed in warm water will take to melt.

Exercises 1 to 6, 8, and 11, described under I2, can be used in the laboratory, with apparatus taking the place of the drawings.

### COMMENTS ON EXERCISES IL2

These exercises differ from those on the knowledge of materials (L1.1) in that the latter involve a single "measurement"—made with the student's eyes, ears, or muscles—of properties that the student has previously measured with instruments, while IL2 exercises require a more complex and less easily verbalized set of physiological "memories." Most of the exercises are in mechanics because most students have probably had a rich background of kinesthetic experience, and because intuitive understanding seems to require extensive familiarity with phenomena, perhaps greater familiarity than many students can get in the laboratory of a single course. Hopefully, intuitive understanding can nevertheless be taught or improved, for it seems to be the prize possession of the engineer and the scientist. Hopefully, too, teachers will experiment with its measurement not so much to reward it with grades—although praise seems in order—as to learn what sort of laboratory experience improves this valuable ability.

### ABILITY L3, ABILITY TO LEARN FROM EXPERIMENT OR OBSERVATION

Facts alone are dumb, and nothing can be learned from them without a conceptual framework. Ability L3, therefore, presupposes symbolic or verbal knowledge and understanding. It can be tested indirectly by a paper-and-pencil test consisting of questions, answers to which the student has most likely obtained in the laboratory. A laboratory report, especially if written under examination conditions, can constitute such a test. In a more direct test the student is asked to react to real phenomena that are new to him; his responses may be written, oral, or manipulative.

### Objective L3.1, Ability to pursue experimental inquiry

Relevant exercises here are the same as exercises L2.2.

### Objective L3.2, Possession of laboratory skills

For non-science majors laboratory skills are not particularly important. Their measurement, however, is, for it may show that bad muscular co-ordination or defective eyesight is the cause of a student's bad showing in a performance test or in learning from observation. If this is the principal reason for measuring skills, these should be tested on just the operations the students have to perform in their scheduled experiments. From fairly casual observations one can identify the probably unskilled. For a more detailed diagnosis, they can be asked to perform the current routine operations: timing with a stop clock, making an electrical connection, measuring the volume of a liquid, reading a micrometer caliper, and lighting a Bunsen burner. To decide whether a student lacks skill or merely experience, his instructor or his laboratory partner should show him a good way to handle the apparatus. If the results are meager, the student may be marked down as lacking in skill. This information might be used in interpreting the results of performance tests.

### Objective L3.3, Disciplined thinking in the laboratory *

The degree of attainment of this objective can be well measured by exercises of the experiment-predict-verify variety. The preliminary design of the experiment can indicate the degree of experimental control the student considers necessary; for example, he may show little faith in theory and decide to test everything for himself—an impractical procedure. Or he may be blind to the necessity for modifying his preliminary design or, at the other extreme, change his attack every time a new datum is added to his knowledge. The report will show how many measurements of a quantity he considers satisfactory; whether he prefers the mode to the mean; and whether he has the courage to abide by his data, as well as the good sense to discard a datum that is clearly the result of a mistake. Both the preliminary design and the report test the student's ability to organize his thoughts.

L3.3-1    You have been given three thin metal containers, identical, except that one is shiny, another is painted dull black, and the third is covered with a *thin* (⅟₁₆ inch) layer of asbestos. Compare qualitatively the rates of heat

---

* This is the same content as in 3.3, except that real phenomena must be involved.

transfer through the walls of the containers by filling them with hot water and observing the rates of cooling.

### Comments on exercise L3.3-1

The experiment has many interesting possibilities, but here only one result is important: the asbestos-covered container loses heat more rapidly than the shiny one. Nevertheless, there are invariably some students who refuse to believe this because asbestos is a well-known insulator. Some of them blame the result on error; a few resort to genteel doctoring of data. (The students are assumed not to have studied radiation.)

### Objective L3.4, Imaginative thinking in the laboratory

L3.4-1    Design an experiment to measure the electrical conductivity of a solution of a salt as a function of concentration.

L3.4-2    Design an experiment to measure thermal conductivity of liquid mercury; of solid ice.

L3.4-3    Design an experiment to measure the specific heat of ice.

L3.4-4    A closed box contains a circuit consisting of a battery and a resistor of known resistance. You have access to the two terminals of the circuit. Devise an experiment to determine the emf and the internal resistance of the battery and whether the battery and the resistor are connected in parallel or in series.

L3.4-5    A closed box contains an electrical circuit. You have access only to two terminals of the circuit. Devise an experiment to determine the circuit as quantitatively as you can.

L3.4-6    A closed box contains a mechanism. You have access only to two chains that go through holes in the bottom of the box. The free end of each chain is attached to a weight that you may not remove. Devise an experiment to determine the mechanism inside the box. (The box may contain a wound spring.)

L3.4-7    The bulb and the lower part of a thermometer are inside a closed container; its upper part is exposed to view. From the readings of the thermometer determine the contents of the box. (The box may contain a dish of liquid whose freezing point is above room temperature. It may also contain a small alcohol flame under the dish that goes out a few minutes after the start of the experiment.)

L3.4-8    Determine the mechanical structure of a cylinder from the following: (1) its period of oscillation about its axis of symmetry; (2) its period of oscillation when loaded with a concentric hoop; (3) the weight of the cylinder and the weight of the hoop; and (4) the time it takes for the cylinder to roll down an inclined plane. (The cylinder may be a solid disk, essentially a hoop, or it may be light and hollow and partly filled with water or mercury.)

### Comments on exercises L3.4

As in testing for 3.4, imaginative thinking about described and idealized phenomena, so here: the difficulty lies in devising exercises that are simple enough for the average student. The exercises must, of course, involve real objects and processes. The first three exercises require designing an experiment. The design must involve choosing among physically present materials and apparatus. With this qualification, exercises 3.4-1 and 3.4-3 may be added to exercises L3.4-1, 2 and 3.

Exercises 4 to 7 are of the black-box variety. They are easy to invent and to administer. As in tests of laboratory knowledge, several different or similar black boxes may be set up in the laboratory and a number of students tested simultaneously. Exercise 8 should be demonstrated by the instructor to prevent the students from hearing the splashing of the liquid. All black-box exercises can be manipulated by the instructor, and data can be given to the whole class. While convenient, such treatment diminishes the validity of the test in two ways: first, the students do not have to decide what measurements to take, and, second, the situation becomes much more abstract—the students can work almost as well from a written description. The test's principal ability thus may come closer to 3.4 than L3.4. To save the instructor's time, various demonstration experiments can be recorded on a motion-picture film to form a library of test exercises. Or, of course, they can be prepared by a testing agency and accompanied by test items, both objective and essay.

For higher validity in tests of laboratory-acquired proficiency, not only the stimulus but at least a part of the student's responses should involve apparatus and materials. It is of course convenient to have the student's answers written down, but if possible he should find it necessary at least to handle the apparatus and materials before he writes down his conclusions. In the motion-picture version, even the stimulus is one step removed from reality.

AAPT questionnaire on testing objectives, 40–41

Abilities: auxiliary, 153, 163, 165; definition of, 81, 203; division of students by, 161, 206; list of, 16–19; measurement of, 103–04, 105, 106–08, 112–13, 123–27, 128, 137, 151–53, 159, 160, 166, 191–92, 199; necessary and sufficient, 106–08; and relevance of exercises, 105–09; in science, 94; taught in present-day science courses, 204; teaching of, 205; unchangeable, 203; use of as basis for grading, 204; use of tests to measure, 206, 207, 208; and weighting, 111

Ability to abide by stated rules: and objective tests, 145; testing for, 151

Ability to conform to scientific modes of thought, testing for, 152

Ability to learn: concept of, 24; definition of, 21; development of, 56, 57; need for teaching, 46–47; as objective, 18–19; teaching of, 120–21, 191, 203; testing for, 109, 110, 121–22, 124–26, 150, 152, 172, 185, 208; tests for, 311–46

Ability to learn from experiment or observation: as objective, 19; tests for, 357–60

Ability to organize: and essay tests, 134, 145; and laboratory tests, 356; and objective tests, 134–35

Ability to pursue experimental inquiry: as objective, 19; tests for, 358

Ability to read: development of, 62; testing for, 124, 152, 171, 172, 304

Ability to understand nonverbal symbolism: as objective, 18–19; tests for, 327–36

Ability to understand prose: as objective, 18; tests for, 311–26

Achievement tests, 100, 102, 103, 107: main function of, 126, 167; recommendations on, 231

Ambiguity in tests, 124, 125, 129, 136, 145, 154

Analytical thinking, testing for, 134

Analytical understanding, testing for, 171, 172

Antiscientific attitudes, 64–66

Behavioral objectives: choice of for testing, 119; of competence, 109–10, 119; content of, 28; and course content, 7–8, 28; examples of, 6; need for descriptions of, 7; need for knowledge of, 5–6; need for in testing, 14–15; and teaching methods, 9. *See also* Objectives

Biases: antiscientific, 64–66; detection of, 164; polar, 163; pro-science, 66; reasons for measuring, 164; sampling of, 163, 165–66

Carleton College conference on physics teaching, 38–40

Certification tests, 118: composition of, 119; function of, 100–02; and measurement of objectives, 122